THE STARS
NIGHT By. NIGHT

The right of Brian Jones to be identified as the Author of the
Work has been asserted by him in accordance with the
Copyright, Designs and Patents Act 1988

Text Copyright: © Brian Jones
Starcharts Copyright: © Garry Blackmore

Edited by Bryn Lloyd and William Rees

Published by
Candy Jar Books
Mackintosh House
136 Newport Road
Cardiff
CF24 1DJ

A catalogue record of this book is available
from the British Library

ISBN: 978-0-9935192-4-6

Printed and bound in the UK by
CPI Group (UK) Ltd, Croydon, CR0 4YY

Inspired by the publication, in 1914, of
The Stars Night By Night by Joseph Henry Elgie.

To my late partner, Anne, an Elgie-inspired
student of the stars.

CONTENTS

About the Author   I
Acknowledgements   II
Introduction   III
Joseph Henry Elgie: A Biography   VIII

Constellations Listed by Ptolemy   1
Constellations Created after Ptolemy   4

The Celestial Sphere
    Night and Day   6
    The Celestial Poles   6
    Altitudes   7
    Circumpolar Stars   9
    The Sun's Path Through the Sky 10
    The Ecliptic   11
    The Seasons   12
    The Solstices   13
    The Equinoxes   13
    Stars For All Seasons   14

Seasonal and Circumpolar Star Charts   16

Monthly Guides to the Night Sky
    January   38
    February   60
    March   83

April	104
May	125
June	152
July	177
August	202
September	230
October	257
November	288
December	323
Glossary	353
Further Reading	364
Index	366

ABOUT THE AUTHOR

Brian Jones hails from Bradford in the West Riding of Yorkshire and was a founder member of the Bradford Astronomical Society. He developed a fascination with astronomy at the age of five, when he first observed the stars through a pair of binoculars, although he spent the first part of his working life developing a career in mechanical engineering. However, his true passion lay in the stars, and his interest in astronomy took him into the realms of writing sky guides for local newspapers, appearing on local radio and television, teaching astronomy and space in schools and, in 1985, leaving engineering to become a full time astronomy and space writer.

In his writing he has covered a range of astronomy and space-related topics for both children and adults, the sixteen books he has to his name including: *The Beginner's Guide to Astronomy*, *Night Sky Identifier*, *Space Exploration* and *Pocket Guide to the Night Sky*. His extensive journalistic work includes writing for the American magazines *Astronomy* and *Odyssey* together with articles and book reviews for the British magazine *Sky at Night*. His passion for bringing an appreciation of the universe to his readers is reflected in his writing.

You can follow Brian on Twitter via @StarsBrian and check out the sky by visiting his blog at www.starlight-nights.co.uk from where you can also access his Facebook group Starlight Nights.

ACKNOWLEDGEMENTS

A number of people have helped with the compilation of this book, first and foremost being my late partner Anne who patiently checked the proofs. My thanks are also due to Jeremy Elgie who has provided sterling service with information relating to Joseph Henry Elgie and his family. I should point out that Jeremy would be happy to supply or exchange information relating either to Joseph Henry Elgie's family or to the Elgie surname in general.

Other people who have also helped include Mandy Fay, Senior Library Officer, Darlington Library; Mike Lucas; Janet Senior; and Anthony Kinder. My thanks are also due to David Sellers of Leeds Astronomical Society for details relating to Joseph's membership of the Society; to Sian Prosser, Librarian and Archivist at the Royal Astronomical Society for information on Elgie's Fellowship of the RAS; and to Tony Kinder of the British Astronomical Association for information relating to Elgie's membership of the BAA.

I am also indebted to Shaun Russell, Bryn Lloyd, William Rees, Hayley Cox and everyone at Candy Jar Books associated with this project for giving me the opportunity to pay tribute to Joseph Henry Elgie. Last, but by no means least, my appreciation goes out to Joseph Henry Elgie himself whose work and achievements inspired me to look at the stars anew and to compile this book in his memory.

Brian Jones

INTRODUCTION

In 1910 the English astronomer and author Joseph Henry Elgie published his book *The Night Skies of a Year*, which was intended to be a non-technical and easily-understood guide to the night sky throughout the seasons. The book was republished in a cheaper, and therefore more-widely accessible, format in 1914 under the title *The Stars Night By Night* and it is this latter publication upon which the current volume is based. In the preface to the 1914 edition Elgie informs us that it was:

'...first and foremost a book for that class of reader who, while interested in the grand science of astronomy, has neither the opportunity nor the inclination to enter deeply into the study of that science. A general acquaintance with the face of the sky is all that (the author) endeavours to teach.'

True to his word, Elgie introduces the readership to the wonders of astronomy at a non-technical level. As its title may suggest, the book was based on observations of the night sky made during the course of a year, these being from his home near Leeds in the West Riding of Yorkshire, England, the year in question being 1907.

Unlike the current volume, Elgie's book did not contain entries for every night of the year, which of course may arise from him having other engagements on those evenings. However, an alternative answer to the errant nights may lie in the entry for June 13th, which highlights his love-hate relationship with clouds. The entry is reproduced in this book, so you can judge for yourself. Clouds are something astronomers can do without, although any thoughts you have in this direction may well be influenced should you ever get the chance to read Elgie's original book and hear his views on them... and perhaps those of you beset by cloudy skies may at least have your opinions of them tweaked a little.

As far as annual guides to the night sky are concerned, these are widely available, although are often more or less limited to the particular year they describe. The book you are holding does not cover the Moon, planets and other members of the Solar System. Consequently, because it describes only the stars and constellations, it is valid for any year you choose. The phases of the Moon and positions of the planets are constantly changing and a guide for a particular year which included them would be largely irrelevant for other years.

As we will see, each of the seasons brings its own array of stars and constellations, and we can rely on these reappearing at the same time in subsequent years. Although Elgie's original book does occasionally mention the planets, by and large it is a book about the stars. As Elgie states in the preface to the 1914 edition: *'Though the diagrams of the stars were drawn by the author in one particular year, as the text indicates, they will serve, of course, for any year.'* Indeed, as a guide to the stars, Elgie's original book is as valid today as it was over a century ago.

In a bid to bring across Elgie's passion for the subject (as well as his relationship and feelings for the weather) I have made regular use of quotations from his original book. All quotations used are italicised and are from Joseph Henry Elgie himself, unless otherwise stated. Some of the quotations are reproduced in places that reflect the area of sky being covered by him on that particular date. Others are randomly selected from whatever date they were used by Elgie simply because he had something interesting to say! Hopefully you, the reader, will forgive this indulgence. Elgie had a passion for the sky and, in keeping with the fact that this book is a tribute to his work, I feel the entries more than merit inclusion.

The basic principle of the book is straightforward and, in keeping with Joseph Henry Elgie's aims, the technical aspects covered in the current volume have been kept to a minimum. Although the original book covered only the night sky visible from Elgie's location in Leeds, this volume offers a tour of the night sky which is open to backyard astronomers across the globe. In addition, although Elgie's book did not contain entries for every night of the year, this one does.

We start our journey with the constellation Orion (see January 1st), a highly prominent pattern of stars which is easy to identify and is visible from every inhabited part of our planet. From here we travel around the sky, moving from constellation to constellation and pausing a while at each to learn about the legends and mythology associated with the group and the stars from which the constellation is formed. Information given for the stars includes their distances and colours. The individual colours of most of the brighter stars in the sky can be made out with the naked eye, those of many of the fainter stars being revealed through either binoculars or small telescopes.

We also take a closer look at some of the other objects, such as double and variable stars, star clusters, nebulae and galaxies that may be found within the borders of each constellation. In many instances these are not visible to the naked eye so finder charts have been provided to help you track them down. These take the form of close-up views of the regions of sky around the objects being sought out and include a guide star, which is also identifiable on the main chart of the constellation in question. Once you have positioned the guide star in the field of view of either binoculars or a small telescope, you can star hop your way from it to the object you are seeking.

As you will see from using the book, details are given as to the visibility of each particular constellation from different locations on the Earth (see also The Celestial Sphere pp 9-15). For the most part each constellation is identified either by using the previously-described constellation, or stars within it, as a guide, or by including a nearby prominent star on the chart to show its location. Should you have any problems, reference to the seasonal and circumpolar star charts, which show large areas of the sky, will enable you to pick out the individual star patterns within their general area and in relation to neighbouring constellations. Although you should manage to identify most of the constellations without too much trouble, some of the fainter groups may present a challenge in that they can be difficult to pick out against the background stars. Good examples are Lynx (the Lynx) (see March 19th), Vulpecula (the Fox - see September 23rd) and Lacerta (the Lizard - see November 27th). In cases like these, a little patience will produce its rewards.

Generally speaking, the constellations are described within the monthly sections of the book closest to the best times of the year for viewing them. In other words, when they are most conveniently placed in the sky for viewing. However, the very nature of the book dictates that we can't adhere to this system precisely, and for this I crave your indulgence. Some constellations, whilst being visible and reasonably placed for observation at the times they are featured, may attain a better and more convenient position in the sky at a slightly different date.

Elgie's love affair with the sky can perhaps be best summed up when he says: *'For my part, with the stars for company – and my books – I sometimes think I should not be lonely in the soundless desert of Sahara nor on an island-rock in mid-Pacific. The starry sky and one's favourite books! And what, indeed, is the starry sky itself but a book? A book whose letters are of gold and silver; a book whose pages turn with the gliding years. How can such true companions ever pall?'*

From reading his books it is clear that, as well as having a deep passion and thorough knowledge of astronomy, Elgie had a romantic and, some would say, philosophical view of the universe. In his book *Star and Weather Gossip* he offers quotes from many of his correspondents including what he refers to as a literary contribution from the American writer and fellow enthusiast Charles Nevers Holmes of Boston who had sent Elgie a description of the night sky in his district which concluded as follows...

'Seasons wax and wane, centuries pass, countless hosts of men and women are born and die, nations arise and fall, even terrestrial life becomes a mausoleum; but these suns, other suns of the universe, blaze on; their satellites still revolve around them; Time – eternity itself – still flows, like some endless, everlasting river, and he who stands beneath the star-lighted dome of night and gazes upon its sparkling and scintillating suns and constellations, will view the same firmament that his ancestors saw, the same firmament that his descendants shall see centuries and centuries in the silent future.'

It seems to me, from learning about Joseph Henry Elgie and his love of astronomy, that he would readily echo these sentiments, and if this book achieves even a fraction of this, then the effort to compile it has been worth while. As Elgie himself would doubtless say... go out and enjoy your journey around the heavens, and may your skies be always clear..!

Happy stargazing!

JOSEPH HENRY ELGIE:
A BIOGRAPHY

George Elgie, the son of Simon Elgie, married Mary Ord at Hart, near Hartlepool, County Durham on 7th May 1851. Records show that Mary bore George eight children, the seventh being their son Joseph Henry Elgie who was born on 5th October 1864 at Union Street, Hartlepool. The last child born to the couple was Simon Kelsey Elgie who came into the world in 1867. No further children followed and George's wife Mary passed away in 1870. She was buried on 24th May 1870, the 1871 census showing George as a widower residing with his six surviving children (the first two had died shortly after birth), including Joseph Henry who by then was aged 6, at 4 Union Street, Hartlepool.

On 18th October 1871, just a few months after the above census was taken, George Elgie remarried, his new bride being Catharine Horner, a spinster of Acomb in the West Riding of Yorkshire, which is where the marriage took place. This union resulted in the births of two additional children to swell the Elgie ranks.

The 1881 census shows Joseph Henry having left the family home and residing on Northgate Street, Hartlepool where he is living with Robert Rowe, a grocer. Joseph Henry is described as a grocer's assistant, a career that was destined to be short-lived, as by 1886 he was working for Furness and Company, a shipping firm based in Hartlepool.

Hartlepool was an important sea port, its rail connections

and first rate facilities making it one of the best harbours on the east coast of England. Joseph had a passion for the sea and everything related to it and it is an interesting and perhaps slightly-romantic notion to think that he may have been drawn towards working for Furness and Company because of the fact that they were involved in the transportation of goods by sea.

Elgie makes his passion for the sea evident to the readers of his book *Star and Weather Gossip*, which was self-published by Elgie in 1915. It contains articles and sketches written by him and which were originally published in T.P.'s Weekly and The Yorkshire Weekly Post. In the introduction to the book Elgie describes his thoughts and feelings for the nautical sketches contained within its pages, telling the reader that *'...born almost on the cliff edge of the north-east coast, they have a warm corner in my heart.'* The location of his home town, on the beautiful and rugged Durham coast overlooking the North Sea, clearly inspired and stimulated the interests of the young Joseph Henry Elgie. Indeed, Elgie's love of nature was destined to formulate much of the rest of his professional life.

Joseph's entry in the 1891 census describes him as a reporter for the North Star, for which he was the Hartlepool representative. It was in 1894 that he was given promotion at the North Star, the report of this in the Hartlepool Mail describing Elgie as having *'...at all times been a genial colleague and reliable journalist, and one who had gained the respect of those with whom he had either business or private relations.'* It is clear that he was held in high esteem by his peers. Joseph worked at the North Star until 1896 when he relocated to the West Riding of Yorkshire, working at the Bradford Observer for a couple of years until his appointment at the Yorkshire Evening Post at Leeds in 1898.

Joseph Henry married Mary Oliver at Darlington St Paul

on 25th May 1896, describing himself as a journalist residing at Bradford, this tying in with his period of employment at the Bradford Observer. By the time of the 1901 census he was living at 9 Kirkstall Road, Leeds with his wife Mary and their son Henry Oliver, the census entry describing him as a journalist and author. In May of that year he was elected to the Leeds Astronomical Society and within a couple of years he was a member of the Society committee. According to Society records, Joseph had moved to 72 Grange Avenue, Chapeltown, Leeds by 1904 and it was from here that he carried out the observations that were to form the basis of his book *The Night Skies Of A Year.*

Originally published in 1910, Joseph's book *The Night Skies Of A Year* took the form of a diary containing entries relating to his observations of the night sky compiled throughout 1907. Paid for by private subscription, it was a comparatively expensive publication. The book was republished in 1914 under the new title *The Stars Night By Night* and in the preface to the 1914 edition, Elgie describes it as being a *'...very cheap edition (which) will give it that wide scope which it could not perhaps enjoy at the higher price'*. It seems clear that Joseph fully intended to make the study of astronomy and the night sky available to a much wider audience.

In both editions of the book Joseph makes occasional mention of someone who he affectionately refers to as the *'Small Stargazer'*. This might be a reference to his son Henry Oliver, who would have been aged around eight at the time his father began to put together the information for his original book. Henry Oliver may have developed an interest in the night sky and accompanied his father as he was carrying out his observations.

Further confirmation of Elgie's desire to encourage public

interest in astronomy and the night sky is seen in the number of letters and articles he had published in newspapers throughout the early 1900s.

The idea that Joseph was keen to popularise astronomy is echoed in the introduction to his book *The Complete Star Guide* where he writes: *'What is the name of that glorious constellation? Is that brilliant star Sirius or Vega? Can that shimmering mass of stellar jewels be the Pleiades or Coma Berenices? And that mysterious-looking cloud-like patch on the face of the night-time sky? Turn over the leaves of this little book and find answer.'* This book didn't carry a publication date although it seems to have appeared in 1916, the Yorkshire Post publishing a favourable review of the book in November of that year. What appears to have been Elgie's final book, *How To Forecast The Weather*, was published in 1922 and again was well received.

Joseph was elected a Fellow of the Royal Astronomical Society in June 1905, his application form describing him as a journalist. He was proposed by Charles Thomas Whitmell, an Inspector of Schools by trade and an accomplished amateur astronomer who lived in the Headingley area of Leeds. Joseph remained a Fellow until 1916. In addition to his RAS Fellowship, Joseph became a member of the British Astronomical Association in October 1910, his membership lasting until September 1924.

The baptism of his second son Rupert at Potternewton near Leeds on 16th May 1906 records Joseph as being a journalist, while the 1911 census entry describes him as a journalist and author and still residing at 72 Grange Avenue. In the household with him is his 12-year-old son Henry Oliver with no sign of either his wife Mary or his son Rupert.

It seems that prior to 1914 Joseph had moved to London, the preface to *The Stars Night By Night* showing him as residing in Brixton. He then relocated to Sussex for a while, Elgie's popularity at the time being such that, in June 1918, the Sussex Agricultural Express saw fit to inform its readers of the move, saying: *'Author and astronomer Mr Joseph Elgie, the well-known writer on astronomical subjects, has settled in Haywards Heath, which he considers to be a very charming locality - we hope he will not change his view in the winter.'*

Joseph eventually moved back to the London area from where his fame as an astronomy populariser grew, the publishing of his books and appearances in newspapers and journals being supplemented by numerous broadcasts on the recently-formed BBC. These broadcasts, usually of around quarter of an hour or so in duration, were transmitted from studios in both London and Nottingham, the topics covered including both astronomy and the weather.

Joseph appears to have remained in London at least until the early-1930s following which he is recorded as residing on Hunsworth Lane, Cleckheaton, near Bradford. Indeed, this was his address at the time of his death, aged 73, on 14th November 1937. Joseph's profession, as given on the death certificate, was *'Formerly a Journalist'* which seems to do little in the way of summing up his achievements. He was buried at Scholemoor Cemetery, Bradford on 20th November 1937, the grave having been purchased by his wife Mary who only made provision for a single interment. The informant for the death was Joseph Henry's son Henry Oliver Elgie who was residing in Shadwell near Leeds at the time. It may be that Joseph Henry and his wife Mary had separated by then, which is something that we will perhaps never know.

Joseph Henry and Mary Elgie had two children, the first being Henry Oliver Elgie who was born in Darlington in July 1898 and who married Doris Sanders at Hunslet Moor Parish Church, near Leeds, in August 1925. Their daughter, Patricia Mary, was born in 1932, following which Henry Oliver and Doris seem to have parted ways. Doris and Patricia Mary appear to have emigrated to the United States during the 1940s and their fate remains unknown. Henry Oliver Elgie remarried in 1949, his second wife being Kathleen Nelson. Henry Oliver and Kathleen ended up in Scarborough in the North Riding of Yorkshire where they both died in the 1980s. A friend of the couple remembers seeing a set of books relating to astronomy, and apparently written by Henry Oliver's father Joseph Henry Elgie, on a shelf at the family home. It would be wonderful to know if there were other items relating to his father and where these eventually ended up.

Rupert, younger brother of Henry Oliver and second child of Joseph Henry and Mary Elgie, was born in 1906. Rupert married Lily Blake in 1930 and records suggest that the couple had no children. The last we hear of Rupert and Lily is in 1945 at which time they are living in Caterham in Surrey although there is strong evidence to suggest that Rupert died in 1970 in Las Palmas.

If any reader can provide further information about Joseph Henry Elgie, or anything relating to either of his children and their families, I would be delighted to hear from you.

This photograph shows Joseph Henry Elgie at work in his study and was taken in the early-1900s, during the time the family were residing in the Leeds area.

LIST OF THE FORTY-EIGHT CONSTELLATIONS LISTED BY THE GREEK ASTRONOMER PTOLEMY

In around 150AD the Greek astronomer Claudius Ptolemaeus of Alexandria drew up a list of the 48 constellations that were known to, and recognised by, the astronomers of the time. These were published in his treatise on astronomy known to us by its Arabic title the *Almagest* and which summarised Greek astronomical knowledge up to that time. The star catalogue and list of constellations were largely based on the observations of an earlier Greek astronomer, Hipparchus of Nicaea, who lived and worked during the 2nd century BC.

Andromeda – Andromeda
Aquarius – The Water Carrier
Aquila – The Eagle
Ara – The Altar
Argo Navis – The Ship Argo
Aries – The Ram
Auriga – The Charioteer
Boötes – The Herdsman
Cancer – The Crab
Canis Major – The Great Dog

Canis Minor – The Little Dog

Capricornus – The Goat

Cassiopeia – Cassiopeia

Centaurus – The Centaur

Cepheus – Cepheus

Cetus – The Whale or Sea Monster

Corona Australis – The Southern Crown

Corona Borealis – The Northern Crown

Corvus – The Crow

Crater – The Cup

Cygnus –The Swan

Delphinus – The Dolphin

Draco – The Dragon

Equuleus – The Little Horse

Eridanus – The River

Gemini – The Twins

Hercules – Hercules

Hydra – The Water Snake

Leo – The Lion

Lepus – The Hare

Libra – The Scales

Lupus – The Wolf

Lyra – The Lyre

Ophiuchus – The Serpent Bearer

Orion – Orion

Pegasus – The Winged Horse

Perseus – Perseus

Pisces – The Fishes

Piscis Austrinus – The Southern Fish

Sagitta – The Arrow

Sagittarius – The Archer
Scorpius – The Scorpion
Serpens – The Serpent
Taurus – The Bull
Triangulum – The Triangle
Ursa Major – The Great Bear
Ursa Minor – The Little Bear
Virgo – The Virgin

CONSTELLATIONS CREATED SINCE THE LIST DEVISED BY PTOLEMY

Johannes Hevelius
Canes Venatici – The Hunting Dogs
Lacerta – The Lizard
Leo Minor – The Little Lion
Lynx – The Lynx
Scutum – The Shield
Sextans – The Sextant
Vulpecula – The Fox

Pieter Dirkszoon Keyser and Frederick de Houtman
Apus – The Bird of Paradise
Chamaeleon – The Chameleon
Dorado – The Goldfish
Grus – The Crane
Hydrus – The Little Water Snake
Indus – The Indian
Musca – The Fly
Pavo – The Peacock
Phoenix – The Phoenix
Triangulum Australe – The Southern Triangle
Tucana – The Toucan
Volans – The Flying Fish

Nicolas Louis de Lacaille
Antlia – The Air Pump
Caelum – The Graving Tool
Carina – The Keel
Circinus – The Compasses
Fornax - The Furnace
Horologium – The Pendulum Clock
Mensa – The Table Mountain
Microscopium – The Microscope
Norma – The Level
Octans – The Octant
Pictor – The Painter's Easel
Puppis – The Poop or Stern
Pyxis – The Mariner's Compass
Reticulum – The Net
Sculptor – The Sculptor
Telescopium – The Telescope
Vela – The Sail

Gerardus Mercator
Coma Berenices – Berenice's Hair

Petrus Plancius
Camelopardalis – The Giraffe
Columba – The Dove
Monoceros – The Unicorn

Andreas Corsali
Crux – The Cross

THE CELESTIAL SPHERE

The night sky is a fascinating place although, at first sight, can be bewildering. When you take your first serious look at our view of the universe, with the purpose of checking out the wonders it has to offer, it may seem difficult to believe that you will soon know your way around. The sky can look confusing with hundreds of pinpoints of light, all vying for your attention and all looking broadly similar. However, certain things soon become obvious. For example, even a cursory glance will reveal that some stars are obviously brighter than others, and it will soon become apparent that many of the stars appear to be arranged in patterns. We call these patterns constellations, and by looking at one area of sky, or constellation, at a time, you will build up your knowledge fairly quickly and, hopefully, start to feel at home under, and familiar with, the star-filled sky.

One thing that will be clear to those of you who have checked out the night sky before is that we see different stars and constellations at different times of the year. To get a full understanding of why this happens we need to examine the reasons behind it. So, before we commence our journey around the sky, let's take a look at some of the basics...

NIGHT AND DAY

The Earth rotates on its axis from west to east. In other words, if we viewed the Earth from above the northern hemisphere, our planet would be seen to rotate in an anti-clockwise direction. It is the rotation of the Earth which causes night and day. Daytime occurs on the side of the Earth facing the Sun, night taking place when that side of our planet moves around and is facing away from the Sun.

As well as giving rise to night and day, the rotation of the Earth from west to east causes the apparent rotation, from east to west, of the sky, containing the Sun, Moon, planets and stars, around the Earth. The stars and other objects in the sky to appear to rise in the east, travel across the sky and set in the west.

THE CELESTIAL POLES

The celestial sphere is the imaginary sphere of sky that completely surrounds the Earth and, for simplicity, the stars are considered to be fixed on the celestial sphere. The Earth's rotation is centred on an imaginary axis passing through the Earth and extending outwards, intercepting the celestial sphere at two points. These points are known as the north and south celestial poles. These are points on the celestial sphere lying directly above the north and south terrestrial poles, through which projections of the Earth's axis would intercept the celestial sphere.

The north celestial pole is marked by the star Polaris in Ursa Minor (see March 13th) while the nearest star to the south celestial pole is the faint Sigma Octantis (see December 16th). As the Earth rotates, the stars on the celestial sphere appear to revolve around these two stars.

In the same way that the celestial poles are projections of the Earth's axis of rotation, the celestial equator is a projection of the Earth's equator onto the sky and is, in effect, an imaginary and continuous line travelling completely around the celestial sphere. Just as its terrestrial counterpart is located at 90° from each pole (these distances normally being expressed in terms of latitude), the celestial equator lies at an angular distance of 90° from each of the celestial poles.

ALTITUDES

The altitude of a star or other celestial object is its angular distance above the horizon. In other words, if a star is located on the horizon, its altitude is 0°. If it is directly overhead its altitude is 90°, placing it at the observer's zenith. (It should be borne in mind that the zenith is not a fixed point on the celestial sphere, but refers to the point in the sky directly above the observer.) If the star is halfway between the horizon and the zenith, its altitude would be 45° and so on.

Taking this a stage further, there is a direct correlation between your location on the Earth and the altitudes of stars in the sky. The best example of this is the altitude of the north celestial pole above the northern horizon (or the south celestial pole above the southern horizon) which, in each case, is equal to the latitude of the observer. An observer at the north pole (latitude 90°N) would see the north celestial pole directly overhead, at an altitude of 90°. In other words, it would be at the observer's zenith.

The further away you travel from the north pole, the lower the north celestial pole will appear to be in the sky. From London (latitude 52°N) it will have an altitude of 52° and from Bombay (latitude 19°N) it will have an altitude of 19°. From the equator (latitude 0°) it will have an altitude of 0° resulting in Polaris being seen on the northern horizon. From south of the equator it will be permanently hidden by the bulk of the Earth and will not be seen at all.

The same is true for Sigma Octantis, the star marking the south celestial pole, as viewed from the southern hemisphere.

From the equator it will be seen at around the level of the southern horizon, while from Johannesburg (latitude 26°S) it will be 26° above the southern horizon. From Sydney (latitude 34°S) it will be 34° above the southern horizon while from the south pole it will be seen at the zenith. The celestial poles lie at compass points north and south. In other words, you would be looking due north if you were gazing at Polaris and due south if gazing at Sigma Octantis.

It is not only Polaris that would be hidden from view to an observer south of the equator. Stars near the north celestial pole would also be hidden, more and more stars being lost to view the further south you go. The same is true for observers north of the equator. The further north you travel, the more stars disappear below the southern horizon. Consequently, from any latitude north (or south) of the equator, there are stars permanently hidden around the south celestial pole (or north celestial pole). From observing locations actually at the north (or south) poles, only those stars north (or south) of the celestial equator will ever be seen. For example, the well-known constellation Cassiopeia (see November 19th) lies so close to the north celestial pole that it is never seen by observers in Tierra del Fuego or Dunedin, in much the same way that the southern constellation Dorado (see December 21st) is permanently hidden to observers in Boston or Paris.

CIRCUMPOLAR STARS

A circumpolar star or constellation is one that never sets as seen from a given location, but always stays above the observer's horizon and can be viewed all year round. If the angular distance of a star from the celestial pole is less than the altitude of the observer, that star will never set as seen from that latitude, and will remain permanently above the horizon.

Such stars are referred to as circumpolar stars. In other words, for an observer in Munich (latitude 48°N) all stars within 48° of the north celestial pole will never disappear below the horizon. As seen from Munich, the star Shedar in Cassiopeia, which is 34° from the north celestial pole, will be circumpolar, while Pollux in Gemini, located 62° from the north celestial pole, will not. The same applies to both the northern and southern hemispheres. For an observer on the equator (latitude 0°) there will be no circumpolar stars, while for an observer at the poles all stars will be circumpolar.

The easy way to determine whether a star is circumpolar is simply to determine your latitude. In the case of Munich (latitude 48°N) all stars located within 48° of the north celestial pole will be circumpolar. Taking this a stage further, an observer in Munich would never see stars which lie more than (90° - 48°) = 42° below the celestial equator. In other words, the number of degrees in latitude you are away from the north celestial pole is equal to the number of degrees (angular distance) you can see south of the celestial equator. The same principle works (albeit in reverse) for southern hemisphere observers.

THE SUN'S PATH THROUGH THE SKY

As we have seen, daytime occurs on the side of the Earth which happens to be facing the Sun, whilst at the same time it is night on the opposite side of our planet. So far so good. However, the axial rotation of the Earth is not the only motion performed by our planet. It is also travelling around our parent star and, as it does so, the position of the Earth in its orbit changes, resulting in us seeing the Sun from a slightly different vantage point each day. This line of sight effect results in the Sun appearing to slowly shift against the backdrop of stars, the consequence of which is that we see it superimposed against a different point on the celestial sphere from day to day.

The Earth makes one complete orbit of our star in a year, the Sun appearing to travel completely around the sky during this time. Of course, the apparent path traced out by the Sun against the background stars is merely a result of perspective. It's rather like having a lamp suspended in the middle of a room to represent the Sun. In this scenario, the walls of the room represent the celestial sphere. As you walk around the lamp, thereby simulating the journey the Earth takes around our parent star, the lamp appears to travel around the room, its position relative to the walls changing as you move around it.

This apparent shift of the Sun against the background stars is not readily observable. After all, the glare from the Sun is so powerful that, even though the stars are still there during the day, their light is blotted out and we are normally prevented from seeing them. However, there are rare moments when we can see the stars during the daytime. During a total solar eclipse, when the Moon momentarily passes in front of, and obscures, the solar disc, the light from the Sun is blotted out. The sky becomes temporarily darker and for a few brief moments we are able to see stars during the daytime with the naked eye.

THE ECLIPTIC

As previously noted, the daily rotation of the Earth on its axis causes the stars and other objects in the sky, including the Sun, to appear to rise in the east, travel across the sky, and set in the west. However, because we are also travelling around the Sun, our star is undergoing yet another apparent motion through the sky. This is caused by the day to day change in the position of the Earth in its orbit. As we have seen, the perspective we get of the Sun due to the Earth's orbital motion is that its position on the celestial sphere shifts by a tiny amount each day. This daily shift is seen against the backdrop of stars. The resulting apparent course around the celestial sphere (not to be confused with night and day) seems to take it from west to east through a band of constellations known as the Zodiac. The actual path of the Sun through the Zodiac is called the ecliptic and, as is the case with the celestial equator, the ecliptic can be imagined and depicted as a continuous line projected onto the celestial sphere.

THE SEASONS

Although the orbit of the Earth around the Sun is elliptical rather than circular, and the distance between our planet and the Sun varies, it is the tilt of the Earth's axis relative to the plane of its orbit around the Sun that give rise to the seasons rather than the variations in distance. In June, for example, the northern hemisphere is tilted *towards* the Sun. As a result, the Sun will appear to be *higher* in the sky when seen from locations in the northern hemisphere. This corresponds to the northern *summer* when the Sun is in the sky for a greater period and the days are longer and warmer. Because the southern hemisphere is tilted *away* from the Sun at this time, the southern *winter* will take place, during which time the Sun will be *lower* in the sky when seen from locations south of the equator. For those in the southern hemisphere, the Sun will be in the sky for a shorter period and the days will be briefer and colder. The situation is reversed six months later. During December, the northern hemisphere is tilted *away* from the Sun and the southern hemisphere *towards* it, thus producing northern *winter* and southern *summer*.

*

THE SOLSTICES

Because the altitude of the Sun is constantly changing, due to a combination of the Earth's axial tilt and the orbit of our planet around the Sun, the apparent path of the Sun through the sky (the ecliptic) takes it both above and below the celestial equator. The Earth is tilted at 23½° relative to the plane of its orbit around the Sun. Therefore, when the northern hemisphere is tilted directly towards the Sun, on or around 21st June each year, the Sun will be 23½° to the north of the celestial equator. At this time, the Sun attains its highest point in the sky for northern hemisphere observers. The Sun is in the sky for the longest period of any day of the year and the northern hemisphere experiences its longest day (and shortest night). From latitude 23½°N (the Tropic of Cancer) the Sun will be seen directly overhead at noon.

Six months later the situation is reversed. The *southern* hemisphere is tilted directly towards the Sun on or around 21st December each year, at which point the Sun attains its highest point in the sky for southern hemisphere observers. The southern hemisphere, therefore, experiences its longest day (and shortest night). At this time, the Sun will be overhead when seen from latitude 23½°S (the Tropic of Capricorn).

The points at which the Sun is at its furthest north (or south) of the celestial equator are known as the summer (and winter) solstices. The word 'solstice' is derived from Latin and means 'Sun stand still', this referring to the fact that, at these times, the apparent motion north or south of the Sun along the ecliptic effectively stops and changes direction.

THE EQUINOXES

As the Sun appears to travel along the ecliptic, moving northwards in its journey, it crosses the celestial equator or around 21st March at a point known as the vernal, or spring, equinox. Similarly, as it moves southwards it crosses the celestial equator on or around 22nd September at a point called the autumnal equinox. At these times, the Earth's axis is tilted neither towards nor away from the Sun. This results in day and night being of nearly equal length at all locations on the Earth, a fact reflected in the word 'equinox', which is derived from the Latin for 'equal night'.

STARS FOR ALL SEASONS

Understanding the axial and orbital motions of the Earth, the apparent journey undertaken by the Sun throughout the year and the reasons why the seasons occur is interesting in itself. However, as far as our Elgie-inspired odyssey around the sky is concerned, the upshot of the progression of the seasons is that, throughout the Earth's annual journey around the Sun, our view of the celestial sphere alters slightly from night to night. On any particular day, or during any particular season, the side of the Earth facing away from the Sun, and therefore experiencing night, is looking out on that section of the celestial sphere opposite that in which the Sun lies.

As the Earth travels along its orbit, the section of sky presented to us alters very slightly from night to night. Over the course of time, and as the days and seasons progress, the stars and constellations on view to us change more appreciably, with a different section of the celestial sphere being presented to us in winter to that which we see in spring, summer and autumn.

The seasonal star charts included in this book show the main stars and constellations visible during the different seasons. There are charts for Northern Summer/Southern Winter;

Northern Autumn/Southern Spring; Northern Winter/Southern Summer; and Northern Spring/Southern Autumn. In addition, there are charts showing the main circumpolar stars, these being the constellations lying around the north and south celestial poles and which (as far as these particular charts are concerned) never set as seen from mid-northern or mid-southern latitudes.

As well as showing the stars and constellations visible during a particular season, the seasonal charts provide a useful back up to help you identify each constellation on your journey around the celestial sphere as they depict each group in relation to those around it. In addition, they overlap slightly with the seasonal chart to either side and to the circumpolar charts. This should help you to link the different sections of the celestial sphere together.

STARS OF THE NORTHERN CIRCUMPOLAR SKY

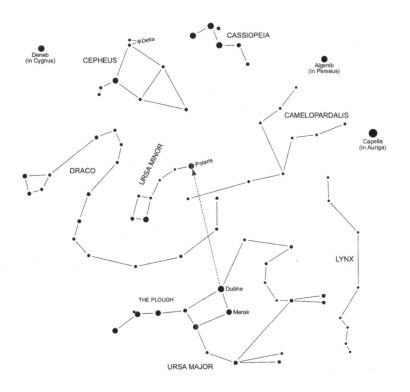

As we have seen, a circumpolar star or constellation is one that never sets as seen from a given location, but always remains above the observer's horizon and can be viewed all year round (see The Celestial Sphere pp 6-15). The area of sky depicted here shows stars which are circumpolar as seen from mid-northern latitudes. They surround the constellation Ursa Minor (the Little Bear), its prominent leading star Polaris, also known as the Pole Star, always being seen to lie due north.

For observers at or around mid-northern latitudes the Plough, together with the rest of Ursa Major (the Great Bear), can be seen near the zenith or overhead point during mid-evenings in spring, whilst summer evenings see Draco (the Dragon) in this position. Cassiopeia takes their place during the autumn months and the faint and somewhat sprawling Camelopardalis (the Giraffe) in winter.

To start your search of the north circumpolar sky, use the Plough as a guide. Hold the chart above your head and rotate it so as to match up the pattern of stars shown with their locations in the sky. Once you've done this, the chart will enable you to identify the stars and constellations you can actually see. Once you've picked out the main constellations shown here, the rest of the (fainter) stars on this chart can be identified (providing the sky is reasonably dark and clear).

By far the most prominent and well-known group in this region is the Plough, a conspicuous pattern of stars formed from the seven brightest members of Ursa Major (see March 7th). The Plough acts as a useful direction finder to many other stars and constellations. One of these is Polaris. If you extend the line from Merak, through Dubhe in the Plough as shown here this will lead you to Polaris, from which the rest of the stars in Ursa Minor (see March 13th) can be picked out.

Now continue the line from Merak and Dubhe roughly as

far again past Polaris and this will bring you to Cassiopeia (see November 19th), a distinct W- or M-shaped group of five bright stars. According to legend, Cassiopeia was the mother of Princess Andromeda and wife of King Cepheus of Ethiopia, Cepheus (see November 23rd) being depicted here as one of the constellations adjoining Cassiopeia.

Other groups in this area of sky include Draco (the Dragon) (see October 9th) which winds its way around Ursa Minor, and the two obscure constellations Camelopardalis (the Giraffe) (see November 18th) and Lynx (the Lynx) (see March 19th). Very clear skies are needed in order to pick out these latter two groups. Neither Camelopardalis nor Lynx contain any particularly bright stars and you may need a pair of binoculars to help you identify them.

STARS OF NORTHERN
WINTER/SOUTHERN SUMMER

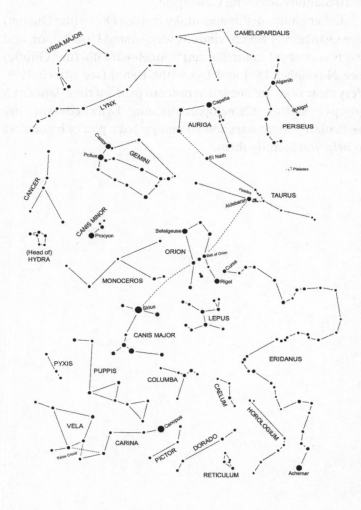

This chart shows the night sky as it appears around this time of year when those at mid-northern latitudes will see the brilliant star Capella in Auriga located at or around the overhead point. Many more prominent stars are in evidence which makes the job of picking out the various star patterns that much easier. Brilliant Capella is the leading star in the constellation Auriga (the Charioteer) (see January 24th). This conspicuous group resembles a large circlet of stars, the overall shape of which includes El Nath, a star which is actually a member of the neighbouring constellation Taurus (the Bull) (see January 28th).

The equally-prominent constellation Gemini (the Twins) (see January 18th) can be found a little way towards the south east of Auriga, its two leading stars Castor and Pollux particularly prominent, as is Procyon, the brightest star in Canis Minor (the Little Dog) (see January 15th) located a little way to the south of Pollux.

The conspicuous form of Perseus (see November 12th) is seen to the west of Auriga, its famous variable star Algol (see November 14th) located a little way to the south of Algenib. Somewhat less obvious is the straggling line of faint stars that forms the constellation Lynx (the Lynx) (see March 19th) which can be made out to the northeast of Gemini.

Immediately to the east of Gemini and Canis Minor we see the faint constellation Cancer (the Crab) (see March 21st) which itself lies just to the north of the tiny circlet of stars forming the Head of Hydra (the Water Snake) (see March 29th and April 14th).

Pride of place, however, goes to Orion (see January 1st), its brightest stars forming a distinctive quadrangle. Betelgeuse and Rigel are unmistakeable, as is the trio of regularly-spaced stars spanning the central region of the group. Representing the Belt of Orion, these three stars act as pointers to two neighbouring constellations. Following the line formed by the Belt of Orion towards the north west we first of all reach Aldebaran, the leading star in Taurus (the Bull) (see January 28th). Extending the line further brings us to the Pleiades, a prominent open star cluster located in the north western reaches of Taurus (see February 4th). Following the line of stars in the Belt of Orion towards the south east brings us to Sirius, the brightest star in Canis Major (the Great Dog) (see January 11th) while just to the south of Orion we see the small gathering of stars forming the constellation Lepus (the Hare) (see February 5th).

The faint constellation Monoceros (the Unicorn) (see February 29th) can be found to the east of Orion and located between the two celestial dogs Canis Major and Canis Minor. The long and winding trail of faint stars forming Eridanus (the River) (see December 28th) stretches away from the star Cursa, located just to the north west of Rigel at the foot of Orion. Eridanus flows southwards to a point deep inside the southern sky, its southernmost point marked by the brilliant star Achernar.

Achernar provides a good reference point from which a number of fainter constellations in this region of the sky can be tracked down, including Horologium (the Pendulum Clock) (see December 26th), visible as an extended trail of faint stars roughly following the southern route of Eridanus and Reticulum (the Net) (see December 24th) located just to the east of Horologium. Lying just to the north of Horologium is the tiny constellation Caelum (the Graving Tool) (see December 18th) which is adjoined by the distinctive shape of Columba (the Dove) (see December 17th). Slightly to the south of these are Dorado (the Goldfish) (see December 21st) and Pictor (the Painter's Easel) (see December 19th), both of which are found to the west of the brilliant Canopus, the leading star of Carina (the Keel) (see February 12th).

Adjoining Carina to the north are Puppis (the Poop or Stern) (see February 22nd) and Vela (the Sail) (see February 19th). Two stars in Carina and two in Vela together make up the prominent asterism the 'False Cross' (see February 17th).

The three constellations Carina, Puppis and Vela were drawn up by the French astronomer Nicolas Louis de Lacaille from the stars forming the old Argo Navis (the Ship Argo) (see February 12th). Lacaille considered Argo Navis as being far too large and unwieldy and he divided the celestial ship into the three separate constellations that grace modern star charts. This leads us nicely on to our final port of call (a suitable expression given the nautical theme of this particular region of sky), which is the tiny constellation Pyxis (the Mariner's Compass) (see February 26th) which lies immediately to the east of Puppis.

STARS OF NORTHERN SPRING/SOUTHERN AUTUMN

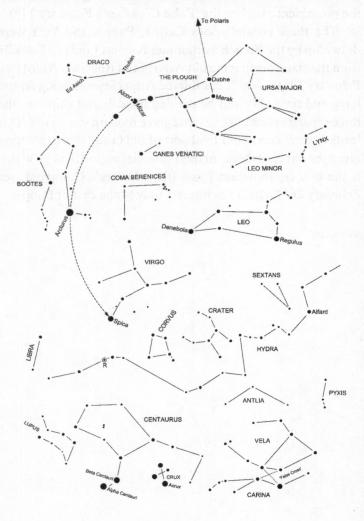

L ocated at or near the overhead point during the spring night sky, as seen from mid-northern latitudes, is the familiar shape of the Plough formed from the seven brightest stars in the constellation Ursa Major (the Great Bear) (see March 7th). The rest of the Great Bear stretches out to the west of the Plough, while immediately to its north is part of the winding constellation Draco (the Dragon) (see October 9th), including the two stars Ed Asich and Thuban.

If you follow the line from Merak, through Dubhe, both located in the 'bowl' of the Plough, you will reach Polaris, the Pole Star (not shown on this chart – see Stars of the Northern Circumpolar Sky). Polaris is the brightest star in Ursa Minor (the Little Bear) (see March 12th) and marks the location of the north celestial pole.

The famous naked-eye double formed from Alcor and Mizar (see March 10th and 11th) lies in the Plough 'handle', and located just to the south of the Plough are the faint constellations Canes Venatici (the Hunting Dogs) (see May 22nd) and Coma Berenices (Berenice's Hair) (see May 25th). Following the curve of the line of stars in the Plough handle southwards as shown here will take you to brilliant Arcturus, the leading star in the constellation Boötes (the Herdsman) (see May 17th). Extending the line further will eventually lead you to Spica, the brightest star in the constellation Virgo (the Virgin) (see May 30th).

The other prominent group in this region of sky is Leo (the Lion) (see April 1st) located to the north west of Virgo. If the sky is dark and clear, you should be able to pick out the small and rather faint constellations Leo Minor (the Little Lion) (see April 11th) and Lynx (the Lynx) (see March 19th), located in the area of sky just to the north of Leo. Clear skies will also be needed to reveal the small constellations Corvus (the Crow) (see June 4th) and Crater (the Cup) (see June 4th) to the south and southwest of Virgo. An even bigger challenge is to pick out the tiny Sextans (the Sextant) (see March 30th), found a little way to the south of the bright star Regulus in Leo.

Spanning the skies to the south of Corvus, Crater and Sextans is the long and winding constellation Hydra (the Water Snake) (see April 14th). The brightest star in Hydra is Alfard, found just to the west of Sextans, from where the rest of the group stretches away. Try finding Alfard and then, with binoculars, make your way along the body of the Water Snake! As you work eastwards you will eventually arrive at the Mira-type variable star R Hydrae (see April 22nd), located a little to the south of Spica in Virgo.

Moving further into the southern sky we arrive at Antlia (the Air Pump) (see February 27th) and Pyxis (the Mariner's Compass) (see February 26th), two tiny and fairly inconspicuous constellations located to the north of the larger and brighter Vela (the Sail) (see February 19th). Immediately to the south of Vela we see part of Carina (the Keel) (see February 12th), these two constellations together playing host to the asterism the 'False Cross' (see February 17th) which is formed from two stars in Carina and two in Vela. The False Cross is often confused with nearby Crux (the Cross) (see April 23rd) which is located some way to the east.

The tiny but distinctive Crux is surrounded by the southern reaches of Centaurus (the Centaur) (see May 2nd), its two brightest stars Alpha and Beta Centauri particularly prominent. Centaurus is bordered to the east by the constellation Lupus (the Wolf) (see June 16th).

STARS OF NORTHERN
SUMMER / SOUTHERN WINTER

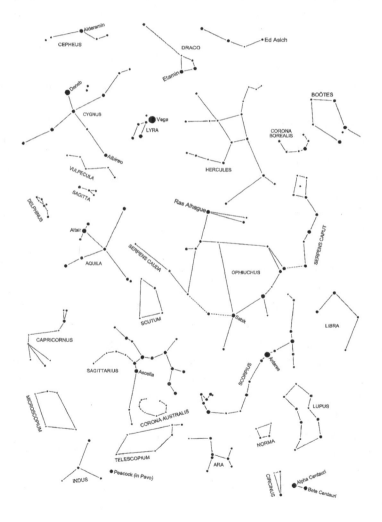

For backyard astronomers in the northern hemisphere, the night sky at this time of year is dominated by the three constellations Cygnus (the Swan) (see September 4th), Lyra (the Lyre) (see September 13th) and Aquila (the Eagle) (see September 1st) which lie close to the overhead point during summer evenings as seen from mid-northern latitudes. Particularly prominent is the triangle formed from the bright stars Deneb in Cygnus, Vega in Lyra and Altair in Aquila. Known as the Summer Triangle (see September 2nd), this trio of stars is unmistakable and from here many of the other constellations on the chart can be located.

If you look in the region of sky between, and slightly to the east of, Aquila and Cygnus you will spot the three smaller groups Vulpecula (the Fox) (see September 23rd), Sagitta (the Arrow) (see September 28th) and Delphinus (the Dolphin) (see October 1st) while to the immediate southwest of Aquila is the faint but distinctive shape of Scutum (the Shield) (see August 27th). All four of these constellations should be visible to the naked eye if the sky is dark and clear, although a pair of binoculars will help you to pick them out.

To the west of Lyra we see the conspicuous quadrilateral of stars marking the constellation of Hercules (see June 30th). Known as the 'Keystone', the rest of Hercules can be seen spreading away from it. Look immediately to the west of Hercules and you'll spot the distinctive circlet of stars forming Corona Borealis (the Northern Crown) (see June 26th) just beyond which is part of the distinctive shape of Boötes (the Herdsman). The whole of Boötes is shown on the Northern Spring / Southern Autumn chart.

If the sky is really dark and clear, you should be able to trace the winding pattern of Serpens Caput (the 'head' of the Serpent) (see July 6th) snaking towards the south. If you follow the line of stars shown here you'll arrive at Ophiuchus (the Serpent Bearer) (see July 13th) with, to the east of Ophiuchus, the smaller line of stars Serpens Cauda (the 'tail' of the Serpent) (see July 6th). According to Greek mythology, Ophiuchus depicts Asclepius, the god of medicine and son of Apollo. He is holding the head of the serpent in his left hand and the tail in his right hand, thereby splitting the constellation Serpens into two parts.

To the southwest of Ophiuchus we can see the brilliant red Antares, the leading star in Scorpius (the Scorpion) (see July 21st). The name Antares means 'rival of Mars' derived from the fact that when Mars (often referred to as the red planet) and Antares are in the same area of sky, the two objects rival each other for prominence.

Immediately to the west of Scorpius is the constellation Libra (the Scales) (see June 21st) while to its east is the large and sprawling Sagittarius (the Archer) (see August 12th). The distinctive circlet of stars forming Corona Australis (the Southern Crown) (see August 10th) can be seen immediately to the south of Sagittarius with the faint constellation Microscopium (the Microscope) (see October 29th) nearby. The two faint constellations Indus (the Indian) (see October 28th) and Telescopium (the Telescope) (see August 8th) occupy the region of sky immediately to the south of this grouping.

Microscopium, Indus and Telescopium are all relatively faint and you may need a fairly dark, clear night in order to pick them out. Somewhat easier to locate is the tiny but distinctive Ara (the Altar) (see August 1st) which can be found just to the south of the prominent curve of stars forming the Sting of Scorpius (see July 22nd). The last three constellations depicted here are Norma (the Level) (see June 14th), Lupus (the Wolf) (see June 16th) and Circinus (the Compasses) (see May

28

15th) which, although not particularly prominent, can be tracked down fairly easily in view of their proximity to the bright pair of stars Alpha and Beta Centauri.

STARS OF NORTHERN
AUTUMN/SOUTHERN SPRING

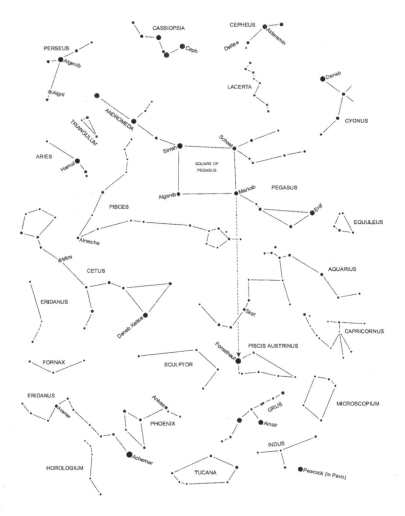

The night sky at this time of year plays host to Cassiopeia (see November 19th), which can be found at or near the overhead point when viewing from mid-northern latitudes. The southern regions of Cepheus, together with the variable star Delta Cephei (see November 26th), lie just to the west of Cassiopeia while just to the south of Cepheus is the tiny constellation Lacerta (the Lizard) (see November 27th). Taking the form of a zigzag line of faint stars, Lacerta may not be easy to pick out without some form of optical aid, unlike the bright star Deneb in the neighbouring constellation Cygnus (the Swan), one of the stars forming the conspicuous Summer Triangle (see September 2nd) which extends beyond the borders of this chart.

A little way to the south of Cassiopeia is the line of stars forming Andromeda (see October 30th) with Sirrah, the westernmost star in Andromeda, being located at the corner of the adjoining and very conspicuous Square of Pegasus (the Winged Horse) (see October 13th). This huge quadrilateral of stars is a striking feature of the night sky at this time of year. The rest of Pegasus extends westward towards Enif, the brightest star in Pegasus, adjoining which we find the tiny constellation Equuleus (the Little Horse) (see October 18th).

Located just to the north east of Andromeda is the bright star Algenib in Perseus (see November 12th) while just to the south of Algenib is the famous variable star Algol (see November 14th).

To the southeast of Andromeda are the two tiny but prominent groups Triangulum (the Triangle) (see November 4th) and Aries (the Ram) (see November 8th) and extending in a meandering line from Andromeda to the region south of the Square of Pegasus is the large but generally faint constellation Pisces (the Fishes) (see November 28th).

Bordering Pegasus we find Aquarius (the Water Carrier) (see October 22nd), located by following a line from Scheat, through Markab, both in the Square of Pegasus, and towards the south as shown here. On the way to the bright star Fomalhaut you will pass just to the east of the star Skat in Aquarius from where you should be able to make out the rest of this large and sprawling constellation. Unless the sky is really dark and clear, you may need binoculars to detect the stars of Aquarius, as well as those forming the constellation Capricornus (the Goat) (see October 3rd), found immediately to the southwest of Aquarius.

Staying with the watery theme, bordering the south-eastern edge of Pisces, and the north western reaches of Eridanus (the River) (see December 28th) is another faint constellation, this being Cetus (the Whale) (see December 2nd). The whale's tail is marked by the fairly prominent star Deneb Kaitos, which can be located by following a line from Sirrah, through Algenib (in the Square of Pegasus) a little way to the south. To the northeast of Deneb Kaitos is the famous long-period variable star Mira (see December 4th).

The bright star Fomalhaut in the constellation Piscis Austrinus (the Southern Fish) (see October 26th) can be found by following a line southwards from Scheat, through Markab, both in the Square of Pegasus. Once you have located Fomalhaut, and providing the sky is reasonably dark and clear, you may be able to pick out some of the fainter stars in Piscis Austrinus, as well as those in the neighbouring constellations Sculptor (the Sculptor) (see December 5th) and, further to the east, Fornax (the Furnace) (see December 27th).

To the south of Piscis Austrinus we have Grus (the Crane) (see October 27th) which in turn is flanked by the quartet of comparatively faint constellations Microscopium (the

Microscope) (see October 29th), Indus (the Indian) (see October 28th), Tucana (the Toucan) (see December 8th) and Phoenix (the Phoenix) (see December 6th), its leading star Ankaa reasonably conspicuous to the southeast of Fomalhaut. Immediately to the southeast of Phoenix is the southern extremity of Eridanus (the River) (see December 28th), marked by its leading star Achernar. As we will see, Achernar is a good guide to locating many of the fainter groups in this region of the sky, including Horologium (the Pendulum Clock) (see December 26th), visible as an extended trail of faint stars located nearby.

STARS OF THE SOUTHERN CIRCUMPOLAR SKY

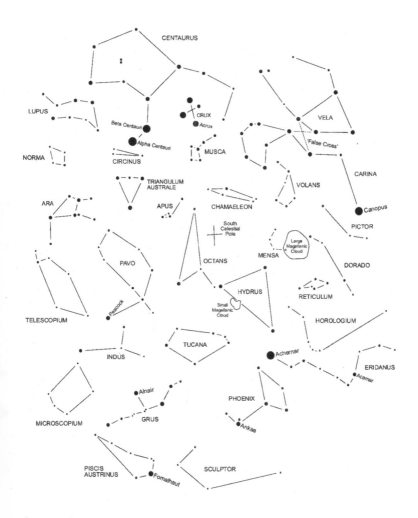

As we have seen, a circumpolar star or constellation is one that never sets as seen from a given location, but always stays above the observer's horizon and can be viewed all year round (see The Celestial Sphere pp 6-15). The area of sky depicted here shows stars which are circumpolar as seen from roughly mid-southern latitudes and includes the constellations that surround Octans (the Octant) (see December 16th), the group which plays host to Sigma Octantis (not depicted on this chart) the faint star which marks the approximate position of the south celestial pole. Unlike its northern counterpart, there is no really bright star marking the south celestial pole position.

Many of the groups in this region of sky are rather faint, including Hydrus (the Little Water Snake) (see December 14th), Tucana (the Toucan) (see December 8th), Mensa (the Table Mountain) (see December 23rd) and Dorado (the Goldfish) (see December 21st) although this quartet of obscure constellations can at least lay claim to the fact that they host the two nearby irregular galaxies the Large and Small Magellanic Clouds. The Large Magellanic Cloud (see December 22nd) lies on the border between Mensa and Dorado, the Small Magellanic Cloud (see December 9th) straddling the region between the two constellations Hydrus and Tucana.

Lying quite close to the triangle of stars forming Hydrus is the bright star Achernar in Eridanus (the River) (see December 28th). Achernar is fairly easy to pick out and acts as a finding aid for the relatively obscure constellations that lie in the same region of sky including Phoenix (the Phoenix) (see December 6th), Horologium (the Pendulum Clock) (see December 26th) and Reticulum (the Net) (see December 24th). Slightly to the north of Phoenix we see the dim Sculptor (the Sculptor) (see December 5th) and the prominent Fomalhaut, the leading star in Piscis Austrinus (the Southern Fish) (see October 26th).

Bordering Piscis Austrinus to the south we have the reasonably prominent Grus (the Crane) (see October 27th) with the fainter and more obscure Microscopium (the Microscope) (see October 29th) nearby. Indus (the Indian) (see October 28th) borders Microscopium, this forming a triangle of constellations with Pavo (the Peacock) (see August 5th) and Telescopium (the Telescope) (see August 8th).

Slightly more noticeable are Ara (the Altar) (see August 1st) and Triangulum Australe (the Southern Triangle) (see June 9th) both of which, along with the fainter trio Norma (the Level) (see June 14th), Circinus (the Compasses) (see May 15th) and Lupus (the Wolf) (see June 16th) can be tracked down by using the bright pair of stars Alpha and Beta Centauri in Centaurus (the Centaur) (see May 2nd) as a location finder.

The southern regions of Centaurus surround the bright constellation Crux (the Cross) (see April 23rd) while immediately to the south of Crux we find the tiny but conspicuous Musca (the Fly) (see May 10th). Lying close to the south celestial pole is the less prominent trio Chamaeleon (the Chameleon) (see May 13th), Apus (the Bird of Paradise) (see June 11th) and Volans (the Flying Fish) (see February 18th).

Located close to the bright star Canopus in Carina (the Keel) (see February 12th) is the bent line of three faint stars forming Pictor (the Painter's Easel) (see December 19th). Carina itself, along with adjoining Vela (the Sail) (see February 19th) are considerably more prominent, as is the asterism the 'False Cross' (see February 17th) which is formed from two stars in Carina and two in Vela. This pattern is often confused with nearby Crux which is located some way to the east.

In spite of this area of sky containing mainly faint and sometimes obscure groups, the region is ringed by the bright stars Alpha and Beta Centauri in Centaurus, Canopus in

Carina and Achernar in Eridanus. Using these stars as a framework, and arming yourself with the accompanying chart, you should be able to identify the south circumpolar constellations.

JANUARY

January 1st

ORION

Orion is arguably the most beautiful constellation in the sky. Straddling the celestial equator, Orion is visible high in the southern winter sky (for northern hemisphere observers) and high in the northern summer sky (for observers in the southern hemisphere).

Orion's conspicuous pattern of bright stars is unmistakable and is visible from almost every inhabited part of the world. Once seen, this splendid constellation is unlikely to be forgotten, and is an excellent starting point for our journey around the night sky...

January 2nd

According to legend, Orion was one of the sons of Neptune and a mighty hunter who boasted far and wide of his prowess. He even went so far as to declare himself a match even for the gods. Naturally, this angered Diana, the goddess of the hunt, who subsequently challenged Orion to a hunting match. Orion gladly accepted and he and Diana spent many days in the chase, but in the end there was nothing to choose between them. The contest was declared a draw and, once more, Orion bragged. In a fit of anger, Diana commanded a scorpion to crawl out of the ground and kill Orion, following which she placed the mighty hunter among the stars where he can be seen to this day. The scorpion was also placed in the sky (see July 21st), although at a point opposite that of Orion, so that the creature can cause him no further harm.

January 3rd

Facing due north, and looking high upward, the gaze meets with five stars of nearly equal brightness, in form resembling a sprawling capital 'W'. They make the principal outline of the constellation Cassiopeia, the Lady in the Chair. I cherish a kindly remembrance for Cassiopeia;

it was the first star group I ever recognised, when, under almost heart-breaking difficulties, I was trying to learn the geography of the sky.

How beautiful is that broad, luminous band against which the 'W' is projected! It is the Milky Way. I can trace it to-night through the Cross, but that constellation is now too near the horizon for me to see the exquisite light and shade of the Galaxy in its neighbourhood.

But of the stellar Milky Way? Is there anything in the universe more awful in its sublimity? One stands appalled on the very threshold of inquiry into so transcendent a mystery as this.

January 4th

One of the most conspicuous stars in Orion is Betelgeuse, the name of this star being derived from the Arabic *'yad al-jauza'* meaning 'the Hand of al-jauza'. Medieval translators mistakenly took the first letter as being a 'B' rather than a 'Y', from which the currently accepted name eventually emerged. The exact identity of 'al-jauza' is not clear, although it appears to be a reference to a female figure that Arabic astronomers saw as being depicted by the stars that represent Orion.

Betelgeuse is a red supergiant and one of the largest stars known to astronomers. It shines from a distance of over 500 light years, its ruddy glow forming a sharp contrast with the brilliant white of Rigel, a supergiant star with a luminosity of over 50,000 times that of our Sun. Checking these two stars out with binoculars brings out the colour difference between them very well. Rigel has a diameter of around 40 million miles and lies at a distance of around 900 light years, which means the light we are seeing now set off on its immense journey towards us only a few years after the Domesday Book was compiled. The name Rigel is derived from the Arabic *'rijl'* meaning 'the Foot'.

January 5th

Along with Betelgeuse and Rigel, the two blue giant stars Bellatrix and Saiph form the conspicuous Rectangle of Orion. Bellatrix is the third brightest star in Orion and lies at a distance of around 250 light years. Saiph, the sixth brightest star in the constellation, is somewhat further away, shining with a magnitude of 2.07 from a distance of over 650 light years. Its name is derived from the Arabic '*saif al-jabbar*' meaning 'the Sword of the Giant.'

January 6th

If the night is really clear, or with the help of binoculars, try to seek out the lion's skin which acts as Orion's shield. This is represented by a faint line of stars from the northernmost Omicron[1] southwards to Pi[6]. The great hunter's club is depicted by a triangle of faint stars located immediately to the north of Betelgeuse and comprised of Mu, Nu and Xi Orionis.

January 7th

Alnitak is the easternmost of the three stars that form the Belt of Orion. Shining from a distance of around 800 light years its name means 'the Girdle' and the area immediately surrounding it is rich in stars and is well worth a look through binoculars. The central star in the Belt of Orion is Alnilam, its name derived from the Arabic for 'String of Pearls'. Alnilam lies at a distance of over 1,300 light years making it somewhat more distant than Mintaka whose light has taken around 900 years to reach us. Mintaka is located just to the west of Alnilam and completes the Belt of Orion.

* * *

January 8th

We know the above three stars as the Belt of Orion, although they have been given other names in the past. Australian natives referred to them as 'Young Men', Greenlanders called them 'The Seal Hunters' and mariners often referred to them as 'The Golden Yardarm'. More common names include 'The Three Kings' and 'Jacob's Rod'. Perhaps the daftest episode relating to the naming of these three stars took place in 1807 when the University of Leipzig christened them 'Napoleon', whereupon an irate Englishman promptly retaliated with the title 'Nelson'. Needless to say, neither name has found its way onto modern star charts!

January 9th

A little to the south of the Belt of Orion can be seen a line of faint stars commonly referred to as the Sword of Orion and here can be found the Orion Nebula, by far the most famous object in the constellation. The Orion Nebula is also known as Messier 42 (M42), derived from its number in the Messier Catalogue of astronomical objects (which includes star clusters, nebulae and galaxies), compiled by the French astronomer Charles Messier in the 18th century. This object is undoubtedly the most famous and eye-catching of all the objects in Messier's Catalogue and records of it go back to the earliest days of recorded astronomy. M42 can be seen as a hazy patch of diffuse light surrounding the group of stars at the southern end of the sword, taking the form of a giant, irregular cloud and shining because of the stars embedded within it.

On really dark and clear nights the Orion Nebula is visible as a faint glowing patch, which seldom fails to impress those who look at it, and it is safe to say that there is little in the heavens to equal this magnificent object. The wide field of view of a pair of binoculars brings out the nebula very well, and the sight leaves the observer with a sense of wonder when it is realised that inside this glowing cloud stars are actually being formed.

January 10th

As with other constellations, the stars in Orion can be used as 'pointers' to help locate other nearby star patterns. Finding our way around the night sky by using stars as pointers will occur with other constellations elsewhere in this book.

But coming back to Orion for the moment, if you follow the line of three stars forming the Belt of Orion to the south east as shown here, you will arrive at Sirius, the leading star in the neighbouring constellation Canis Major (the Great Dog) and by far the brightest star in the sky (apart from the Sun, of course).

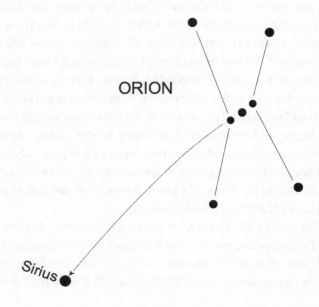

ORION

Sirius

January 11th

Canis Major represents one of Orion's hunting dogs, the other being the adjoining Canis Minor (the Little Dog) (see January 15th), located just to the north east. Together the trio are chasing a hare, depicted by the constellation Lepus and located immediately to the south of Orion (see February 5th). Canis Major can be seen in its entirety from central Canada, northern Europe and central Russia and from all locations further south.

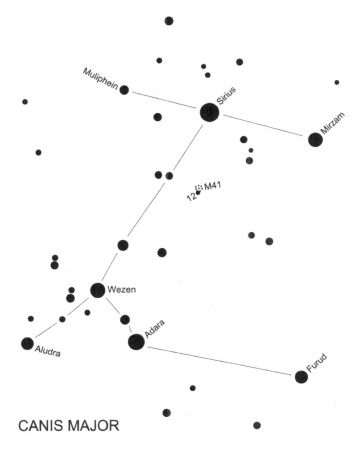

CANIS MAJOR

January 12th

At magnitude −1.46 brilliant blue-white Sirius is the brightest star in the sky. It is also one of the closest stars to the Earth, shining from a distance of just 8.6 light years. Sirius is also known as the Dog Star, from its role as the leading star in Canis Major. The rising of this star at dawn during the time of the Greeks heralded the approach of summer and its hot (or 'dog') days. So bright and prominent is this star that the Greeks believed it to have a heating effect on the Earth, its name being derived from the Greek *'seirius'* meaning 'scorching' or 'glowing'.

'Sirius the Superb, the King of Suns. It is the brightest star in the whole firmament, and the wonder and admiration of mankind over most of the inhabited globe. Lustrous to the last degree is the Dog Star...'

January 13th

To either side of Sirius are Muliphein and Mirzam while the rest of Canis Major stretches to the south from this trio. Wezen, Aludra, Adara and Furud can be seen very close to the southern horizon when viewed from mid-northern latitudes and can be difficult to spot, although they may be picked out with binoculars if the sky is dark and clear.

January 14th

Canis Major contains a number of open star clusters, one of the brightest being M41, the discovery of which is credited to the Italian astronomer Giovanni Batista Hodierna during the early part of the 17th century. If the sky is really dark and clear, M41 is actually visible to the naked eye and may have been spotted by the Greek philosopher Aristotle during the 4th century BC. Messier added it to his catalogue in 1765, describing it as: *'A cluster of stars below Sirius; this cluster appears nebulous in an ordinary telescope ...it is nothing more than a cluster of small stars'*. With a magnitude of 4.5 and located at a distance of 2,400 light years, M41 contains about 100 stars and measures around 25 light years across.

This cluster is easily seen through binoculars and you can track it down by checking out the area of sky a little way to the south of Sirius. Look out for a misty patch of light, rather than a star like point. M41 forms a triangle with Sirius and the star Nu². The faint star 12, which lies on the southern edge of the cluster, is also a guide.

January 15th

CANIS MINOR

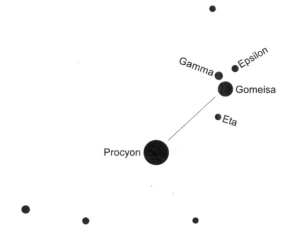

The tiny constellation of Canis Minor (the Little Dog) is located a little to the north east of Canis Major and is marked by its leading star Procyon. This group can be seen from every inhabited part of the world.

Although generally identified as one of Orion's hunting dogs, the astronomers of ancient Egypt linked Canis Minor with Anubis, the jackal-headed dog in Egyptian mythology associated with mummification and the after-life. The group is also identified with the gigantic Teumessian Fox, a creature that, according to legend, was destined never to be caught. This huge fox was one of the children of Echidna, a fearsome being who was half-woman, half-snake and known as the 'Mother of All Monsters'. The Theban general Amphitron was given the seemingly-impossible task of destroying the Teumessian Fox to which end he fetched the magical dog Laelaps who had the distinction of catching every creature he chased. However, the abilities of these two creatures were mutually excluding and Zeus, seeing the situation as being irresolvable, placed them both in the sky where they can be seen to this day. Laelaps is identified with the neighbouring constellation Canis Major.

January 16th

Sirius (in Canis Major) and Procyon are two of the closest stars to our solar system. Procyon shines from a distance of just over 11 light years, a couple of light years or so further away than Sirius. To the naked eye Procyon looks white, although a good pair of binoculars may reveal its slightly yellowish tint. Procyon has a true luminosity of around six times that of our Sun.

January 17th

Procyon derives its name from the Greek for 'before the dog', alluding to the fact that Canis Minor rises before the neighbouring celestial dog Canis Major. Gomeisa, on the other hand, has a name derived from the Arabic *'al-ghumaisa'* meaning 'the Dim, Watery-eyed or Weeping One', a name that was originally applied by Arabic astronomers to the constellation as a whole and one which illustrates the point that star names are quite often nothing if not imaginative! Shining from a distance of around 170 light years Gomeisa is a white star with a true luminosity of some 250 times that of our Sun. Gamma, which shines from a distance of over 300 light years, has a distinctly orange-yellow tint which can be spotted through binoculars. The area of sky containing Gomeisa, Gamma, Epsilon and Eta is quite pretty and well worth a look through binoculars.

January 18th
Located a little to the north of Procyon are the two bright stars Castor and Pollux, the leading stars in the constellation of Gemini (the Twins). Gemini is one of the oldest groups in the heavens and was depicted on the star charts of Babylonian astronomers as long ago as 1,500 BC. Both Greeks and Romans looked upon these two stars as representing Castor and Pollux, the twin sons of Jupiter and Leda. They were regarded as being patrons of navigators and there is a Biblical reference (Acts 28:11) to this effect:

> *And after three months we departed in a ship of Alexandria, which had wintered in the isle, whose sign was Castor and Pollux.*

When suitably placed in the sky, the entire constellation can be viewed from virtually every inhabited part of the world. Once you have identified the two leading stars of Gemini, the distinctive shape of the constellation can be picked out in the form of lines of stars stretching away to the west of Castor and Pollux in the general direction of Orion.

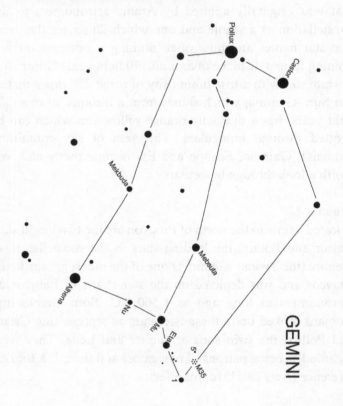

January 19th

Shining from a distance of around 50 light years, Castor is a rather unusual star. It is a binary system with two companion stars in orbit around each other, each orbit taking a little under four centuries to complete. It was first seen as a double by the Italian astronomer Giovanni Cassini in 1678, and a fairly large telescope is needed to resolve this pair. A third member of the group has also been discovered, this being a faint red dwarf star which orbits the main pair. What complicates matters even further is that each of these three stars has been found to be a binary star in its own right, making Castor a rather elaborate sextuple system!

January 20th
Pollux is a little brighter than Castor and is also a bit closer, its light having taken around 35 years to reach us. Pollux has a true luminosity of over 40 times that of our own Sun, its yellow-orange tint being easily seen in binoculars and contrasting with the whiteness of Castor.

January 21st
Alhena lies at a distance of just over 100 light years, shining with a magnitude of 1.93 and a true luminosity of around 160 times that of our Sun. Somewhat further away are Mebsuta and Mekbuda, which lie at distances of around 850 light years and 1,200 light years respectively. Both of these stars are very luminous, each with a true brightness of several thousand times that of our parent star.

January 22nd
Through binoculars, the orange hues of Mu and Eta are fairly conspicuous. The western region of Gemini, including the stars Mu, Nu and nearby Eta, straddles the Milky Way, and binoculars or a small telescope will show many star fields in this area, of particular interest being the open star cluster M35 seen in the area of sky a little way to the north west of Eta and forming a triangle with Eta and the star 1 Geminorum.

*

January 23rd

If the night is really dark and clear, M35 can be glimpsed with the naked eye as a faint, misty patch of light immediately to the north east of the star 1 Geminorum, and binoculars bring the cluster out quite well. Discovered independently during the 1740s by the Swiss astronomer Jean-Philippe Loys de Cheseaux and the English astronomer John Bevis, it was described by de Cheseaux as: *'A star cluster above the northern feet of Gemini.'*

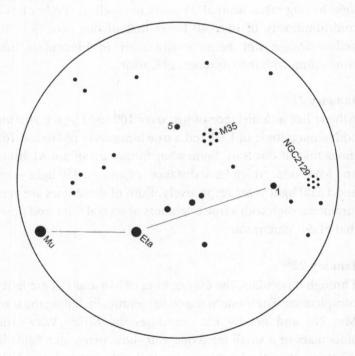

M35 contains well over a hundred stars and lies at a distance of around 2,800 light years. Providing the sky is dark and clear, binoculars may also reveal NGC 2129, another open cluster located at a distance of over 7,000 light years and seen more or less on the opposite side of the star 1 Geminorum as shown. This object may be a little difficult to spot, although with perseverance you should pick it up. This finder chart shows the area around these two star clusters in more detail, the individual stars shown being those visible through binoculars. Use the finder chart to help you star-hop your way from Mu, through Eta and on towards your target! Binoculars will probably not resolve any individual stars within NGC 2129, although you may have a bit more luck with M35.

The reference for NGC 2129 is derived from its number in the New General Catalogue of Nebulae and Clusters of Stars (NGC) first published in 1888 by the Danish astronomer John Louis Emil Dreyer and which contains details of 7,840 star clusters, nebulae and galaxies.

January 24th

Auriga (the Charioteer) is one of the most prominent of the constellations and there are numerous legends attached to it, one being its identification as Myrtilus, the son of Hermes and charioteer of King Oenomaus of Elis, a district of southern Greece. The King had a beautiful daughter, Hippodamia, who had many suitors but who her father was reluctant to let go. This is perhaps understandable as Oenomaus had been told by an oracle that his son-in-law would cause his death. Therefore Oenomaus set a challenge whereby whoever could beat him in a chariot race would win his daughter's hand in marriage. Unfortunately for the would-be suitors, Oenomaus had the fastest chariot in Greece which, together with the fact that his charioteer was the skilful Myrtilus, ensured that between them they easily beat any challenge they met.

AURIGA

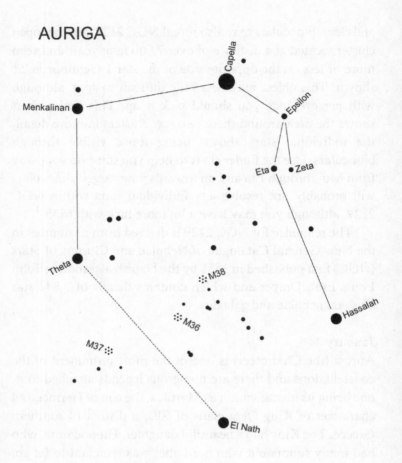

After a dozen or so suitors met the challenge, and failed, along came the handsome Pelops, the son of Tantalus and grandson of Zeus. Pelops and Hippodamia fell in love, so much so that Myrtilus was persuaded by Hippodamia to throw the race and let Pelops win. This he duly did by sabotaging the chariot, which resulted in King Oenomaus being thrown off and killed. Unfortunately Myrtilus was also in love with Hippodamia which set up a rather awkward love triangle. The problem was solved, however, when Pelops drowned his rival in the sea, following which unfortunate event, Hermes placed his son Myrtilus in the sky where we see him today.

January 25th

Auriga can be seen in its entirety from most of South America and South Africa and the northern half of Australia and from locations to the north of these. At first sight, the stars of Auriga appear to form a striking circlet. This is a little deceptive and what appears to be the southernmost star in the group, El Nath, is now a member of the neighbouring constellation Taurus (the Bull) (see January 28th). El Nath depicts the tip of the bull's northern horn, its title derived from the Arabic for 'the Butting One'. Historically, the star has been considered as belonging to either constellation and, when linked to Auriga, Arabic astronomers knew it as 'Heel of the Rein-holder'. In keeping with the charioteer theme, the name of the star Menkalinan is derived from the Arabic for 'Shoulder of the Rein-holder'.

January 26th

Auriga's leading star Capella has a distinctive yellow colour. Ranked as the sixth brightest star in the entire sky, Capella has a magnitude of 0.08 and shines from a distance of around 42 light years. Its name is derived from the Latin for 'she-goat' and one of the legends attached to this star refers to a Cretan goat named Amalthea who suckled the infant Zeus and who was repaid for her efforts by being placed among the stars. Alongside Capella are her two kids, known collectively by their Latin name Haedi (the Kids) and represented by the two stars Eta and Zeta Aurigae. These two stars form a distinctive little triangle with Epsilon, a star which was known to Arabic astronomers as *'al-ma'az'* (the He Goat).

January 27th
Because Auriga straddles the Milky Way, the whole constellation is rich in stars and carefully sweeping the area with binoculars will reveal many beautiful star fields. However, pride of place must go to the three open star clusters M36, M37 and M38 which lie in a neat line straddling the area between Theta and El Nath.

These three clusters were discovered by the Italian astronomer Giovanni Batista Hodierna during the early part of the 17th century. Hodierna described them as: *'...nebulous patch(es) in Auriga.'* Providing the sky is really dark and clear you should be able to spot these three objects with binoculars, through which they will appear as faint misty patches of light, much as they will have done to Hodierna. M37 is the brightest of the three and is also considered to be the finest of the trio. M36 is a little fainter and less bright still is M38. Although binoculars will enable you to pick these three clusters out against the backdrop of sky, you'll need at least a small telescope in order to bring out any of the individual stars within them.

In his book *'Star and Weather Gossip'*, Elgie quotes a few lines of verse, written by the American writer Charles Nevers Holmes and culled from the American magazine Popular Astronomy, offering a romantic view of the section of night sky described in the paragraphs above:

> *When royal Rigel glitters like a gem*
> *Where gleams Orion's glory in the sky*
> *And Queen Capella like a diadem*

Reigns o'er Auriga with a watchful eye;
When winter's thraldom rests on vale and hill,
And skies are clear, and stars shine coldly bright,
Ere most men dream or city's voice is still,
King Sirius again adorns the night.

January 28th

The prominent constellation of Taurus (the Bull) adjoins Orion, its leading star Aldebaran easily located by following the line of stars in the Belt of Orion to the north west as shown here. Alternatively, the star El Nath can be used as a guide to locating Taurus from the neighbouring constellation Auriga (see January 25th). At around this time of year, and when suitably placed in the sky, the whole of Taurus is visible from every inhabited part of the world.

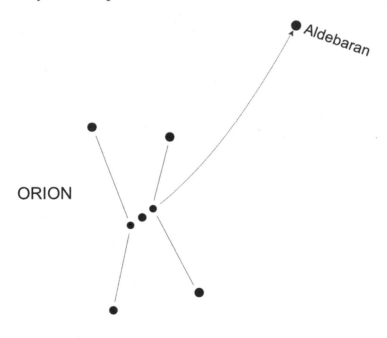

January 29th

Eight o'clock! After a day of blinding snow squalls, which have turned the city and district into Fairyland, a keen frost has set in. Through the streets a howling wind blows, deadly chill, and above its uproar there arise the excited cries of youthful toboganners as they dash down the snow-covered slopes of the adjacent streets. What a scouring has the sky received from those blizzards! And how brilliantly starlit it would be were not the moon – now almost full – shining so brightly yonder between Castor and Pollux and the eastern horizon!

January 30th

According to one legend, Taurus represents Zeus who, during one of his extra-marital affairs, disguised himself as a white bull with the sole intention of abducting Europa, the beautiful daughter of King Agenor of Phoenica.

Europa was playing on the beach when Zeus joined her father's herd of bulls which was grazing nearby. Entranced by the beautiful white coat and splendid shiny horns of Zeus, Europa wandered closer to take a look, eventually climbing onto the bull's back. At this point Zeus quickly entered the sea and swam away with Europa while she was clinging tightly to his back. They eventually reached Crete where Zeus revealed his true identity. He gave her a number of gifts including a beautiful necklace made by the Greek god Hephaestus and Laelaps, a hunting dog which never failed to catch its prey. As previously noted, Laelaps is identified with the constellation Canis Major (see January 15th).

* * *

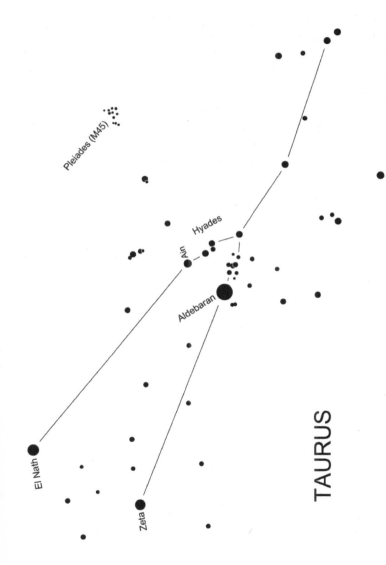

Pleiades (M45)

Hyades

Ain

Aldebaran

El Nath

Zeta

TAURUS

January 31st

The brightest star in Taurus is the orange giant Aldebaran, which shines at magnitude 0.87 from a distance of around 65 light years. Its name is derived from the Arabic '*al-dabaran*' meaning 'the Follower', testimony to the fact that the star 'follows' the nearby Pleiades star cluster through the heavens. This giant star has a diameter of more than 40 times that of the Sun and a true luminosity of over 400 times that of our parent star. Aldebaran represents the southern eye of the celestial bull, the northern eye denoted by the yellow giant star Ain (see February 1st).

FEBRUARY

February 1st
Another giant star is El Nath, shining with a magnitude of 1.65 from a distance of around 135 light years. This is the second brightest star in Taurus and represents one of the horns of the bull, the other horn marked by magnitude 2.97 Zeta Tauri, visible a short way to the south and the light from which has taken around 440 years to reach us. As we have seen (see January 25th) El Nath appears at first sight to be associated with the constellation Auriga, although this is not the case.

The yellow giant star Ain derives its name from the Arabic *'ain al-thaur'* meaning 'the Bull's Eye' and denotes the northern eye of Taurus, the southern eye marked by the orange giant star Aldebaran (see January 31st). Shining with a magnitude of 3.53 from a distance of around 145 light years, Ain is one of the brighter members of the Hyades open star cluster (see February 2nd).

February 2nd
Taurus plays host to two famous open star clusters – the Hyades and the Pleiades. Visible close to the star Aldebaran, as seen from Earth, the Hyades marks the head of Taurus and is a V-shaped collection of around 200 stars of which Aldebaran is not actually a member. The Hyades cluster lies at a distance of around 150 light years, over twice the distance of Aldebaran, and only appears in the same line of sight as viewed from our planet.

*

February 3rd

Ten-thirty o'clock! Out of a dark, featureless sky snow is falling. The beauties of the heavens are concealed, but the earth is lovely to look upon this wintry night of early February. She invites us to gaze on the landscape wearing its new white mantle, a mantle whose reflection is the sole illuminant of the gloom, and which seems to arrest the earthward advance of the leaden sky. And has not Nature generously provided her lovers with stars of earth to-night? What beauty is there not in the myriads of glittering points that bejewel the surface of the freshly-fallen, unsullied snow! Humble stars, in truth, and evanescent! But the stars of heaven? Are they, too, not evanescent – compared with eternity?

February 4th

Somewhat more impressive than the Hyades is the Pleiades, also known as Messier 45, perhaps the most famous open star cluster in the heavens and which was eloquently described by Alfred Lord Tennyson in his poem 'Locksley Hall':

Many a night I saw the Pleiads, rising thro' the mellow shade,
Glitter like a swarm of fireflies tangled in a silver braid.

Located at a distance of around 500 light years, the stars forming this beautiful cluster are spread out over an area of space roughly equal to that of a full Moon as seen from Earth. The naked eye will show around half-a-dozen cluster members while binoculars bring out many more. However, even a small telescope will reveal dozens of individual stars within the cluster. Some of the stars in the Pleiades are enveloped in nebulosity. Visible only through large telescopes, this nebulosity is the remnant of the gas cloud from which the stars in the cluster were formed. This close-up chart shows the named individual members of the Pleiades that are visible through binoculars.

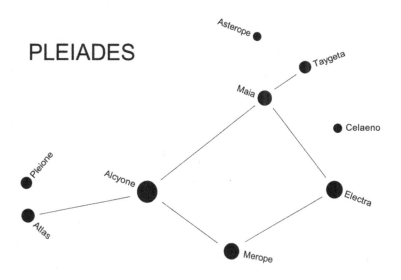

Joseph Henry Elgie outlines some interesting thoughts on the Pleiades, in particular relating to the views of William Herschel and the subject of averted vision (see Glossary) when he says:

(Alcyone) is supposed to have become brighter since Ptolemy's time. Its magnitude is now 3½, whilst the magnitudes of its companions may be taken as follows: Electra 4, Atlas 4½, Maia, Taygeta and Merope 5, Pleione 5½, Celone 7, and Asterope 8. The inclusion of three of the fainter Pleiades and the futile endeavours the vast proportion of observers make to see them with the naked eye, remind me that Herschel associates the cluster as a whole with the subject of averted vision in viewing faint objects. This is what he says:

"There is a group called the Pleiades in which six or seven stars may be noticed if the eye be directed full upon it, and many more if the eye be turned carelessly aside, while the attention is kept directed upon the group". A footnote reads: *"It is a remarkable fact that the centre of the visual area is far less sensible to feeble impressions of light than the exterior portions of the retina... the fact accounts for the multitude of stars with which we are impressed by a general view of the heavens, their paucity when we come to count them."*

February 5ᵗʰ

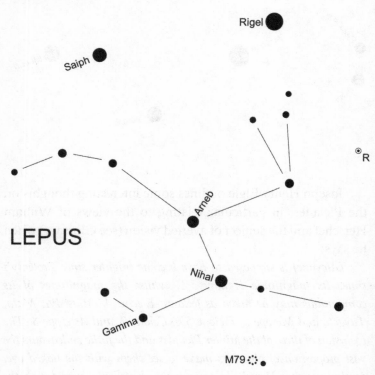

Visible immediately to the south of the conspicuous constellation Orion is Lepus (the Hare), depicted here with the two bright stars Rigel and Saiph in Orion as a guide to locating the group. A comparatively small but distinct pattern of stars, Lepus can be viewed in its entirety from central Canada, northern Europe and central Russia and from anywhere south of these regions. The origins of Lepus are somewhat uncertain although the most popular story comes from Sicily and tells us that in early times there was a great deal of crop devastation wrought by the local hare population. The Greeks who inhabited the island placed the animal up in the sky quite close to the mighty hunter Orion, presumably so that he could keep their numbers under control. The Egyptians, however, identified the stars in Lepus as the legendary Boat of Osiris, the powerful Egyptian god whose form was depicted by the nearby group of stars we now know as Orion.

February 6th

The brightest star in Lepus is the white supergiant Arneb which shines at magnitude 2.58 from a distance of a little over 2,000 light years. Arneb derives its name from the Arabic *'al-arnab'* meaning 'the Hare'. Located just to the south is the magnitude 2.81 yellow giant Nihal which, although appearing only slightly fainter than Arneb, is also a great deal closer to us, its light having taken only 160 years to reach our eyes. The true luminosity of Nihal is considerably less than that of Arneb and appears to be of roughly the same brightness simply because it is so much closer to us.

February 7th

Just to the east of Nihal is magnitude 3.59 Gamma, another yellowish-white star shining from a distance of only 29 light years. Gamma has a companion star with a distinctly orange tint which can be seen through a good pair of binoculars with a magnification of at least 12x, provided that you can hold them really steady. When seen together this pair of stars forms a pretty colour contrast.

February 8th

Lepus plays host to the globular cluster M79 which can be detected with binoculars. Discovered by the French astronomer Pierre François André Méchain in 1780, M79 lies at a distance of a little over 40,000 light years and can be detected as a hazy star-like object lying roughly on a line from Arneb, through Nihal, and projected for approximately the same distance again. Although visible in binoculars, observers at mid-northern latitudes may have trouble tracking M79 down if there is any moonlight or horizon mist or glow present, which will tend to hide it from view. For those at more southerly latitudes, however, M79 will be higher in the sky and should be picked up fairly easily.

February 9th

The Mira-type (see December 4th) variable star R Leporis, also known as Hind's Crimson Star, is located near the western boundary of the constellation as shown. This class of variable star is named after the prototype long-period variable Mira in the constellation Cetus. R Leporis shines from a distance in excess of 1,000 light years and varies in brightness between magnitudes 5.5 and 11.5 over a period of around 430 days. Its variability was discovered by the English astronomer John Russell Hind in 1845. If you take a look for the star and have difficulty in finding it, this may well be because it is at or near minimum magnitude. With a little patience, and given the fact that the star is distinguished by its strong red colour, R Leporis should eventually come into view as it brightens again. Under clear, dark skies, you should be able to follow the star through its entire period of variability with binoculars or a small telescope. It should be borne in mind, however, that variable stars of this type can take a year or more to undergo their complete cycles, so any observations you start now may not be complete until the following year!

February 10th

Let's now take our exploration of the night sky into the region of sky which lies well to the south of the celestial equator. Using the stars in Orion as a guide, follow the line from Mintaka, through Saiph as shown. This will bring you to brilliant Canopus, the leading star in the constellation Carina (the Keel) and, at magnitude − 0.72, the second brightest star in the entire sky.

February 11th

*Tonight there is a keen frost, and the cold is intensified by a brisk breeze; so here am I star-gazing in a heavy overcoat and thick gloves. The latter **will** persist in letting the pencil slip from my fingers whenever I clumsily make an attempt to write.*

February 12th

Carina is one of a trio of constellations - the others being Puppis (the Poop or Stern) and Vela (the Sail) - all of which lie in the same general area of sky and all of which represent a part or section of a ship. This is no coincidence...

During the second century, the Greek astronomer Ptolemy drew up a list of the 48 constellations that were known to, and recognised by, the astronomers of the time. One of these was Argo Navis (the Ship Argo), representing the ship in which Jason and the Argonauts journeyed to Colchis in their quest for the Golden Fleece. Argo Navis was, to say the least, large and somewhat unwieldy and its size was to prove its downfall. The constellation was eventually dismantled by the French astronomer Nicolas Louis de Lacaille who described Argo Navis as being: '...*composed of more than 160 easily visible stars...*' Lacaille divided the celestial ship into the three separate constellations Carina, Puppis and Vela, all of which have survived and made their way onto modern star charts.

Parts of Carina can be seen from the southern United States, southern Europe and southern China although it is only from latitudes south of 15°N that the whole of this constellation can be observed.

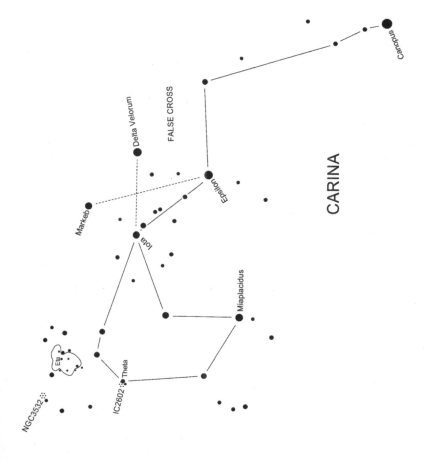

February 13th

The brilliant Canopus lies at the western end of Carina, the rest of the constellation trailing off towards the east. Canopus itself is a white supergiant star shining from a distance of over 300 light years and with a true luminosity of more than 10,000 times that of our own Sun. The star represents the pilot of the ship belonging to the Greek King Menelaus and his wife, Helen of Troy. While on their way back home from Troy their ship was blown off course and they eventually ended up in Egypt where Canopus, unfortunately, was killed by a snake shortly after he went ashore. Fittingly, and perhaps in keeping with the identification of the star as the pilot of Menelaus' ship, Canopus is often used as a navigation star by space probes.

February 14th

Other prominent stars in Carina include Miaplacidus which, at magnitude 1.67, shines from a distance of around 110 light years. The origins of this name are uncertain, although it may be derived from *'Mi'ah'*, the plural form of the Arabic for water. To the north east of Miaplacidus is the magnitude 1.86 orange giant Epsilon Carinae which is somewhat more distant, its light having taken over 600 years to reach us. Magnitude 2.74 Theta Carinae, located near the eastern border of the constellation, is a blue white star whose main claim to fame is that it is the brightest and most prominent member of the open star cluster IC 2602.

February 15th

The open cluster IC 2602, located at a distance of nearly 500 light years and containing around 60 member stars, is just one of many objects of this type found within the constellation Carina, and is well worth seeking out. Also known as the Theta Carinae Cluster, IC 2602 shines with an overall magnitude of 1.9 and is easily visible to the unaided eye. This cluster occupies an area of sky somewhat larger than the full Moon, so the wide field of view obtained with binoculars make them the ideal instrument with which to view this lovely object.

The reference for IC 2602 is derived from its number in the Index Catalogue (IC), published in 1895 as the first of two supplements (the second was published in 1908) to his New General Catalogue of Nebulae and Clusters of Stars (NGC) by the Danish astronomer John Louis Emil Dreyer (see January 23rd). Between them, the two Index Catalogues contain details of an additional 5,386 objects.

February 16th

As well as being rich in open star clusters, Carina also contains the Eta Carinae Nebula, a vast cloud of gas surrounding the variable star Eta Carinae and which rivals the Orion Nebula for splendour. Also known as the Carina Nebula, this highly luminous object is thought to lie at a distance of around 8,000 light years. The Eta Carinae Nebula was discovered by Nicolas Louis de Lacaille in 1751, during his stay in South Africa cataloguing the southern stars, and around the same time he was dismantling the constellation Argo Navis (see February 12th).

When first catalogued, the star Eta Carinae was of 3rd magnitude, although it was seen to vary considerably over the following years, reaching magnitude −0.8 in 1843, before sinking to 6th magnitude obscurity by 1868 where it remains today. Material ejected from the star, or from dust clouds around the star, are thought to play a role in the variability of Eta Carinae.

The Eta Carinae Nebula is well worth observing, even with binoculars or a small telescope, as is the nearby magnificent open cluster NGC 3532, a magnitude 3 object containing around 150 stars and shining from a distance of some 1,400 light years. Wide fields of view, such as those obtained through binoculars, are essential when viewing NGC 3532 as this cluster occupies an area of sky greater than the full Moon.

February 17th

Two of the stars in Carina – Iota and Epsilon – along with the two stars Delta and Markeb from the neighbouring constellation Vela, make up the False Cross, an asterism which is often confused with Crux (the Cross or Southern Cross) (see April 23rd), a constellation which is located some way to the east. However, when the two are compared the differences are fairly evident, the False Cross being both fainter and somewhat larger than Crux.

February 18th

The tiny constellation Volans (the Flying Fish) lies immediately to the south of Carina and is shown here along with the two neighbouring bright stars Miaplacidus and Epsilon Carinae as a guide. Volans lies quite close to the south celestial pole and is one of the constellations introduced by Pieter Dirkszoon Keyser and Frederick de Houtman in the 1590s (see May 10th). Originally known as Piscis Volans, this constellation appeared on the celestial globe produced by Petrus Plancius in 1598, following which it was depicted in the star atlas *Uranometria*, produced in 1603 by the German astronomer and celestial cartographer Johann Bayer. There are no legends attached to the constellation and none of its stars are named.

Located a little to the north of Miaplacidus, in the neighbouring constellation Carina, is magnitude 4.00 Alpha Volantis, the light from which has taken around 125 years to reach us. Alpha lies on the border of Volans and from here the rest of the constellation can be picked out. The brightest star in Volans is the magnitude 3.77 orange giant Beta Volantis which shines from a distance of a little over 100 light years. Gamma Volantis is a pretty double star with magnitude 3.78 and 5.68 yellowish components which can be resolved in small telescopes.

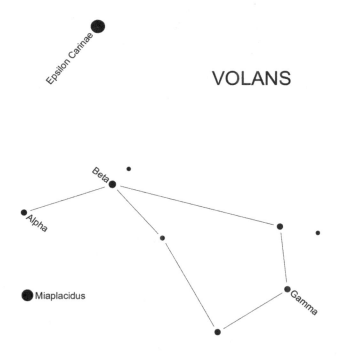

VOLANS

February 19th

Our next port of call is the constellation Vela (the Sail) located immediately to the north of Carina and which represents the sails of the dismantled ship Argo Navis. The whole of Vela can be observed from anywhere south of latitude 33°N although the entire constellation is hidden from view to those located at latitudes north of Winnipeg, Canada and London, England.

The brightest star in Vela is Gamma Velorum, which is actually a four-star system with two of the components visible as a double star. With magnitudes of 1.9 and 4.2 they are far enough apart to be resolvable either in high-magnification binoculars or a small telescope.

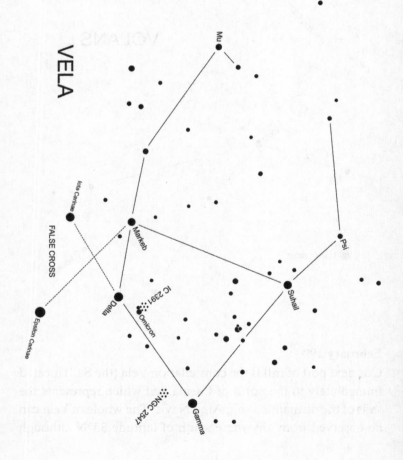

Suhail is the third brightest star in Vela. Located at a distance of well over 500 light years, this supergiant star shines at magnitude 2.23 and has a distinctly orange hue which can be seen in binoculars. Somewhat confusingly, the name is occasionally applied to Gamma. Located near the southern border of Vela is Markeb, the light from this magnitude 2.47 star having taken around 570 years to reach us. Although the origins of this name are not certain, it probably derives from the Arabic *'markab'* meaning 'a ship or any vehicle'.

The star located near the eastern border of Vela is Mu Velorum, a magnitude 2.69 yellow giant whose light has taken around 115 years to reach us. Marking the northern border is Psi which, at magnitude 3.60, shines from a distance of 61 light years. As can be seen from the chart, the two stars Markeb and Delta, along with Iota and Epsilon from the neighbouring constellation Carina, form the famous asterism known as the False Cross (see February 17th).

February 20th
Vela contains a number of open star clusters, by far the brightest of which is IC 2391 which contains around 30 stars and is located just to the north of the star Delta. Binoculars show this object very well and reveal a roughly-cruciform appearance to the cluster. Also known as the Omicron Velorum Cluster, its brightest member being the star Omicron Velorum, IC 2391 shines with an overall magnitude of 2.5 from a distance of over 500 light years. The cluster can be seen with the naked eye and appears to have been first described as long ago as the tenth century when the Persian astronomer Al-Sufi noted: *'...a nebulous star'* at this location. It was independently discovered by the French astronomer Nicolas Louis de Lacaille in 1751 during his expedition to South Africa.

February 21st

Also discovered by Lacaille, the open cluster NGC 2547 is somewhat fainter than IC 2391 although it can be seen with the naked eye and is worth seeking out with binoculars. Located a little way to the south of the star Gamma, NGC 2547 shines with an overall magnitude of 4.7 from a distance of around 1,500 light years.

February 22nd

We now move on to the constellation Puppis (the Poop or Stern) which can be found to the north of Carina and north west of Vela, bordering both constellations.

Puppis is the largest of the three constellations created when Lacaille dismantled Argo Navis and extends from a point near Canopus in Carina, along the Carina/Vela borders and northwards past Sirius in Canis Major. Indeed, its northern border matches that of Canis Major and, although generally regarded as a southern constellation, the northern extremities of Puppis can be seen from mid-northern latitudes. However, the entire group is only visible from the central United States, southern Europe and locations south of these. The bright star Canopus in Carina (see February 10th), as well as the trio of stars Sirius, Mirzam and Muliphein in Canis Major (see January 10th), are shown on the chart to help you locate Puppis.

The brightest star in Puppis is Naos, a name derived from the Greek for 'Ship'. This magnitude 2.21 blue supergiant star shines from a distance of over 1,000 light years. To the north of Naos is the yellow supergiant star Azmidiske whose magnitude 3.34 glow has taken over 1,100 years to reach us. Markeb, located just to the south west of Azmidiske, is a double star with components of magnitudes 4.5 and 4.6 which can be resolved in a small telescope.

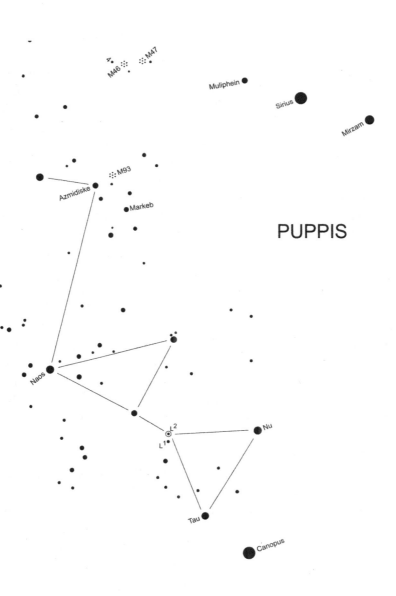

M46 M47

Muliphein

Sirius

Mirzam

M93

Azmidiske

Markeb

PUPPIS

Naos

L^2
L^1

Nu

Tau

Canopus

February 23rd

Puppis contains a number of fairly bright open star clusters, two of which, M46 and M47, are found near the northern border of the constellation towards the east of the bright star Sirius in the neighbouring constellation Canis Major. Although the discoveries of both M46 and M47 are credited to the French astronomer Charles Messier in 1771, M47 was originally discovered by the Italian astronomer Giovanni Batista Hodierna during the early part of the 17th century.

M46 lies at a distance of around 5,400 light years and shines at around magnitude 6 making it an easy target for binoculars or a small telescope. This cluster contains up to around 500 member stars, making it somewhat larger than M47 which has around 50 stars. M47, lying at a distance of around 1,600 light years, is brighter that M46 and, at 4th magnitude, can be seen with the naked eye if the sky is dark and clear.

To locate M46 and M47, extend the line from Mirzam, through Sirius and Muliphein in Canis Major towards the east, and veering very slightly south, until you reach the small triangle of faint stars which includes 4 Puppis, as shown here. M46 and M47 are actually close enough to each other to be visible in the same wide field of view of a pair of binoculars.

February 24th

Another bright open cluster is M93 which can be found close to the star Azmidiske. Discovered by Charles Messier in 1782, M93 lies at a distance of around 3,600 light years and contains around 50 individual stars. Its magnitude is around 6 which puts it at the threshold of naked-eye visibility although to see it without optical aid would require exceptionally dark, clear and moonless skies. Using a pair of binoculars, first of all locate the star Azmidiske and then check out the area immediately to its north west where M93 should be visible as a misty patch of light.

February 25th

The star Tau, located at the southern end of Puppis (a little to the north east of Canopus in Carina) forms one corner of a small triangle of stars which includes Nu and the pair L¹ and L². All these stars can be identified from the chart.

L² Puppis is interesting in that it is a semi-regular variable star which, when at its brightest, shines at around magnitude 3, this dropping to magnitude 6.2 when at its faintest, after which its brightness increases again. The whole cycle takes just over 140 days. Once you identify the star, you can easily follow its entire cycle, either with the naked eye or binoculars. The fact that L² Puppis varies so much in brightness means that, when at or near its maximum magnitude it is a fairly prominent member of the constellation. When at its faintest, however, the opposite is the case. L² Puppis shines from a little over 200 light years away and its orange colour is fairly evident when viewed through binoculars.

February 26th

Next we move onto the small and obscure constellation Pyxis (the Mariner's Compass) which takes the form of a line of faint stars and which can be found immediately to the east of the northern reaches of Puppis. Located as it is near the stern of the dismantled Argo Navis, the constellation Pyxis was created by Nicolas Louis de Lacaille to represent the magnetic compass used by seamen.

The chart shows Pyxis together with the neighbouring constellation Antlia (see February 27th), the bright star Naos in Puppis (see February 22ⁿᵈ) being included here as a guide to tracking down these two faint groups. The whole of both Pyxis and Antlia can be viewed from the northern United States, central Europe, northern China and from any latitude to the south of these.

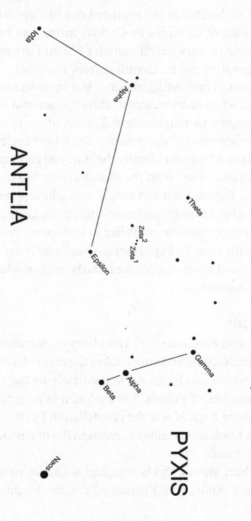

The brightest member of this somewhat-inconspicuous group is magnitude 3.68 Alpha Pyxidis, a blue giant star shining from a distance of almost 900 light years. Immediately to the south of Alpha is Beta, the magnitude 3.97 glow from which has taken a little over 400 years to reach us. Located at a distance of just over 200 light years is Gamma, this magnitude 4.02 orange giant completing the trio of stars marking the main part of Pyxis.

February 27th
Adjoining Pyxis we find the equally-obscure Antlia (the Air Pump), another constellation devised by Lacaille and created to commemorate the air pump invented by the French physicist Denis Papin. Both Pyxis and Antlia lie in an area of sky devoid of prominent stars and, as Lacaille stated at the time: *'To fill up the big spaces between the ancient constellations I have proposed new ones, namely the principal figures of the arts.'* In all, Lacaille devised 14 new constellations and, in keeping with his intentions, these included no creatures, mythological or otherwise.

The brightest star in Antlia is Alpha Antliae, a magnitude 4.28 orange giant whose light has taken over 350 years to reach us. Located a short way to the west of Alpha is magnitude 4.51 Epsilon, another orange giant star, this one shining from a distance of around 700 light years. Near the eastern border of Antlia, and completing the crooked line of stars forming this somewhat unimpressive constellation, we find magnitude 4.60 Iota Antliae.

February 28th
Although obscure, Antlia does have one potential target for binoculars or small telescope. This is the double star comprising Zeta[1] and Zeta[2] Antliae and located just to the west

of a line from Epsilon to Theta as shown on the chart. Shining from a distance of over 350 light years, their magnitudes are almost equal at 5.75 and 5.91 and both components are easily seen in binoculars. If you have a small telescope, however, you can take a closer look at Zeta[1] which has a seventh magnitude companion star lying quite close by.

February 29th

Our journey around the sky now takes us back northwards to the constellation Monoceros (the Unicorn) which occupies the area of sky between Orion, Canis Major, Canis Minor and Hydra and which depicts the legendary animal with the body of a horse and a single horn in the middle of its forehead.

Monoceros straddles the celestial equator and is visible in its entirety from virtually anywhere on Earth. This constellation was originally devised by the Dutch celestial cartographer Petrus Plancius and depicted on a globe produced by him in 1613. Although none of the stars in Monoceros are particularly bright, the constellation is reasonably easy to locate as the bulk of it lies within the so-called Winter Triangle, an asterism formed by the three bright stars Betelgeuse (in Orion), Procyon (in Canis Minor) and Sirius (in Canis Major), as shown on the chart overleaf.

* * *

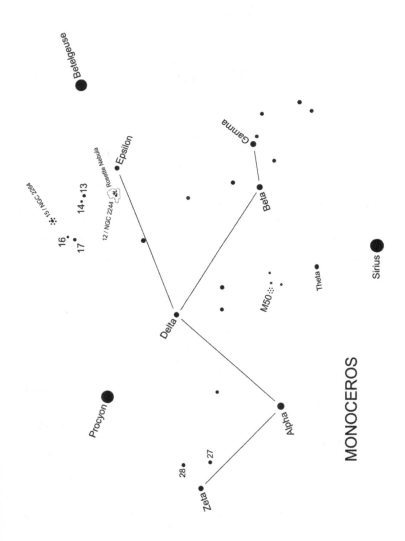

MONOCEROS

Betelgeuse

Epsilon

Gamma

Rosette Nebula

14 • • 13

12 / NGC 2244

vs224

15 / NGC

16

17

Beta

Delta

Sirius

M50

Theta

Procyon

Alpha

27

28 •

Zeta

MARCH

March 1st

The main stars forming Monoceros include Alpha Monocerotis, an orange giant shining at magnitude 3.9 from a distance of around 150 light years. Another orange star is magnitude 3.99 Gamma, the light from which has taken around 500 years to reach us. Zeta lies at the eastern end of the constellation and, at magnitude 4.36, shines from a distance of around a thousand light years. Lying at just under 400 light years away, magnitude 4.15 Delta is somewhat closer. Epsilon is located at the north western end of Monoceros, not far from Betelgeuse in Orion. This magnitude 4.39 star can be spotted by following a line slightly south of eastwards from Betelgeuse. Once you have found Epsilon you can trace out the rest of Monoceros by using the chart as a guide. Because the stars in this constellation are all relatively faint you will need a clear, dark and moonless sky to see them with the naked eye. Binoculars will make your search easier.

March 2nd

Monoceros lies on the Milky Way and contains a number of open star clusters. One of these is M50 which can be found near the southern border of the constellation. Although Charles Messier is credited with the discovery of M50 in 1772, it may be that the Italian born astronomer Giovanni Domenico Cassini saw it prior to 1711.

M50 lies at a distance of around 3,200 light years and

contains anything up to 200 stars. Shining with an overall magnitude of 5.9 this cluster is just visible to the naked eye under skies which are really dark and clear. The English astronomer John Herschel described this object as: *'A remarkable cluster, very large and rich.'* As Herschel's description suggests, M50 is pretty easy to find and is an excellent target for binoculars or a small telescope even from areas which are not perfectly dark. Using binoculars, follow a line from Sirius northwards through Theta (both in Canis Major) and on roughly as far again and you will reach M50 which will be visible as a misty patch of light against the background stars and located just to the east of the small triangle of stars as shown on the chart. Large binoculars or a small telescope should reveal lots of individual stars within the M50 cluster.

March 3rd

Another cluster in Monoceros worthy of note is NGC 2244 which shines from a distance of over 5,000 light years and which was discovered by the English astronomer John Flamsteed in around 1690. This cluster surrounds the star 12 Monocerotis and can be tracked down fairly easily in binoculars. NGC 2244 can be found just to the east of Epsilon, lying within the same binocular field of view and forming a small triangle with Epsilon and the nearby star 13 Monocerotis.

March 4th

Once you've located NGC 2244 you can then take up a real challenge! Extremely difficult to observe, the Rosette Nebula is a large ring of nebulosity surrounding the NGC 2244 cluster. The Rosette is an example of an emission nebula in that it shines through the effects of young, hot stars embedded within it. These stars release energy which excites the atoms in the surrounding nebula, causing them to shine and thereby produce the nebula we see. When photographed with telescopes the Rosette is one of the most stunning and attractive of the nebulae. However, when viewed visually it is very difficult to see at all. With good binoculars or a small telescope it can just be made out as a patch of very soft light surrounding the NGC 2244 cluster. If you can't see it directly, averted vision (see Glossary) may help you to catch a glimpse of this visually-elusive object.

March 5th

Also known as the Christmas Tree Cluster, due to its visual appearance when viewed through telescopes, NGC 2264 contains around 30 stars and is another of the large number of open clusters found in Monoceros. The star 15, located a little way to the north east of 13, lies on the edge of the cluster. An easy target for binoculars, NGC 2264 shines with an overall magnitude of 3.9 from a distance of around 2,400 light years and can be glimpsed with the naked eye provided the sky is really dark and clear.

March 6th

Let's now take our night-by-night journey around the sky further to the north. One of the most famous and easily-recognisable star patterns is the Plough which, when viewed from mid-northern latitudes, is easily located lying fairly well up in the north eastern sky during March evenings. As far as observers in the southern hemisphere are concerned, this is the best time to see Ursa Major although even then it's not easy. From most of South Africa, Australia and southern South America the parts of Ursa Major that rise at all are very low in the northern sky and from locations further south very little if any of the constellation can ever be seen.

Shaped rather like a gigantic heavenly spoon the Plough is probably the best-known asterism in the sky, being part of the much larger constellation Ursa Major (the Great Bear). Although the other stars in the Ursa Major are all comparatively faint, the Plough itself, which marks the hind quarters and tail of the bear, stands out quite well.

March 7th

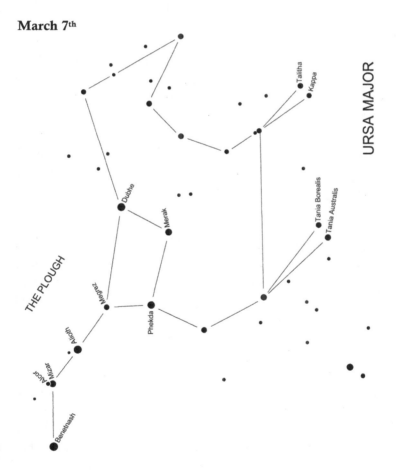

From mid-northern latitudes the Plough, together with the rest of Ursa Major, is located high in the north eastern sky during winter evenings and at or near the overhead point during spring. As the year wears on the constellation drops down into the high north west, eventually ending up over the northern horizon during autumn. This annual cycle around the northern sky gave rise to one of the many legends attached to the Plough, this being the one devised by the North American Indians which identifies the four stars in the 'bowl' of the Plough as a bear. This is being chased around the sky by three hunters, represented by the three stars in the Plough 'handle'. The faint star Alcor (see March 10th) represents the cooking pot carried by the middle of the three hunters! Over the course of a year the bear is chased around the sky until autumn when it is eventually caught. At this time, and from mid-northern latitudes, the group can be seen low over the northern horizon, the blood from the bear supposedly dripping down onto the earth, turning the leaves brown.

March 8th

One of Ursa Major's claims to fame is that the constellation actually does resemble the object or character that it depicts! Checking out the group as a whole you will see that the legs and head of the Great Bear are clearly represented. Its hind feet are depicted by the two stars Tania Borealis and Tania Australis while the bear's front paws are marked by the stars Kappa and Talitha.

However, as with most of the constellations, the stars that we see in Ursa Major only happen to lie in more-or-less the same line of sight as seen from our planet and so only appear to be close together in the sky. If seen from elsewhere in our Galaxy the arrangement of these stars would be somewhat different to the constellation we see from Earth.

An example is the star Dubhe, which lies around 125 light years from Earth. Merak, on the other hand, lies at a distance of around 80 light years, not much more than half the distance of Dubhe. However, because they happen to lie in roughly the same direction as seen from our vantage point on Earth, they appear to be close to each other in the sky. Lying at roughly the same distance as Merak is magnitude 1.76 Alioth, one of the stars in the Plough handle.

March 9th

As we have seen is the case with many of the stars in the heavens, the names of the stars in Ursa Major are quite interesting and varied. The star Dubhe derives its name from the Arabic *'al-dubb'* meaning 'the Bear' whilst Merak comes from the Arabic for 'the Groin (of the Great Bear)'. Megrez derives its name from an abbreviation of the Arabic for 'the Root of the Tail' and, keeping on the theme of ursine body parts, the star Phekda derives its name from the Arabic *'fakhidh al-dubb al-akbar'* meaning 'the Thigh'. These names are certainly descriptive!

March 10th

While you're looking at the Plough, check out the star in the middle of the Plough 'handle'. You will see that this is actually a pair of stars comprising Mizar - the brighter of the two at magnitude 2.23 – and a nearby magnitude 3.99 companion star Alcor. Both Alcor and Mizar can be made out individually if you have keen eyesight and if the sky is really dark and clear, although binoculars may be needed to bring the pair out well. If you have powerful binoculars, or a small telescope, you may see another, much fainter star, forming a triangle with Alcor and Mizar. This 8th magnitude star bears the somewhat-clumsy name of Sidus Ludoviciana and was named as such by the eccentric German astronomer Johann Georg Liebknecht in December 1722. Spotting the star in his telescope and thinking he had discovered a new planet he named it after his sovereign and patron the Landgrave Ludwig of Hessen-Darmstadt. Liebknecht published his 'find' and notified many of the leading astronomers of the time. The discovery was erroneous, but the name stuck (unlike Liebknecht's reputation, which doubtless became unstuck once the new 'planet' turned out to be an ordinary star).

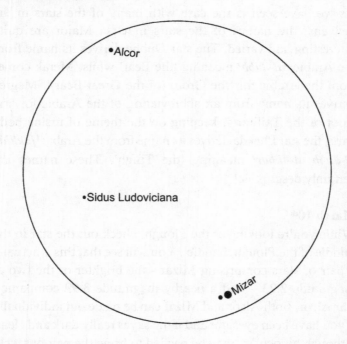

March 11ᵗʰ

A small telescope will show that Mizar itself is a close double star with a faint magnitude 4 companion lying close by. Mizar appears to be one of the first double stars to be discovered with a telescope, this being around 1650 by the Italian astronomer Giovanni Battista Riccioli.

Mizar and Alcor are gravitationally-bound to each other and have been found to share a common motion through space. Research has also shown that the Mizar and Alcor system is more complicated than at first thought. In 1889 the American astronomer Edward Charles Pickering discovered that the brighter of the two stars forming Mizar is in fact a binary with two components in orbit around each other. Subsequent observation then revealed that Mizar's fainter component is also a binary. Adding further interest was the discovery in 2009 that Alcor is itself a binary, making the Mizar and Alcor grouping a six-star system with Mizar comprising four stars and Alcor two. It should be pointed out that these three binary systems can not be resolved with normal telescopes, their true natures being discovered through the use of specialized instruments.

Sidus Ludoviciana, the star which lies in the same telescopic field as Mizar and Alcor, is not actually associated with the pair and only happens to lie in the same line of sight. Both Mizar and Alcor lie at a distance of around 82 light years, somewhat closer than Sidus Ludoviciana whose light has taken around 400 years to reach us.

March 12ᵗʰ

Along with Ursa Major, nearby Ursa Minor (the Little Bear) is one of the oldest depicted star patterns and appears in the catalogue of constellations compiled during the second century by the Greek astronomer Ptolemy. Visible high in the northern sky as seen from mid-northern latitudes, the Little Bear is easily found by using the two end stars in the 'bowl' of the Plough as pointers, as shown here. If you follow a line from Merak through Dubhe you will reach the star Polaris. This is the brightest star in Ursa Minor and represents the end of the Little Bear's tail.

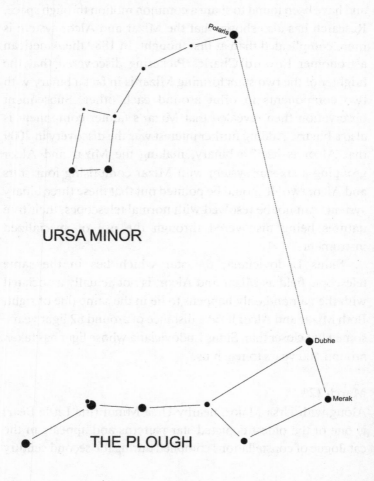

URSA MINOR

THE PLOUGH

March 13th

Although Ursa Minor is not the most prominent of
constellations, it can be picked out fairly easily as the area
around it is devoid of bright stars. It roughly resembles the
Plough in shape and stretches away from Polaris, the Pole Star,
the main star in the group. When suitably placed in the sky
Ursa Minor can be seen in its entirety from anywhere north of
the equator, although from latitudes below around 25°S it is
permanently hidden from view.

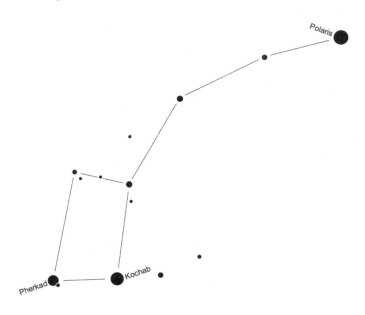

URSA MINOR

As its name suggests, Polaris marks the position of the north celestial pole. The north (and south) celestial poles are the points on the celestial sphere through which extensions of the Earth's axis of rotation would pass. Consequently, the north celestial pole would be seen directly overhead when viewed from the North Pole and the south celestial pole directly overhead when seen from the South Pole.

Taking this further, the north celestial pole lies in the direction of north when viewed from elsewhere on the Earth's surface in the same way that the south celestial pole lies in the direction of south when seen from other locations.

The south celestial pole is located in the tiny constellation Octans (the Octant) although, as we will discover (see December 16th), there is no particularly bright star marking its position, as is the case with Polaris and the north celestial pole.

March 14th

Because the position of Polaris is in line with the Earth's axis of rotation, it appears to remain stationary as the Earth turns on its axis, with all the other stars appearing to go round it every 24 hours. The fact that the other stars appear to travel around Polaris is echoed in an Arabic legend which identified Polaris with a notorious villain who was cast into the sky upon his death. His coffin is represented by the Pole Star and was placed at the northernmost part of the sky where it remains to this day, with all the other stars keeping their distance as they travel around the heavens.

March 15th

If you look at the celestial bears you will notice that they both have long tails, unlike their earthly counterparts. Of course, there is a legend which explains this! Ursa Major represents the legendary maiden Callisto who was so beautiful that the Roman goddess Juno, wife of Jupiter, the King of the Gods, became jealous, and turned her into a bear. Years later, Callisto's son Arcas almost killed the bear while out hunting. Jupiter rescued the situation by turning Arcas into a bear and, in order to render them both safe from Juno's clutches, grabbed both animals by their tails and swung them high up into the sky where they can be seen to this day. Naturally, the tails of both animals became stretched in the process!

March 16th

Polaris shines from a distance of around 430 light years. In other words, the light we are seeing from Polaris set off towards us around the reign of Elizabeth I! Shining at magnitude 2.02, the star appears relatively faint although in reality it is around 2,500 times as luminous as our Sun and only appears faint due to the fact that it lies at such a great distance from us.

March 17th

Some nights have been wholly unfriended of the stars of late. Last night the sullenness of the skies gave way to wild rage, with frequent showers of cold rain. The winds were not the winds of mid-March, but those of a tempestuous November. For several minutes at a time the air poured past at a hurricane rate, producing the sound of a vast, deep, sustained peal of thunder or of a grand prolonged organ note running through the majestic music of the elements.

March 18th

Kochab and Pherkad are known collectively as the Guardians of the Pole in view of the fact that they appear to circle around Polaris as the Earth rotates. Pherkad lies at a distance of around 490 light years, making it slightly more remote that Polaris.

Kochab is somewhat nearer and, at a distance of 130 light years, is one of the closest stars in Ursa Minor. A pair of binoculars will bring out the orange colour of Kochab, which contrasts well with the white of Polaris.

The very small star close to (Pherkad) is visible to me but seldom. I can just see it at this moment – a shivering moment, for the piercingly cold wind hums about me the while. The Form of the Lesser Bear (Ursa Minor) always reminds me of the Great Bear turned inside out.

March 19th

LYNX

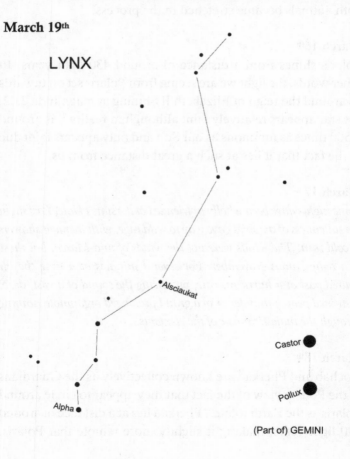

The constellation Lynx (the Lynx) takes the form of a zigzag line of stars occupying the barren region between Ursa Major to the north east and Auriga and Gemini to the south west. It was introduced in the 17th century by the Polish astronomer Johannes Hevelius in order to fill this gap. The whole of Lynx is visible from central South America, northern Australia and latitudes north of these and at least in part from almost every inhabited part of the world.

The constellation is very faint and contains no stars brighter than third magnitude. When Elgie was compiling his book, and drawing the star charts to illustrate it, he wrote: *'I cannot see any prominent star in the constellation Lynx, which occupies nearly all the space between (Ursa Major) and Castor and Pollux. Consequently, I am compelled to leave it starless.'*

Lynx can be picked out by using the two stars Castor and Pollux in Gemini as guides. Providing the sky is dark and clear you should be able to locate the wandering form of this faint constellation. Hevelius explained the constellation name by saying that those who examined the Lynx ought to be lynx-eyed (keen-sighted). It seems he wasn't wrong there...

March 20th

The brightest star in Lynx is Alpha Lyncis, a magnitude 3.14 orange giant whose light has taken around 200 years to reach us. The only named star in this group is Alsciaukat, another orange giant star shining at magnitude 4.25 from a distance of nearly 400 light years. The title Alsciaukat is derived from the Arabic for 'Thorn'. An alternative name for this star is Mabsuthat, derived from the Arabic for 'Expanded', referring perhaps to the outstretched paw of the creature depicted by the constellation.

*

March 21st

Only slightly more eye-catching than Lynx is Cancer (the Crab), a faint constellation which lies between the two prominent groups Gemini and Leo and which can be tracked down by using the two stars Castor and Pollux as a guide. Located as it is a little way to the north of the celestial equator, the constellation of Cancer can be seen in its entirety from virtually anywhere in the world.

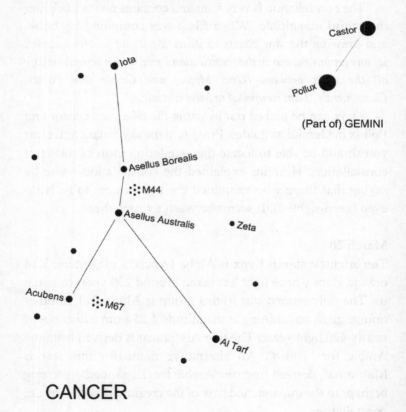

As the second of his labours, Hercules battled the fearsome Hydra in the swamps near Lerna (see April 15th). During the confrontation, the goddess Hera commanded a crab to crawl out of the swamp and bite Hercules on the foot. Hercules promptly responded by killing the crab, following which Hera placed the animal amongst the stars.

March 22nd

Although not a particularly bright or impressive constellation, Cancer does contain a number of stars with interesting names. The brightest of these is the orange giant Al Tarf which shines at magnitude 3.53 from a distance of around 300 light years. Its name is derived from the Arabic for 'the End', alluding to the fact that it depicts the southern foot of the crab. Acubens, whose name is derived from the Arabic for 'the Claws', has a magnitude of 4.26 and lies at a distance of around 190 light years.

March 23rd

The central region of the constellation is occupied by the two stars Asellus Borealis and Asellus Australis. The names of these stars are derived from the Latin for the Northern and Southern Ass Colts. Asellus Borealis is a white supergiant star which shines at magnitude 4.66 from a distance of around 180 light years. Slightly brighter is magnitude 3.94 Asellus Australis, a yellow giant star whose light has taken 130 years to reach us.

March 24th

*The nomenclature of many stars has often seemed to me hauntingly melodious, no matter how bizarre the names should appear in cold type. I would instance Antares, Arcturus, Betelgeuse, Vega, Capella, Canopus. Then how resonantly **royal** is the name of Regulus!*

And of the constellations, too; how full and majestic is the sound of Orion! What could be more in keeping with the rhythm, the majesty of Orion itself!

How pleasantly on the ear fall the names of Cepheus, of Andromeda, Perseus, Cassiopeia! And what is there to mate the music of Praesepe! From these, surely, must spring that sweet celestial harmony besung so tenderly of the poets.

March 25th

Two fairly prominent open star clusters can be found in Cancer, the brightest of these being M44, also known as Praesepe. M44 shines with an overall magnitude of around 3.7 and can be seen as a nebulous patch with the naked eye providing the sky is dark and clear. Virtually the whole of M44 will fit into the field of view of binoculars, which will bring the cluster out well. The Greek astronomer Ptolemy described this object as being the *'Centre of the cloud-shaped convolutions in the breast (of Cancer), called Praesepe'*. Roman mythology identifies M44 as a manger, provided as a source of food for the two nearby asses – Asellus Borealis and Asellus Australis. Shining from a distance of around 580 light years, M44 contains at least 350 stars and is one of the nearest open star clusters to us.

*A poor constellation would Cancer be if it were not for the presence of Praesepe, which now looks as cloudy to me as does Andromeda's superb nebula. Yet somehow there is a difference. But how shall I describe that difference? Shall I say that Praesepe is, to the naked eye, inanimate, whilst the Andromeda Nebula breathes and palpitates like a sentient being – the one, clay; the other, animated marble. But assist the sight with even the most modest of opera-glasses. Then does Praesepe leap into life. Its vivacity is exhilarating. Its crowded components seem to dance for the very **joie de vivre**, and their innumerable laughter to be infectious.*

March 26th

Discovered by the German astronomer Johann Gottfried Koehler prior to 1779, the open star cluster M67 contains over 500 stars and lies just to the west of the star Acubens. Shining with an overall magnitude of 6.1 from a distance of over 2,500 light years, M67 can be located fairly easily in binoculars which will reveal it as a misty patch of light. Described by Koehler at the time of discovery as: *'A rather conspicuous nebula...'* M67 is one of the oldest open star clusters known to astronomers.

March 27th

There are a number of double stars in Cancer, two of which – Iota and Zeta - can be resolved in binoculars or small telescopes. Iota Cancri, located at the northern end of the constellation, shines with an overall magnitude of 4.03 from a distance of around 300 light years. The two components of this double are a yellow giant and a white dwarf, and checking them out carefully with binoculars may reveal their individual colours.

March 28th

Zeta Cancri, which shines at magnitude 4.67 a little way to the west of Asellus Australis, was found to be a double star by the German astronomer Johann Tobias Mayer in 1756. Although the two individual stars are too close to each other to be resolvable in binoculars, a small telescope will show them both quite well. Located at a distance of around 82 light years, both of the main components of Zeta have since been found to be very close binary systems, each one of which is comprised of two stars orbiting each other. However, these two individual pairs are so close together that large telescopes are needed to see them.

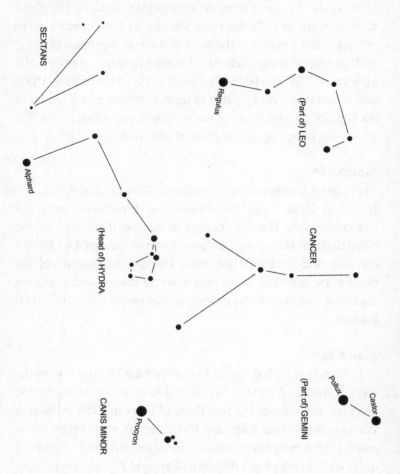

Moving a little further south we come to a region of sky occupied by the western end of the constellation Hydra (the Water Snake) which will be described later (see April 14th). For observers in the southern hemisphere, this area can be best seen looking towards the north around March and April.

The Head of Hydra is located at the centre of an area flanked by the small constellation Canis Minor to the west; the two leading stars of Gemini – Castor and Pollux – to the north west; the faint constellation of Cancer to the north; and the western region of the constellation Leo (the Lion) (see April 1st), including the bright star Regulus, to the north east. The faint constellation Sextans (the Sextant) (see March 30th) can be made out immediately to the east of the Head of Hydra.

March 30th

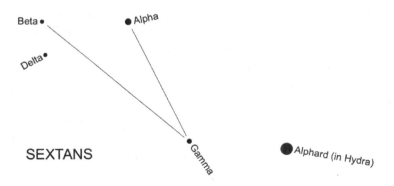

Lying a little way to the east of the circlet of stars forming the Head of Hydra, the constellation Sextans (the Sextant) takes the form of a small triangle of faint stars. Sextans is shown here along with the nearby stars Regulus in Leo and Alphard in Hydra (see March 29th), both of which can be used as guides to locating the group. Parts of Sextans can be seen from anywhere on the planet and the whole of the constellation is visible from almost every inhabited region.

This rather dim and unimpressive group was introduced by the Polish astronomer Johannes Hevelius in the 17th century to commemorate the sextant, an instrument used by Hevelius to measure star positions. None of the stars in Sextans have individual names although the constellation itself can, with just a little imagination, be seen to at-least vaguely resemble the object it depicts!

March 31st

As far as the individual stars in Sextans are concerned, the brightest is Alpha, a blue giant star which shines with a magnitude of 4.48 from a distance of around 280 light years. Slightly fainter, at magnitude 5.08, is Beta which lies at a distance of 400 light years. Somewhat closer than Beta, and with an almost identical brightness, is magnitude 5.07 Gamma, the light from which reaches us from a distance of around 275 light years. To complete the obscure group we have the even-fainter magnitude 5.19 Delta which lies around 320 light years away.

Provided the sky is dark and clear, you might be able to pick out Sextans with the naked eye, although a pair of binoculars would probably be an asset to your search!

APRIL

April 1st

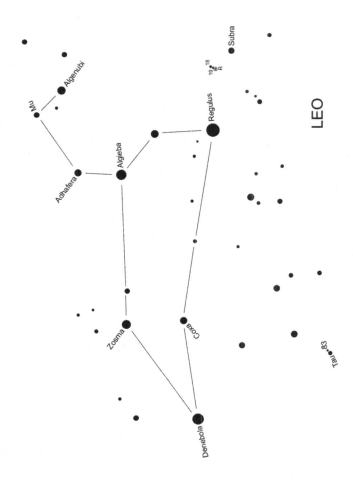

From mid-northern latitudes, the constellation of Leo (the Lion) can be seen high up in the southern sky during March and April evenings, whilst for observers located at latitudes south of the equator Leo graces the northern heavens. Situated as it is a little way to the north of the celestial equator, Leo can be seen in its entirety from almost every inhabited part of the world. Its distinctive shape is really unmistakeable and it is one of the few constellations actually resembling the object or character that it depicts, in this case the Nemean lion which Hercules slew as the first of his twelve labours. The whole group does indeed echo the appearance of a crouching lion, with the curve of stars northwards from Regulus depicting the head, mane and paws. This curve of stars is often known as the Sickle. At the opposite end of the constellation we have the triangle of stars formed from Denebola, Coxa and Zosma which together form the lion's hindquarters and tail.

April 2nd

The above story, associating the lion with Hercules, originates in Greek mythology, although there are other accounts of how the lion came to be among the stars. One of these comes down from the ancient Egyptians who associated the group with the heat of summer. This was because members of the lion population left the hot desert regions for the cooler areas surrounding the Nile during the summer months, at great inconvenience to the communities living on the banks of the river!

April 3rd

For northern hemisphere observers, Leo is the leading spring constellation and contains over a hundred naked-eye stars, the brightest of which is Regulus. This name is derived from the

Latin for 'the Little King', and was first applied to the star during the early 16th century. Shining from a distance of around 80 light years, magnitude 1.36 blue-white Regulus has a fainter 8th magnitude yellowish companion lying quite close by, both stars being resolvable in small telescopes.

April 4th

Slightly fainter than Regulus is Denebola, its name derived from the Arabic *'al dhanab al-asad'* meaning 'the Lion's Tail'. This magnitude 2.14 star is white in colour and is located 36 light years away. Denebola, along with the nearby bright stars Arcturus in Boötes (see May 18th), Spica in Virgo (see May 30th) and Cor Caroli in Canes Venatici (see May 23rd), forms the conspicuous and celebrated asterism the Diamond of Virgo which surrounds the constellation Coma Berenices (see May 25th).

April 5th

Together with the two stars Coxa and Zosma, Denebola forms the hind quarters of Leo. Zosma is a white star shining from a distance of 58 light years with a magnitude of 2.56, slightly brighter than its neighbour Coxa, another white star with a magnitude of 3.33 and whose light has taken over 160 years to reach us.

April 6th

Nine o'clock! The gentian is not more blue than was the sky this morning; though, alas! Spring smiled but was again to deceive. Night has fallen swathed in neutral clouds. They come up out of the south, grimly, sullenly, and hanging low, as if their aqueous burden were dragging them to earth. Even now a sputtering of ice-cold rain falls on my upturned face.

April 7th

Another of Leo's bright stars is the orange-red Algieba, a name derived from the Arabic *'al jabha'* meaning 'the Lion's Forehead or Mane'. Algieba has a magnitude of 2.3 and its orange tint offers a contrast with a fainter magnitude 3.5 yellowish companion star. Both Algieba and its companion can just be resolved in a small telescope, although they may present something of a challenge!

April 8th

Another interesting object that can be seen through binoculars is the double star Tau which is located someway to the south of the main constellation. Lying very close by to Tau is the star 83 Leonis and when seen together they are a pretty sight in binoculars. However, if you look closely you will see that each of these two stars is a double, Tau comprising a brighter yellow-orange star and a fainter bluish companion, both of which should be visible in binoculars. However, the yellowish and violet stars forming 83 will need a telescope to resolve them. Of the two, Tau is the most distant, shining from a distance of around 600 light years, roughly ten times further away than 83 Leonis, which lies at a distance of around 58 light years.

April 9th

The star Algenubi derives its name from the Arabic *'ras al-asad al-janubi'*, meaning 'the Southern (Star) in the Lion's Head'. Algenubi shines at magnitude 2.97 from a distance of around 250 light years and, along with nearby Mu and Adhafera, forms the main outline of the lion's mane. Through binoculars each of these stars presents a pretty sight under dark, clear and moonless skies. Due to their location in the head of Leo, the two stars Mu and Algenubi were collectively known to Arabic astronomers as *'al-ashfar'* meaning 'the Eyebrows'.

April 10th

Before we take our leave of Leo, let's take a look at the Mira-type (see December 4th) variable star R Leonis. Shining from a distance of around 380 light years, and located a little way to the west of Regulus as shown on the chart. R Leonis has an average magnitude range of between 5 and 10 and a period of 312 days. You can track R Leonis down with binoculars by working your way slightly to the west of Regulus. The two faint stars 18 and 19 lie just above a line from Regulus to Subra and R Leonis can be found next to this pair. Described by the English astronomer Edwin Dunkin as having a *'...blood-red appearance, which is very striking to the eye when viewed for the first time through a good telescope'*, the ruddy hue of R Leonis should be clearly visible when you see the star. This is one of the most widely-observed objects of its type in the sky. The variability of R Leonis was first noted by the Polish astronomer Julius August Koch as far back as 1782, and it has continued to be a target for backyard astronomers ever since.

April 11th

Another of the faint and obscure constellations introduced during the 17th century by the Polish astronomer Johannes Hevelius, Leo Minor (the Little Lion) takes the form of a short line of stars running between Ursa Major and Leo. It can be located by using the stars of Leo as a guide, some of which are shown here. When suitably placed in the sky, the whole of this constellation can be seen from locations anywhere to the north of latitude 48°S, ruling out only the southernmost regions of South America and New Zealand as potential vantage points.

As with other faint groups, Leo Minor can be seen with the naked eye although tracking it down will be made easier with binoculars.

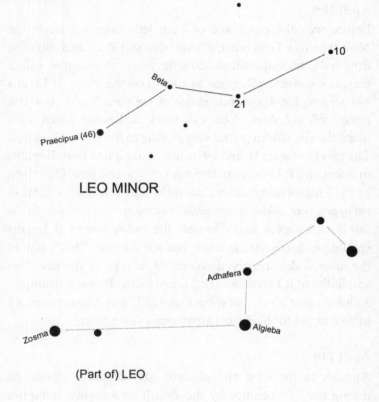

LEO MINOR

(Part of) LEO

April 12th

Midnight! Black and forbidding. Never for a single moment since darkness set in has the rain ceased, and now it is driving from the north-east in heavy sheets. The air has that clearness which I have observed on the Durham coast during what is commonly called an equinoctial gale, though the connection between the storms which occur there in early October and the autumnal equinox does not seem to me to rest on very solid basis. But, oh! for a full-starred sky again. Why does the new-born Spring refuse to smile? Why should she frown so persistently?

April 13th

Leo Minor has no star designated Alpha and the one named Beta isn't actually the brightest star in the group. Pride of place here goes to Praecipua, a name which means 'Chief' and which, located at the extreme eastern end of the line of stars forming Leo Minor, shines with a magnitude of 3.79 from a distance of around 95 light years. The star was given this name by Hevelius, although it never really became popular, and it is usually known by its Flamsteed number 46.

Beta Leonis Minoris is a yellow giant star lying at a distance of just over 150 light years and shining at magnitude 4.20. Completing the Leo Minor group are the stars 10 and 21. Shining from a distance of around 90 light years, 21 is a white star with a magnitude of 4.49, marginally brighter than the yellow giant 10 which, at magnitude 4.54. is located at a distance of 185 light years.

April 14th

Now let's take our journey around the sky to the long and sprawling constellation Hydra (the Water Snake). As we have seen (see March 29th) the Head of Hydra lies in the region of sky immediately to the east of Canis Minor (the Little Dog) and to the south of Cancer (the Crab).

* * *

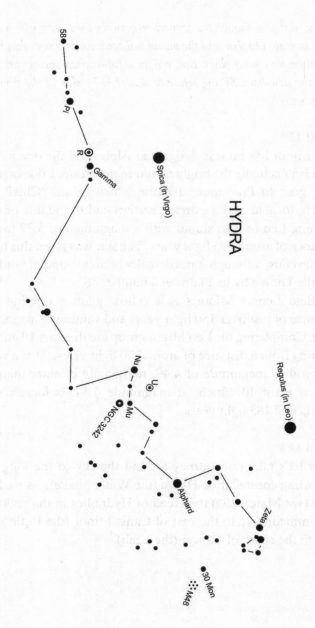

HYDRA

58

Pi

R

Gamma

Spica (in Virgo)

Regulus (in Leo)

Nu

Mu

U

NGC 3242

Alphard

Zeta

30 Mon

M48

From here the celestial snake winds its way eastwards, passing immediately to the south of Sextans (the Sextant), Crater (the Cup) and Corvus (the Crow) and onwards to its tail, located between the constellations Libra (the Scales) and Centaurus (the Centaur). The chart shows Hydra along with two prominent guide stars – Spica (in Virgo) and Regulus (in Leo) – to help you locate and follow the constellation along its whole length. The entire constellation can be seen from anywhere south of latitude 55°N and portions of it are visible from any location on the Earth.

Hydra is the largest of the 88 modern-day constellations and one of the 48 star groups drawn up by the Greek astronomer Ptolemy during the 2nd century. However, despite its size, there is nothing about Hydra that stands out particularly well. The constellation is best seen during the months of March and April when its winding form can be seen straddling an extended region of sky on and to the south of the celestial equator. The stars forming Hydra are not particularly bright and observers at mid-northern latitudes may need clear and dark skies in order to identify the entire constellation. To make the job easier, you can use binoculars to try and pick out the individual stars forming the group, working your way eastwards from the Head of Hydra. Observers in more southerly latitudes will have less trouble tracking Hydra down as the constellation will, of course, be located higher in the sky and away from horizon glow.

Not far below Procyon there is a group of fairly bright stars forming a graceful curve to the west. They form the head of the great sinuous constellation of Hydra, the Water Snake, a fearful monster, worthy to rank among the weird creatures seen by Coleridge's Ancient Mariner when that immortal seafarer lay becalmed in the tropics. The position of these stars is from four to seven degrees north of the equator. When once this curve has been recognised the feeling of the observer is that it constitutes one of the most striking configurations in the heavens.

April 15th

According to legend, Hydra represents the fearsome multi-headed monster which lived near to the town of Lerna in the Pelopponesus region of southern Greece. The area it occupied was ideal territory for such a creature, containing as it did a lake, numerous springs and areas of swampland. From here the monster spread fear and panic amongst the local inhabitants as it wandered around destroying the countryside and eating various and assorted livestock. Its reign of terror eventually came to an end when Hercules battled and killed the creature as the second of his labours. The victory was hard-won, however, due to the fact that Hydra had nine heads and, as if this wasn't bad enough, each time he cut off one of the heads, another two grew in its place. Hercules eventually managed to overcome this problem by burning out the roots of each severed head to prevent others growing.

April 16th

Another legend associates Hydra with a water snake. Apollo asked a crow to fly to a spring and fetch him the water of life, giving him a cup in which to carry it. However, the crow loitered in order to eat some fruit from a fig tree and, in so doing, dropped the cup onto the ground. When he had finished feasting the crow panicked. He picked up the cup again, along with a water snake, and returned to Apollo to try and explain the delay, blaming the snake for hampering his attempts to extract water from the spring. In spite of the various excuses offered by the hapless crow, Apollo didn't really believe him. He wasn't at all pleased and promptly banished the trio to the

113

sky where both the crow and cup can be seen balanced on the back of the water snake (see June 4th).

April 17th

The brightest of the stars that form Hydra is the magnitude 1.99 Alphard which can be found by following the line of stars southwards from Zeta, a magnitude 3.11 yellow giant star located at a distance of over 160 light years and situated at the eastern end of the Head of Hydra. Alphard is an orange giant star shining from a distance of around 180 light years. Its name is derived from the Arabic *'al-fard'* meaning 'the Solitary One', a fitting title taking into account its position in relation to the surrounding field of comparatively faint stars.

Proceeding along the constellation we soon come to the two stars Nu and Mu which together act as a guide to the variable star U Hydrae (see April 21st). Approaching the eastern end of Hydra we come to Gamma Hydrae, a yellow giant star shining with a magnitude of 2.99 and whose light has taken over 130 years to reach us. This star is located a short way to the south of the brilliant Spica in the neighbouring constellation Virgo which can be used as a guide to help you track down Gamma Hydrae and the nearby variable star R Hydrae (see April 22nd). From Gamma the winding form of Hydra continues through the magnitude 3.25 Pi and on to the faint star 58 which, located at a distance of around 330 light years and shining at a rather dim magnitude 4.42, marks the tail of the celestial water snake.

April 18th

What Hydra lacks in prominent stars it makes up for to some extent with a few interesting objects, including the open star cluster M48. Located a little way to the south west of the star

30 Mon as shown here, this cluster contains up to 80 stars and shines at an overall magnitude of around 5.5 making it just visible to the naked eye under really dark and clear skies. It was originally discovered by the French astronomer Charles Messier in 1771 who described it as being '...*a little distance from the three stars which are at the root of the tail of Monoceros.*'

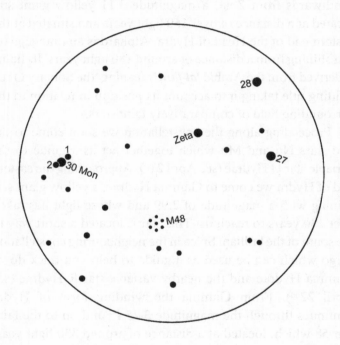

To locate M48 in binoculars, first of all find the star 30 Mon which can be seen a little way to the south west of the Head of Hydra. From here, using the finder chart will allow you to identify the cluster amongst the faint stars in its immediate vicinity. The three stars alluded to by Messier were 27, 28 and

Zeta Monocerotis. These are shown on the star chart for Monoceros (see February 29th) as well as on the finder chart here, where they act as a useful finding aid for the M48 cluster. Your initial view of M48 will be as an extended patch of faint light, although closer and more careful examination will bring out a few of its member stars.

April 19th

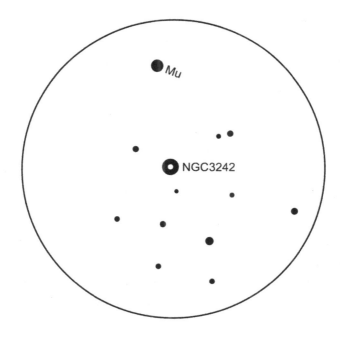

Located a little to the south of the star Mu Hydrae is the planetary nebula NGC 3242 which offers a bit of a challenge if you feel like trying to track it down. The finder chart shows the faint stars immediately to the south of Mu, in the area of NGC 3242, and should help you to locate this object. Discovered in 1785 by William Herschel, NGC 3242 is located at a distance of approximately 1,500 light years and shines with a magnitude of around 8.5, making it visible in good binoculars or a small telescope. When you carry out your search, remember to look for a diffuse patch of light rather than a star like point.

Planetary nebulae are created when gas is ejected from old stars. They take the appearance of shells of gas surrounding the parent star, the gas within them being illuminated by energy from the star from whose outer layers they were formed. The term 'planetary nebula' was coined by the astronomer William Herschel when he likened their appearance in telescopes to that of planetary discs. They have nothing whatsoever to do with planets, although the perhaps-misleading description given by Herschel has stuck!

Planetary nebulae occur in a variety of colours and shapes, NGC 3242 itself often being referred to as the 'Ghost of Jupiter', presumably due to the fact that early observers likened its visual appearance to that of the planet Jupiter.

April 20th

Ten-fifteen! A delicious evening. The hovering clouds send down their liquid sweetness, and the grateful Earth breathes back a breath of perfume. So is this starless eve of April filled with Spring's most fragrant odours. And how jealously the clouds guard them, lest they should be dissipated into space.

April 21st

Before we leave Hydra we should take a closer look at a couple of variable stars which can be located and observed fairly easily. The first of these is U Hydrae which forms a small triangle with nearby Nu and Mu, all three of which lie in the same binocular field of view. U Hydrae is what is known as a semi-regular variable star and ranges in brightness between around 4th and 5th magnitude over a period of about 115 days. It has the reddish colour typical of stars of this type and which should be noticeable when you check this star out.

April 22nd

The other variable we should check out is the Mira-type (see December 4th) R Hydrae, which is located immediately to the east of Gamma and is regarded as being one of the easiest variable stars to observe. The discovery of its variability is generally credited to the Italian-born astronomer Giacomo Filippo Maraldi in 1704, although it may have been noticed earlier than this. Estimates as to how much this star varies in brightness differ although its average magnitude range is around 4.5 to 9.5 with the whole cycle taking place over a period of around 385 days. Located within the same binocular field as Gamma, R Hydrae is easy to find and is an ideal candidate for those backyard astronomers armed with binoculars or a small telescope, or even the naked eye when the star is at or near maximum brightness!

April 23rd

Crux (the Cross) is the smallest of the constellations, but is also one of the most famous. The stars forming this tiny group were once part of the neighbouring Centaurus (the Centaur) noted by Ptolemy on the list of 48 constellations he drew up during the 2nd century.

*

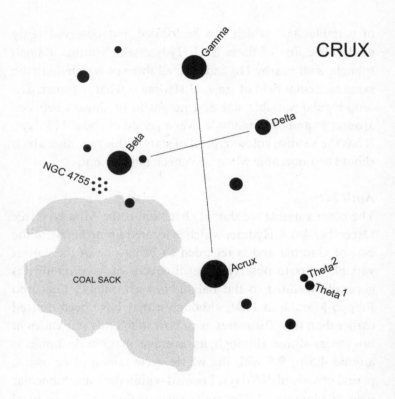

CRUX

Crux was first described as a separate constellation by the Italian navigator Andreas Corsali in 1516. However, in 1504 his countryman and fellow navigator Amerigo Vespucci had described a number of important southern stars, including a particular group of six which were probably the four main stars in Crux together with the nearby Alpha and Beta Centauri. The first appearance of Crux as a individual constellation were on celestial globes made by the English globe maker Emery Molyneux in 1592 and by the Dutch cartographer Petrus Plancius in 1598. From then on the constellation gained its own identity as a separate group, appearing on other celestial globes and in various atlases throughout the 17th century. Modern star charts depict it surrounded on three sides by Centaurus.

Because Crux lies not far from the south celestial pole it can never be seen from mid-northern latitudes and only really rises from locations south of Central America and southern India. From places on or south of the equator the constellation is easily seen, being best placed for viewing around April when it is located fairly high up in the sky.

The constellation Crux should not be confused with the asterism of four stars which straddle the borders of the nearby constellations Carina and Vela (see February 17th). Known collectively as the False Cross, these are found a little to the west of Crux and form a similar, albeit slightly larger, pattern.

April 24th
The tiny but noticeable constellation of Crux has long been a source of inspiration to those journeying south. Typical of the sentiments aroused by the sight of the Cross are those expressed by the German explorer Friedrich Wilhelm Heinrich Alexander von Humboldt who, presumably during his Latin American expedition in 1799, saw it for the first time. He noted that: *'We saw distinctly, for the first time, the Cross of the South, on the night of the fourth and fifth of July, in the sixteenth degree of latitude... The pleasure felt on discovering the Southern Cross was warmly shared by such of the crew as had lived in the colonies. In the solitude of the seas we hail a star as a friend, from whom we have been long separated.'*

In 1817, during their scientific expedition to Brazil, the German biologist Johann Baptist Ritter von Spix and his companion, the German explorer and botanist Carl Friedrich

Philipp von Martius, recorded that: '...on the 15th of June, in latitude 14° S., we beheld for the first time that glorious constellation of the southern heavens, the Cross, which is to navigators a token of peace... We had long wished for this constellation as a guide to the other hemisphere; we therefore felt inexpressible pleasure when we perceived it in the resplendent firmament.'

April 25th

Although the smallest of the constellations, Crux is home to numerous objects of interest to the backyard astronomer, all of which are set against the backdrop of the Milky Way which forms a wonderful backdrop. Three of the four stars making up the Cross are obviously blue or blue-white in colour while the other, Gamma, has a definite orange/red tint.

The brightest star in the Cross is Acrux. The name of this star appears to be a combination of the full Bayer reference for the star Alpha Crucis and seems to have been first coined by the American astronomy writer and cartographer Elijah Hinsdale Burritt in a star atlas compiled by him in the 1830s. In keeping with the fact that the stars of Crux were once part of the constellation Centaurus, the 16th century Arabian astronomer Al Tizini defined the position of this star as being near the ankle of the right hind foot of the Centaur.

Acrux is in fact a double star which shines at a combined magnitude 0.77 from a distance of around 320 light years. At magnitudes 1.4 and 1.9, the white and blue-white components of Acrux are resolvable in small telescopes.

April 26th

Beta Crucis is a magnitude 1.25 blue star whose light has taken around 280 years to reach us, and is somewhat closer than the blue giant star Delta Crucis which shines at magnitude 2.79

from a distance of a little under 350 light years. Offsetting the symmetry of the Cross is Epsilon, an orange giant star shining at magnitude 3.59 from a distance of approximately 230 light years.

Another double worth checking out is the orange-red Gamma Crucis which can be seen as a magnitude 1.6 star seemingly accompanied by a fainter magnitude 6.7 companion. Both components can be resolved in binoculars. However, the association is merely a line of sight effect and the two stars are not physically related. Gamma itself lies at a distance of 89 light years, roughly a quarter of the distance of its fainter companion.

April 27th

The stars Theta[1] and Theta[2] Crucis form a pretty pair when viewed through binoculars and seen against the backdrop of star fields against which they lie. Magnitude 4.32 Theta[1] lies at a distance of around 230 light years, a little over a quarter of the distance of magnitude 4.72 Theta[2] which shines from around 800 light years. Closer examination has shown that each of these two stars is actually a binary system, although the individual components of each are far too close to each other to be resolvable with conventional telescopes.

April 28th

The open star cluster NGC 4755, also known as the Jewel Box, is a splendid object. Resolvable into individual stars even through binoculars, this cluster lies at a distance of around 6,500 light years. It contains over 100 individual stars and can be spotted with the naked eye as a 4th-magnitude fuzzy star like object just to the south east of Beta Crucis, both objects lying within the same field of view of binoculars.

This fine cluster was discovered by the French astronomer Nicolas Louis de Lacaille who, after viewing it through his admittedly-small ½-inch (1.2cm) telescope, described it as being slightly nebulous and containing: *'Five or six stars between two mag. 6 stars.'* It was the English astronomer John Herschel who named this cluster the Jewel Box, describing it as: *'...an extremely brilliant and beautiful object when viewed through an instrument of sufficient aperture to show distinctly the very different colour of its constituent stars, which give it the effect of a superb piece of fancy jewellery.'*

When viewed through binoculars or a small telescope the Jewel Box can be seen to contain a number of very bright bluish-white stars. However, there is one supergiant star within the cluster which has a distinctly red tint and, when viewed through telescopes, lends a beautiful splash of colour to this stunning object.

April 29th
The Coal Sack dark nebula is visible to the naked eye and, apart from the presence of a few faint foreground stars, takes on the appearance of a dark patch silhouetted against the brighter background of the Milky Way. The Jewel Box cluster appears to be situated close to the northern edge of the Coal Sack, although this association is no more than a line of sight effect, the Coal Sack itself being located only around 500 light years away. The Coal Sack is the most prominent object of its type in the entire sky and, as its name suggests, takes the form of a huge, dark cloud of absorbing dust which blots out the light from the stars beyond, the overall effect being that of a huge hole in the surrounding star fields. Although most of the nebula lies within the constellation Crux, it overlaps into the neighbouring groups Centaurus and Musca.

April 30th

Nine-thirty! April, from whose brow the clouds seem rarely to have lifted, is passing in a fit of black and foul sullenness. Small wonder that the stars have all withdrawn themselves from her presence. So, unattended and unmourned, this inharmonious April is being submerged in the infinite ocean of time. Ungenial month! And never more ungenial than in these her last hours.

MAY

May 1st

Ten o'clock! Ugh! How drear and dismal is the night, a night unrelieved by star or moon. Rain is beginning to fall. The tempting gleam of a brightly burning fire comes out to me through my window, so I will indoors and try to think that this really is the opening of the "merrie month." Then, to round off the evening pleasantly, I will study anew an appropriate article on the old, old question of "Is the climate changing?" If matters do not mend soon I shall alter my opinion on that subject, and persist that the climate is changing.

May 2nd

Crux is surrounded on three sides by Centaurus (the Centaur), a much larger group and the ninth largest constellation in the sky. Containing over 100 naked-eye stars, this constellation is visible in its entirety from anywhere south of latitude 25°N, although from mid-European latitudes the whole group is essentially hidden from view.

Centaurus depicts the legendary Chiron, the half-man and half-horse son of Cronos, king of the Titans, and the sea nymph Philyra. As Chiron grew up he became well liked both by the gods and by many Greek heroes. He became a proficient teacher and passed on many skills, including hunting and archery, music and medicine, to all who visited his home at Mount Pelion in central Greece, including Achilles, Ajax, Asclepius, Perseus, Jason and Hercules.

*

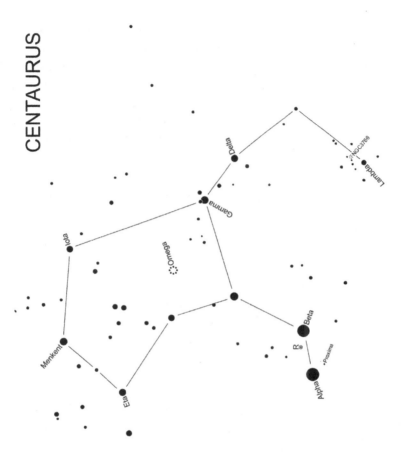

CENTAURUS

Sadly, however, this idyllic state of affairs was not to last. Chiron was accidentally killed by an arrow fired by Hercules who had been entertained by another centaur, the wise and respected Pholus. Unfortunately Pholus seems to have suffered a temporary loss of wisdom and gave Hercules a drink from the wine normally reserved for the centaurs who, upon hearing about this, became angry and attacked Pholus and Hercules. Hercules repelled the angry mob with a volley of poisoned arrows, one of which accidentally struck Chiron, who wasn't really part of the attack. Hercules did his best to save him by pulling out the arrow, but to no avail. Chiron continued to suffer although, because he was immortal, didn't die but remained in pain. When he learned of the situation, Zeus took away Chiron's immortality, allowing him to pass away peacefully, following which he was placed among the stars.

May 3rd

Lying at a distance of 4.3 light years, Alpha Centauri is the closest naked-eye star to us. Also known as Rigil Kentaurus, a name derived from the Arabic *'rijl qanturis'* meaning 'the Centaur's Foot', Alpha Centauri was discovered to be a double star by the French astronomer and Jesuit missionary Father Jean Richaud in 1689 from his observatory at Pondicherry in India. The magnitude 0 and 1.2 yellow components of Alpha Centauri actually form a binary system, the two stars orbiting each other over a period of 80 years.

Both components of Alpha Centauri are easily resolvable in small telescopes, unlike the much fainter Proxima Centauri, the location of which is shown on the chart. This dim 11th magnitude red dwarf star is probably gravitationally linked to the Alpha Centauri system, and is thought to be orbiting the main pair of stars over a period of many thousands of years. Proxima Centauri, its name derived from the Latin *'proxima'* meaning 'nearest' or 'closest', lies at a distance of just 4.24 light years, making it the closest star to our solar system.

May 4th

Located a little to the west of Alpha Centauri is Beta Centauri, a blue giant star shining at magnitude 0.60 from a distance of around 350 light years. Beta is also known by the traditional names of either Hadar or Agena, the latter title being given to the star by the American astronomy writer and cartographer Elijah Hinsdale Burritt, although the meaning of the word is unclear. It may, however, be derived from the Latin *'genu'* meaning 'the Knee (of the Centaur)'.

Alpha and Beta Centauri are known collectively as the Southern Pointers, alluding to the fact that a line drawn from Alpha through Beta leads to a point in the sky very close to Gamma Crucis, the star at the northern point of the nearby constellation Crux (see April 23rd). The direction of south can then be determined by following a line from Gamma Crucis through Acrux, the star at the lower, or southern end, of Crux.

May 5th

The western sky was splashed with purple clouds at sunset. By half-past eight, however, these had drifted into the north-west, and had become black, wide-spreading stratified masses. And there they lay in brooding stillness, like so many sombre-clad Army Corps waiting for the battle signal. So grand an air of solemnity and repose did they give to the scene as to make even the sounds of distant music incongruous.

May 6th

The constellation Centaurus covers a large area of sky and among the many bright stars in contains is Menkent, a yellow-orange magnitude 2.06 giant shining from a distance of 59 light years and found at the northern end of the Centaur. Its name is probably derived from the Arabic word *'mankib'* meaning 'the Shoulder (of the Centaur)'. Menkent is flanked by the two stars Iota and Eta Centauri. Magnitude 2.75 Iota is located at around the same distance as Menkent, while somewhat further away is Eta, the light from this magnitude 2.33 star having taken a little over 300 years to reach us.

One of the southernmost members of Centaurus is Lambda, a white star shining at magnitude 3.10 and located at a distance of just over 400 light years. Another white star is Gamma Centauri, somewhat closer than Lambda at just 130 light years and shining with a magnitude of 2.20. A short way from Gamma is the bluish magnitude 2.58 Delta Centauri, the light from which has taken a little over 400 years to reach us.

May 7th

Located a little way to the north of the line from Alpha to Beta Centauri is the long-period Mira-type (see December 4th) variable star R Centauri, the reddish tint of which should be easily identifiable in binoculars. Located at a distance of over 1,000 light years, its average magnitude range is 5.3 to around 11, the whole cycle taking place over a period of around 550 days. If you have the patience to keep a look out for this star you will eventually catch it at or near maximum brightness, from where you can watch it decrease and brighten again. Although most of its cycle can be followed through binoculars, you will need a small telescope (or very large binoculars) to keep it in view when at or near its dimmest. A definite target for the backyard astronomer!

May 8th

The southern reaches of Centaurus straddle the Milky Way and the area is well worth sweeping with binoculars which will reveal many rich and attractive star fields, in particular the region around the star Delta Centauri. In addition, there are quite a number of open star clusters, a particularly fine example being NGC 3766. Also known as the Pearl Cluster, NGC 3766 was discovered by the French astronomer Nicolas Louis de Lacaille during his stay in South Africa cataloguing the southern stars. Located just to the north of the star Lambda Centauri, and lying in the same binocular field of view, NGC 3766 shines at magnitude 5.3 and can be made out with the naked eye if the sky is really dark and clear. Most of the 40 or so stars within this cluster are bluish in colour, although there are a couple of red giant stars which you may be able to pick out.

May 9th

Easily visible to the naked eye, Omega Centauri (NGC 5139) is one of the finest examples of all the globular clusters. Unlike open clusters, which are found within the main galactic plane and have no really well-defined shape, globular clusters are vast spherical collections of stars located in the area of space surrounding the Galaxy (see Glossary). In contrast to the young hot stars from which open clusters are typically formed, globular clusters are made up of old stars with little or none of the nebulosity sometimes seen in open clusters.

With a diameter in excess of 150 light years, Omega Centauri is the largest globular cluster in our Milky Way Galaxy. Shining from a distance of nearly 16,000 light years, this huge object contains several million individual stars. To locate Omega Centauri, follow a line from Beta Centauri, through Epsilon and on nearly as far again. When viewed without optical aid, it will appear as a nebulous star and binoculars will reveal Omega Centauri as a large nebulous patch. With magnifications of 20x or more individual stars will be visible and small telescopes will offer even better views of this magnificent cluster.

The German astronomer and celestial cartographer Johann Bayer named this object Omega Centauri in his *Uranometria*, a star atlas published by him in 1603. Because it appeared to be the 24th brightest star in Centaurus, he used the 24th letter of the Greek alphabet to identify it. Bayer saw it as nothing more than a hazy 4th-magnitude star, and it wasn't until the advent of the telescope that its true nature was revealed. However, in spite of the object not actually being a star, the name has remained in use.

May 10th

Immediately to the south of Crux is the small but conspicuous pattern of stars we call Musca (the Fly). This tiny constellation was introduced by the Dutch navigators and explorers Pieter Dirkszoon Keyser and Frederick de Houtman following their expedition to the East Indies in the 1590s. Keyser had been asked by his fellow countryman and celestial cartographer Petrus Plancius to chart the southern hemisphere stars during the voyage. Unfortunately, Keyser died in 1596, although the observations made were passed on to Plancius when the expedition returned in 1597. This constellation was given the name Apis (the Bee) and it appeared on a celestial globe produced by Plancius in 1598, as well as in the *Uranometria*, a star atlas produced by the German astronomer and celestial cartographer Johann Bayer in 1603.

The diminutive form of Musca can only be readily seen from locations on or south of the equator and is completely hidden to observers north of latitude 25°N. Nicolas Louis de Lacaille renamed the constellation Musca Australis (the Southern Fly) in 1752, this to avoid confusion with the constellation Musca Borealis (the Northern Fly) which existed at the time (see November 11th), located immediately to the north east of the constellation Aries (the Ram). Musca Borealis eventually disappeared from star charts leaving Musca Australis, the name of which has since been reduced to Musca.

131

To add to the confusion, the northern counterpart Musca Borealis was originally known as Apes (a slight variation on Apis - the Bee) when originally introduced by Plancius on another of his globes, this one produced in 1613.

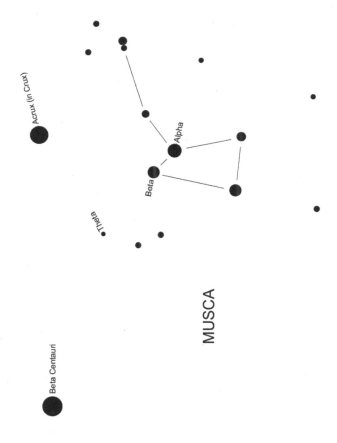

May 11th
The chart shows Musca together with the two nearby

prominent stars Acrux in Crux and Beta Centauri in Centaurus which should help you to locate this constellation. The two brightest stars in Musca are Alpha and Beta Muscae. Alpha shines at magnitude 2.69 from a distance of 315 light years whilst Beta is a little further away, the light from this magnitude 3.04 star having taken 340 years to reach us.

If you have a small telescope you might like to try and resolve the two components of the double star Theta Muscae. Musca lies on the edge of the Milky Way and the yellowish and white magnitude 5.7 and 7.3 components of Theta form a pretty sight when viewed against the rich field of stars that act as a backdrop to this pair.

May 12th

This has been an odour-diffusing day, all vivid sunshine and soft, warm . Gentle May has come at last, but how weary has been the breezes wait!

Nine o'clock! After an impressive display of lightning in the south-west at sunset, the sky cleared, and the north became beautifully transparent, pearly; the air refreshingly cool after the hot day.

May 13th

The constellation Chamaeleon (the Chameleon) can be found close to the south celestial pole, immediately to the south of Musca and Carina. The chart shows the constellation together with the four main stars in Musca, which can be used as a guide to locating this group. As with Musca, Chamaeleon can only be readily seen from locations on or south of the equator and the constellation is completely hidden from view to observers north of latitude 15°N. Taking the form of a small extended diamond, this is another of the constellations introduced following observations made by Pieter Dirkszoon Keyser and

Frederick de Houtman (see May 10th) during the 1590s.

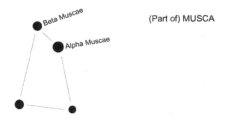

(Part of) MUSCA

CHAMAELEON

May 14th

The stars in Chamaeleon are all faint and none of them are named. The brightest is Alpha, a white star shining at magnitude 4.05 from a distance of 64 light years. Located immediately to its south west is Theta, a magnitude 4.34 orange giant star lying at a distance of 155 light years. When seen in binoculars Alpha and Theta form a wide pair with a pretty colour contrast. At the opposite end of the diamond we have Beta Chamaeleontis, a magnitude 4.24 blue star whose light has taken nearly 300 years to reach us.

Perhaps of most interest to the backyard astronomer is Delta Chamaeleontis which is actually made up of two unrelated stars. The colour of blue-white Delta[1] contrasts nicely with the orange tint of the slightly-brighter Delta[2] when viewed through binoculars.

May 15th

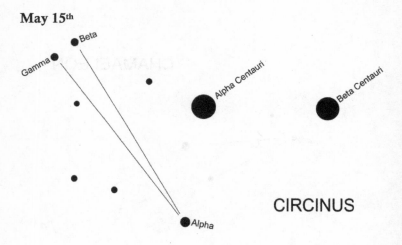

CIRCINUS

Our final port of call during this visit to the stars of the southern hemisphere, before we once again divert our attentions to the northern skies, is the constellation Circinus (the Compasses) which was devised by the French astronomer Nicolas Louis de Lacaille to represent either the instrument used by navigators or pair of the dividing compasses used by draughtsmen to measure distances. It seems to most closely resemble the latter, taking the form of a tiny elongated triangle located immediately to the west of the two bright stars Alpha and Beta Centauri, both of which are shown on the chart.

Circinus can be viewed in its entirety from most of Mexico, northern Africa and most of India and from locations to the south of these. None of the stars in the constellation are particularly prominent, the brightest being Alpha Circini which shines at magnitude 3.18 from a distance of 54 light years. The two 4th magnitude stars Beta and Gamma complete the triangle.

May 16th

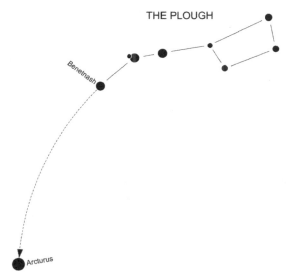

Now we turn our attentions back to the northern skies, in particular to the prominent constellation Boötes (the Herdsman), its leading star Arcturus very prominent in the northern spring night sky. If you do need help tracking Arcturus down, first of all locate the Plough, its familiar shape formed from the seven brightest stars in the constellation Ursa Major (see March 6th). For observers in or around mid-northern latitudes, the Plough is located at or near the overhead point at this time of year. Using the line of stars in the Plough handle as direction finders, follow their curve until you reach brilliant yellow-orange Arcturus, from where the rest of the stars in Boötes can be traced out. For additional reference Benetnash, the 'end star' in the Plough handle, is also shown on the chart.

Although predominantly a northern constellation, portions of Boötes are visible from almost every inhabited part of the world and the whole of the constellation can be seen from South Africa and from most of Australia and South America, albeit fairly low down on the northern horizon.

May 17th

Boötes has rather a mixed and uncertain origin and different backgrounds describe a whole host of mythological sources. The constellation is usually taken to depict a herdsman who is chasing the Great Bear around the northern sky, the name of its leading star Arcturus being derived from the Greek title meaning 'the Bear Watcher'. Some legends associate him with a hunter leading a pair of hunting dogs, depicted by Canes Venatici (see May 22nd) on a chase, whilst other Greek stories associate the constellation with a Ploughman. Extending the mix of possible origins for the group are tales from early Rome which depict the group as a Wagoner, and early English accounts which refer to the constellation as a Bear Driver, due to its proximity to Ursa Major (the Great Bear).

* * *

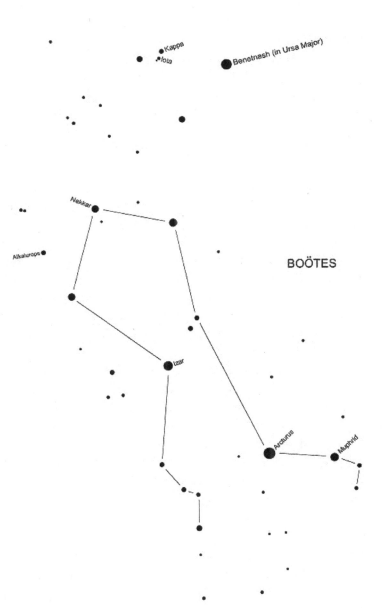

Kappa

Iota

Benetnash (in Ursa Major)

Nekkar

Alkalurops

BOÖTES

Izar

Arcturus

Muphrid

138

May 18th

At magnitude –0.04 and located at a distance of 37 light years, Arcturus is the 4th brightest star in the entire sky, and the most prominent member of the Diamond of Virgo, an asterism formed from Arcturus, Spica in Virgo (see May 30th), Denebola in Leo (see April 4th) and Cor Caroli in Canes Venatici (see May 23rd) and which is depicted on the chart of Coma Berenices (see May 25th). One of this star's main claims to fame is that it was the first star to be observed in daylight, this feat being accomplished by the French astronomer Jean-Baptiste Morin in 1635.

Arcturus was one of Joseph Elgie's favourite stars, and he says of it: *'I have ever had the kindliest regard for golden-hued Arcturus. Glittering night after night, it is to me associated with everything that is beautiful and fair. Its changing colour, according to its altitude, is a source of never-ending delight. It is unique in its beauty and in its power of arousing kindly sentiment. To me, not only is it the harbinger of Spring, but the apotheosis of summer also.'*

Somewhat further away than Arcturus is magnitude 3.49 Nekkar, a yellow giant star which shines from a distance of around 225 light years. Another yellow star is Muphrid, named after the Arabic for 'the Solitary Star of the Lancer' and which shines at magnitude 2.68 from a distance of 37 light years. Chinese astronomers gave this star the rather grand name of Yew She Ti, meaning 'The officer standing on the right of the Emperor'!

May 19th

Boötes contains a number of double stars including Alkalurops which, shining from a distance of around 120 light years, has magnitude 4.5 and 6.7 components which can be resolved through binoculars. Iota is one of a tiny triangle of stars located just to the east of Benetnash, the end star in the handle of the Plough. This is another double worth checking out, the magnitude 4.8 and 6.7 components of Iota being far enough apart to be split with binoculars. The magnitude 4.6 and 6.6 components of Kappa situated immediately to the north of Iota are both white in colour and, although not resolvable in binoculars, can be seen with a small telescope.

May 20th

Like Arcturus, Izar is a yellow-orange giant star, its light having taken around 200 years to reach us and the colour of which is fairly obvious in binoculars. Its name is derived from the Arabic *'al-mi'zar'* meaning 'the Girdle', perhaps a fitting title in view of the fact that Izar is located near the middle of the constellation. Shining with an overall magnitude of 2.35, Izar is also a double star system, although the two components are very difficult to resolve in small telescopes.

May 21st

May is still disposed to be vixenish. This morning we had a smart shower of hail, and to-night would be cold even for February. There is, too, that hard glint in the clear sky which so often follows an atmospheric scouring by winter-like squalls. Winter, indeed, leaves us this year with greater reluctance than ever. It is bold in its reluctance, and dares the quickening sun of Spring to banish it.

May 22nd

As we have seen, the Plough is a useful pointer to many other star patterns, one of which is the constellation Canes Venatici. Known to Arabic astronomers as *'Al Karb al Ibl'* meaning 'the Camel's Burden', the main part of the tiny constellation of Canes Venatici (the Hunting Dogs) is visible as a pair of stars immediately to the south of the 'handle' of the Plough. Benetnash, the star at the end of the Plough handle, is shown here for reference along with the bright star Arcturus in the neighbouring constellation Boötes. As is the case with Boötes, the whole of Canes Venatici can be seen from South Africa and from most of Australia and South America, from where it will be seen fairly low down on the northern horizon.

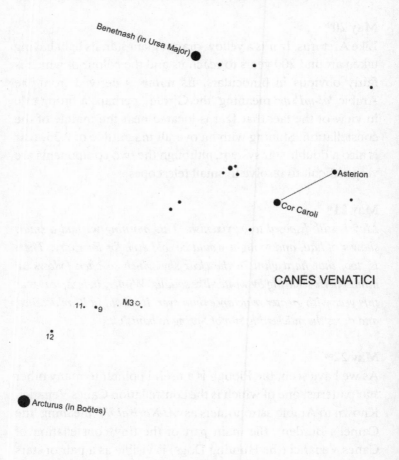

Benetnash (in Ursa Major)

Asterion

Cor Caroli

CANES VENATICI

11·   ·9   · M3☼·

·
12

Arcturus (in Boötes)

Canes Venatici was introduced by the Polish astronomer Johannes Hevelius in the late-17th century and represents a pair of hunting dogs held by Boötes (see May 17th), the three of them involved in an eternal pursuit of the Great Bear around the sky. Canes Venatici is one of only three constellations that depict dogs, the other two being Canis Major (see January 11th) and Canis Minor (see January 15th).

May 23rd

The brightest star in Canes Venatici is Cor Caroli, or Charles' Heart. Along with the nearby bright stars Arcturus in Boötes (see May 18th), Spica in Virgo (see May 30th) and Denebola in Leo (see April 4th), Cor Caroli forms the conspicuous and celebrated asterism the Diamond of Virgo, depicted on the chart showing Coma Berenices (see May 25th). Accounts differ as to exactly who this star was named after. Some authorities say it was named in memory of Charles I, who was executed in 1649 during the English Civil War, whilst others believe the star was named after his son, Charles II, following his return to England in 1660 and his restoring of the English monarchy to the throne.

Cor Caroli shines from a distance of 110 light years and is a double star. The individual components are of magnitudes 2.8 and 5.6 and the pair is easily resolvable through a small telescope.

As well as commemorating one of the two English kings mentioned above, Cor Caroli also depicts one of the two hunting dogs featuring in the legend surrounding this constellation. Indeed, an alternative name for this star is Chara, one of the two dogs alluded to in the legend. Located a short distance to the north west of Cor Caroli is Asterion, the star depicting the other dog from the mythological account.

Asterion shines at magnitude 4.24, its light having taken 28 years to reach us.

May 24th

Although only a tiny constellation, Canes Venatici is notable in that it plays host to the celestial showpiece M3, a member of a class of objects known to astronomers as globular clusters. Like all globular clusters, M3 lies outside our Galaxy, located at a distance of well over 30,000 light years. Discovered by the French astronomer Charles Messier in 1764, this magnificent object contains around half-a-million stars compressed, as its descriptive name suggests, into a globe-shape with an actual diameter of around 180 light years.

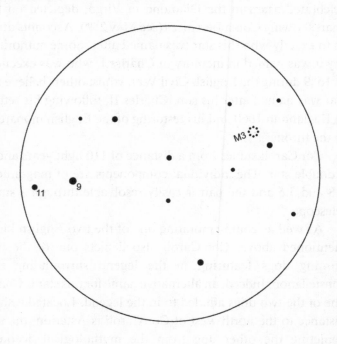

M3 shines at magnitude 6.2 and, if you have really keen eyesight, and the sky is very dark, clear and moonless, you might just be able to pick it out with no optical aid whatsoever. However, you are best looking for it with a pair of binoculars. M3 is located almost on a direct line from Asterion through Cor Caroli and extended towards the bright star Arcturus in the neighbouring constellation Boötes. Starting your search from Arcturus, slowly work your way up towards Canes Venatici and look for the faint stars 12, 11 and 9 (all in Boötes). Once you have spotted 11 and 9, you can star hop your way to M3 using the detailed finder chart. When seeking out this object, and others of its type, try to look for a patch of luminosity rather than a point of light. Once you find it, M3 should be visible as a tiny, spherical cloud.

It is a sobering thought that, should you manage to glimpse M3, the light you are seeing from this remote object set off on its journey towards us over six times as long ago as the age during which Stonehenge and the Great Pyramid of Giza were constructed ...the universe is truly a huge place!

May 25th

During May evenings, the scattering of faint stars known as Coma Berenices (Berenice's Hair) can be located a little way to the east and slightly north of the bright star Denebola in the tail of the neighbouring constellation of Leo as shown here. Coma Berenices lies within the Diamond of Virgo, an asterism of the bright stars Arcturus in Boötes (see May 18th), Spica in Virgo (see May 30th), Denebola in Leo (see April 4th) and Cor Caroli in Canes Venatici (see May 23rd). The chart shows the group along with the four bright stars in the Diamond of Virgo. Coma Berenices takes the form of a pretty collection of faint stars spread out over a small area of sky, and is best seen when the sky is really dark and clear and free of moonlight.

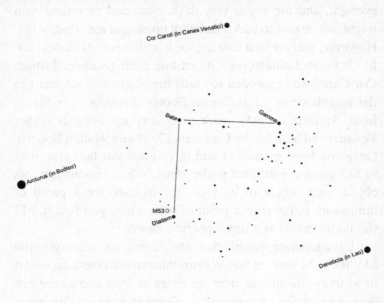

Cor Caroli (in Canes Venatici) ●

Beta ●
Gamma ●

Arcturus (in Boötes) ●

M53 ✧
Diadem ●

Denebola (in Leo) ●

Spica (in Virgo) ●

COMA BERENICES

The whole of Coma Berenices is visible from latitudes north of 56°S, which makes it accessible to backyard astronomers in Australia, New Zealand and in all but the very southern tip of South America. However, when viewed from these locations Coma Berenices may be quite difficult to pick out should there be mist, hazy cloud or any form of light pollution over the horizon. Bearing in mind that the constellation contains no particularly bright stars, seeing it at all from locations so far south may be an achievement in itself.

How exquisite is the delicate shimmering of Berenice's fabled hair at this hour! Coma Berenices is, to me, one of the most fairylike objects in the sky. To see its tiny diamond-like stars in their full beauty one should use an opera glass, for then do they appear of a texture that Arachne herself may have spun.

Like Praesepe, Coma Berenices may afford at times some broad indication of what the weather will be on the following day. I have seen this shimmering cluster grow dim with the mists of gathering condensation, and have asked myself if it meant rain; and rain, sometimes very heavy, has not infrequently come. Such results have arisen merely from the working of a simple physical law. They do not enter into the dangerous domain of weather prophecy.

May 26th

The early Egyptians knew this group as 'Many Stars' while Arabic astronomers referred to it as the 'Coarse Hair' or 'Tuft' in the tail of the nearby constellation of Leo (the Lion). The group itself is not an ancient one, however, and was only made into an official constellation by the Dutch cartographer Gerardus Mercator in the mid-16th century. However, the region was noted and observed by ancient star-gazers and there is quite an enchanting legend behind Coma Berenices.

According to the story, King Ptolemy III of Egypt was

away fighting a war in Asia. His wife, Queen Berenice II, was worried that he would not return safely home, and she offered to sacrifice her hair to the gods if they safeguarded his return. Ptolemy came back alive and well, and Berenice kept her promise, cutting off her hair and placing it in the temple of Aphrodite at Zephyrium. The gods were so pleased with this that they took the hair and transformed it into a constellation, placing it forever among the stars.

May 27th

The fact that Coma Berenices resembles a large and loosely scattered collection of stars is no illusion, and in fact the Coma group is an open star cluster containing around 40 members. The stars within the cluster range in brightness between around 5th and 10th magnitude, ensuring that some are visible to the naked eye. Also known as Melotte 111, after its inclusion in a catalogue of star clusters compiled by the English astronomer Philibert Jacques Melotte in 1915, the Coma Star Cluster lies at a distance of around 250 light years. This makes it one of the closest objects of its type in the sky and the area is rich and well worth sweeping with binoculars.

May 28th

The three leading stars of Coma Berenices are not actually members of the Coma Star Cluster and are, in effect, seen superimposed against it. The first of these is Diadem which has a magnitude of 4.32 and shines from a distance of 58 light years. Diadem is in fact a binary star, although the two 5th magnitude components, which orbit each other every 25 years or so, are too close together to be seen in anything other than a large telescope.

Diadem has a yellowish-white tinge, similar to yellow Beta,

a star roughly comparable in size and actual brightness to our own Sun and located to the north of Diadem. Beta shines at magnitude 4.23 from a distance of around 30 light years. Gamma, a magnitude 4.35 star whose light has taken around 170 years to reach us, has a slightly orange hue. Diadem, Beta and Gamma are the brightest stars in Coma Berenices, although all three are probably too faint to be seen with the naked eye from light polluted urban areas, and are best sought out with binoculars.

May 29th

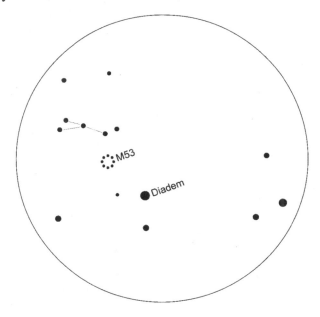

Coma Berenices plays host to a large number of faint galaxies which are spread out across the southern regions of the group.

However, large telescopes are required to bring these out, although there is one interesting object in Coma Berenices which is within the light grasp of a good pair of binoculars. This is the globular star cluster M53, situated just to the north east of Diadem.

This vast, spherical collection of stars was discovered by the German astronomer Johann Elert Bode in 1775 and measurements have put the cluster at a distance of around 58,000 light years. M53 shines at magnitude 7.6 and, under really clear, dark skies, will be revealed in binoculars as a small, diffuse patch of light. This finder chart will help you to find M53. First of all locate Diadem. You'll then see a tiny dart-shaped pattern of stars immediately to the north east. M53 is located between these stars and Diadem. Remember, you will need to look for a patch of luminosity rather than an actual point of light.

May 30th

We now turn our attention to the constellation Virgo (the Virgin), a long and sprawling pattern of stars which can be found straddling the celestial equator. The stars of Virgo form a conspicuous Y-shape and the brightest star in the constellation, Spica, is quite prominent. The fact that Virgo lies on the celestial equator ensures that the whole of the constellation is visible from every inhabited part of the world lying south of latitude 68°N.

Northern hemisphere observers can locate Spica by using the stars in the Plough as pointers. If you extend the curve of these stars southwards you will pass through Arcturus in Boötes and, extending the line as far again, eventually arrive at Spica. For those observers in the southern hemisphere who are perhaps unable to see the Plough, the two bright stars

Arcturus in Boötes and Denebola in Leo can be seen to form a prominent triangle with Spica high in the northern sky and should help you pick it out.

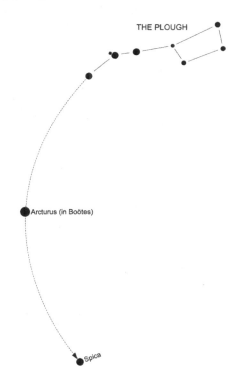

THE PLOUGH

Arcturus (in Boötes)

Spica

May 31st

According to the early Greeks the constellation symbolised a pure and unpolluted Earth, although other legends associate Virgo with Ceres, the goddess of the harvest. In these accounts Spica represents an ear of wheat held in Virgo's left hand. Egyptian mythology states that the misty band of light we see as the Milky Way was formed by Virgo throwing millions of wheat heads up into the sky. On a somewhat more bizarre note, the Greek philosopher Pliny said that if ever a comet was seen in the constellation, then great misfortune would befall all females here on Earth.

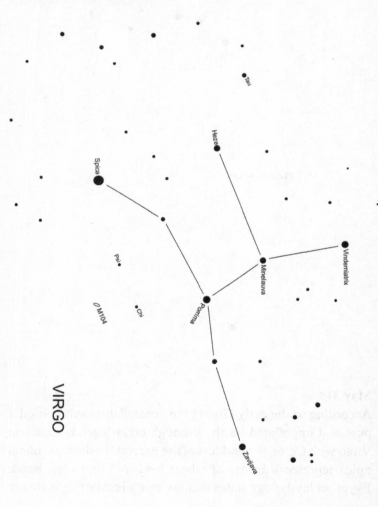

JUNE

June 1st

Brilliant blue-white Spica takes its name from its Roman title meaning 'the Ear of Grain', the light from this magnitude 0.98 star having taken around 250 years to reach us. Spica is actually a binary system, comprising two stars in orbit around each other, although the components are so close together that they cannot be resolved in ordinary telescopes. Along with the nearby bright stars Arcturus in Boötes (see May 18th), Denebola in Leo (see April 4th) and Cor Caroli in Canes Venatici (see May 23rd), Spica forms the conspicuous and celebrated asterism known as the Diamond of Virgo, and which is depicted on the chart showing Coma Berenices (see May 25th).

Found a little way to the northwest of Spica is magnitude 2.74 Porrima which shines from a distance of 38 light years.

A little fainter than Porrima is magnitude 3.59 Zavijava, a yellow-white star located at the western end of Virgo and shining from a distance of 36 light years. Located at a distance of around 200 light years, the orange-red tint of magnitude 3.39 Minelauva, situated to the north east of Porrima, can be seen quite well in binoculars.

The name given to the yellow giant star Vindemiatrix takes its from the Latin for 'the Grape Gatherer', deriving from the fact that the star was seen to rise just before the Sun at around the time of the annual harvest. The light from Vindemiatrix has taken around 110 years to reach us and, when seen through binoculars, offers a nice colour contrast with the magnitude 3.38 white star Heze which shines from a distance of around 74 light years.

June 2nd

Located a little way to the east-northeast of Heze is the slightly fainter double star Tau Virginis which, with an overall magnitude of 4.23, shines from a distance of around 220 light years. Close examination will reveal its 9th magnitude companion star lying close by. The two individual stars making up the Tau system can be resolved in small telescopes or even powerful binoculars, and this pair is definitely worth tracking down.

June 3rd

Discovered by the French astronomer Pierre Méchain in 1781, Messier 104 is one of Virgo's most celebrated sights. Lying at a distance of around 30 million light years, M104 is also known as the 'Sombrero Hat Galaxy', a name derived from its appearance when viewed through large telescopes. From our position in space we see M104 edge-on and there is a conspicuous lane of dark, dusty material spread out along its main plane. The bright central region of the galaxy is seen to project outwards at either side of this dust lane.

When Méchain discovered this object he will have seen little more than a diffuse patch of light and it would seem that the dust lane was first observed by William Herschel through one of his large telescopes. Indeed, to see this feature a large telescope is normally required, although the galaxy itself may be glimpsed with only moderate optical aid.

A good pair of binoculars or a small telescope should help you to locate M104. Plenty of patience, coupled with a dark, clear sky devoid of any moonlight, will be essential in your search, and don't forget that you are looking for a patch of light rather than a star-like point. The accompanying finder chart will lead you towards M104. First of all, track down the two guide stars Psi and Chi, which are located in the area of sky just to the south of Porrima. Once these have been found, you can 'star-hop' your way to the Sombrero Hat Galaxy by carefully following the patterns of faint stars show on the chart.

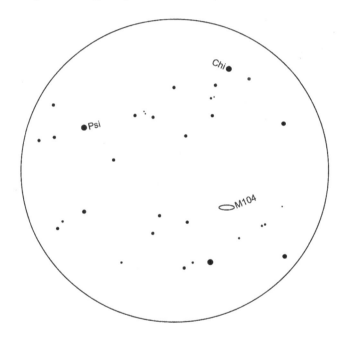

Whether or not you manage to locate the Sombrero Hat Galazy, it is a sobering thought that the light we are now receiving from this distant star system set off on its journey towards us around 30 million years ago. It is also fascinating to imagine that other astronomers may be situated on a planet orbiting one of the millions of stars that make up M104. Indeed, they may be thinking the same thoughts as they train their telescopes on our own Milky Way Galaxy.

June 4th

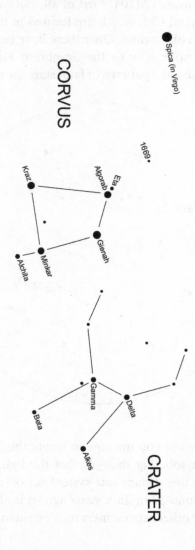

The Sombrero Hat Galaxy is found virtually on the border between the constellations Virgo and Corvus, the latter being located immediately to the south of Virgo, and our next port of call. Both Corvus (the Crow) and the neighbouring constellation Crater (the Cup) can be found a little way to the south of the celestial equator, resulting in both constellations being visible in their entirety from every inhabited part of the world lying south of latitude 65°N.

Corvus and Crater are associated with the legend involving Apollo and his request that the crow fetch him a cup of the water of life (see April 16th). As we have seen, the crow kept Apollo waiting, the result of which delay resulted in the crow and the cup being banished to the sky. Both can be found immediately to the north, and on the back of, the long and meandering constellation Hydra (the Water Snake) (see April 14th) who guards the cup and its contents from the crow, thereby condemning the unfortunate bird to eternal thirst.

June 5th

Although the stars forming Corvus and Crater are not particularly bright, the shapes of these two groups are quite distinctive. Both constellations can be located fairly easily in the area of sky immediately to the south and south west of Virgo, the bright star Spica in Virgo included on the chart for guidance. The leading star in Corvus is Gienah which shines at magnitude 2.58 from a distance of around 160 light years. The name Gienah is derived from the Arabic *'janah'* meaning 'wing' and can be confusing in that the same name is used for stars in two different constellations. Although here it represents the wing of a crow, it also represents the outstretched wing of the constellation Cygnus (see September 5th).

Slightly fainter than Gienah is the magnitude 2.65 yellow

giant star Kraz, the light from which has taken 140 years to reach us. Magnitude 2.94 Algorab, the name of which comes from the Arabic *'janah al-ghurab'* meaning 'the Raven's Wing', is somewhat closer at only 87 light years. These three stars, together with the orange giant Minkar, form the distinctive quadrilateral shape of Corvus, adjoining to the south of which is the 4th magnitude white star Alchita, the light from which set off towards us around 50 years ago.

June 6th

Although Corvus doesn't have much in the way of interesting objects for the backyard astronomer to look at, there are some double stars you can check out. One of these is an optical double formed from Algorab and 4th magnitude Eta, the latter lying somewhat closer to us than Algorab, at a distance of 60 light years. The pair form a pretty sight when viewed through binoculars, although the fact that they appear close together in the sky is merely a line of sight effect. Algorab itself is a double with an 9th magnitude bluish companion, both stars being resolvable in a small telescope.

Another double worth seeking out is Struve 1669 which can be seen a short way to the north east of Algorab and Eta. Struve 1669 is formed from two 6th magnitude yellowish stars which together form an attractive pair for small telescopes.

The reference for Struve 1669 is derived from its number in the catalogue of double stars compiled by the German astronomer Friedrich Georg Wilhelm von Struve and his son Otto Wilhelm von Struve during the 19th century.

June 7th

While the shape of Corvus may not particularly resemble that of a crow, that of neighbouring Crater does at least bear a distinct likeness to a cup complete with base. Generally speaking, the stars forming Crater are fainter than those in Corvus, the brightest being Delta Crateris, a yellow giant star shining at magnitude 3.56 from a distance of around 180 light years. Slightly fainter is Gamma, a magnitude 4.06 white star whose light has taken 82 years to reach us. Alkes is another yellow giant, the magnitude 4.08 glow of which set off on its journey towards us around 160 years ago. Alkes derives its name from the Arabic *'al-ka's'* meaning 'the (Wine) Cup', alluding to the constellation itself. Completing the shape of what may be taken as the base of the cup is magnitude 4.46 Beta, a white star shining from a distance of around 340 light years.

June 8th

The twilight month of June! The month when roses blush by day and the stars are coy by night.

Ten o'clock! A delicious evening; so transparent has been the air that Polaris did not become visible until twenty minutes past nine. Ten minutes later Altair emerged with conspicuous lustre from the low fringe of murk over the eastern horizon, winking with hysterical vigour. Spica was then well past the meridian. Its light was cold and hard against the soft twilit sky. And what a contrast it presented with the golden gleam of tender-eyed Arcturus! The great star of Boötes was then far above Spica, and somewhat to the eastward.

June 9th

Now we again divert our attentions to the southern hemisphere stars, our next port of call being the distinctively-shaped Triangulum Australe (the Southern Triangle). This group is known as the Southern Triangle to distinguish it from its northern counterpart Triangulum (the Triangle) (see November

4th). Taking the form of a small triangle of stars (as its name would suggest) Triangulum Australe is located a little way to the east of the prominent pair Alpha and Beta Centauri, both included on the chart for guidance, and the tiny constellation Circinus (see May 15th).

TRIANGULUM AUSTRALE

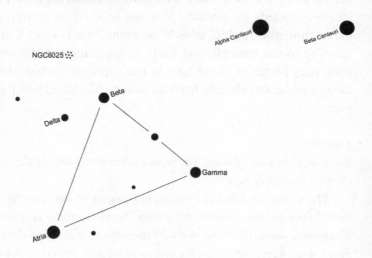

The whole of Triangulum Australe can be viewed from the Earth's equatorial regions and from anywhere further south, although the constellation is completely hidden from view to those north of latitude 30°N. Triangulum Australe is one of the constellations introduced by Pieter Dirkszoon Keyser and Frederick de Houtman in the 1590s (see May 10th) following which it appeared on the celestial globe produced by Petrus Plancius in 1598. The stars in the group were charted by the French astronomer Nicolas Louis de Lacaille following his stay in South Africa during 1751 and 1752 and it was Lacaille who gave the brightest stars in the constellation their Bayer designations (see Glossary – Star Names).

The brightest star in Triangulum Australe is Atria, its name being a contraction of its Bayer reference Alpha Trianguli Australis. This magnitude 1.91 orange giant shines from a distance of 390 light years. Somewhat fainter than Atria is Beta Trianguli Australis, a magnitude 2.83 white star whose light has taken just 40 years to reach us. Completing the triangle is Gamma, another white star which shines at magnitude 2.87 and lies at a distance of around 180 light years.

June 10th

Although Triangulum Australe doesn't contain a great deal of interest to the backyard astronomer, one object definitely worth looking for is the open star cluster NGC 6025. Discovered by Nicolas Louis de Lacaille, NGC 6025 is located on the northern edge of Triangulum Australe, near its border with the neighbouring constellation Norma (see June 14th). This cluster is fairly easy to find as it lies more or less in line with the two stars Atria and Delta. Containing around 30 individual stars, NGC 6025 shines at magnitude 5.3 and is an easy object for binoculars.

June 11th

Triangulum Australe is bordered to the south by the tiny constellation Apus (the Bird of Paradise), shown here with the bright pair Alpha and Beta Centauri, together with the three stars Atria and Beta and Gamma Trianguli Australis, as guides to locating the group. Apus lies quite close to the south celestial pole, the whole constellation being visible from anywhere south of latitude 7°N. This is one of the constellations introduced by Pieter Dirkszoon Keyser and Frederick de

Houtman in the 1590s (see May 10th) following which it appeared on the celestial globe produced by Petrus Plancius in 1598. Apus was also depicted in the star atlas *Uranometria*, produced in 1603 by the German astronomer and celestial cartographer Johann Bayer.

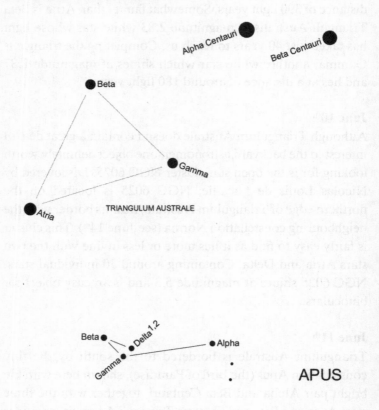

June 12th

The brightest star in Apus is the magnitude 3.83 orange giant Alpha Apodis which lies at a distance of around 440 light years.

Slightly fainter is the yellow giant Gamma at magnitude 3.86. The light from Gamma has taken 160 years to reach us. Beta Apodis is another orange giant star, shining at magnitude 4.23 from a distance of around 160 light years.

Delta Apodis is a wide optical double star which can be easily resolved in binoculars. The two stars forming Delta are not actually related, the distance between them being around 150 light years. The main component is the magnitude 4.68 red giant Delta[1] Apodis which lies at a distance of around 750 light years. Somewhat closer is the slightly fainter Delta[2] Apodis, an orange giant of magnitude 5.27 shining from around 610 light years.

June 13th

I think I shall always remember this present year of grace one thousand nine hundred and seven – so far as it has gone, at any rate – as the Year of Cloud. I know this, that I have never had to tire in vigilance over the sky o' nights so that I might present a proper sequence of stellar observations as the months have glided by. Yet has it a fascination, this conflict with the clouds – great, sullen, slow-moving adversaries – and so accustomed to their grim presence have I become of late that when they are absent and the stars are shining I experience all the pride of a victory over the forces of Nature – the sweet recompense of a ceaseless vigil.

June 14th

Located just to the north of Triangulum Australe is the tiny constellation Norma (the Level). Devised by the French astronomer Nicolas Louis de Lacaille to represent the set square used by draughtsmen, Norma can be viewed in its entirety from anywhere south of latitude 30°N and takes the form of a tiny quadrilateral of faint stars located a little way to the northeast of the two bright stars Alpha and Beta Centauri and the tiny constellation Circinus. Alpha and Beta Centauri are included on the chart as guides to locating Norma.

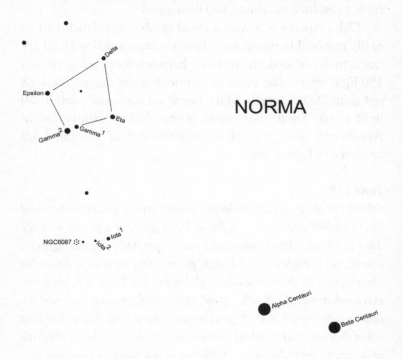

NONE of the stars in the constellation are named and none are particularly prominent, the brightest being Gamma^2 Normae, a 4th magnitude orange giant shining from a distance of around 130 light years. The 5th magnitude white supergiant Gamma^1 Normae lies close to Gamma^2 although the two stars are not related and the pair only form an optical double. Measurements reveal that Gamma^1 shines from a distance of well over 1,000 light years.

The rest of the main quadrilateral of Norma is made up of the three stars Delta, Eta and Epsilon, the latter being a double star resolvable in small telescopes. Located at a distance of around 530 light years, the main component of Epsilon is blue and shines at magnitude 4.8 although a small telescope, or powerful binoculars, will reveal a magnitude 7.5 companion star.

June 15th

Located a little way to the east of the stars Iota^1 and Iota^2 Normae is the open star cluster NGC 6087 which contains around 40 member stars and shines with an overall magnitude of 5.4 from a distance of around 3,500 light years. This is an easy binocular object although at least a small telescope will be needed to resolve any individual stars in the cluster.

June 16th

Lupus (the Wolf) occupies the area of sky immediately to the east of Centaurus (the Centaur) and just to the north of the bright pair of stars Alpha and Beta Centauri, which can be used as guide stars to locate the group.

The whole of Lupus can be viewed from the southern United States, Egypt, central China and from latitudes further south of these. Although Lupus was one of the 48 constellations drawn up by the Greek astronomer Ptolemy during the 2nd century, there appear to be no legends associated with it. This particular group of stars used to be depicted as being combined with Centaurus, representing an animal impaled on a long pole held by the Centaur who was facing in the general direction of Ara (the Altar) (see August 1st), presumably so that he could offer the animal to the gods as a sacrifice.

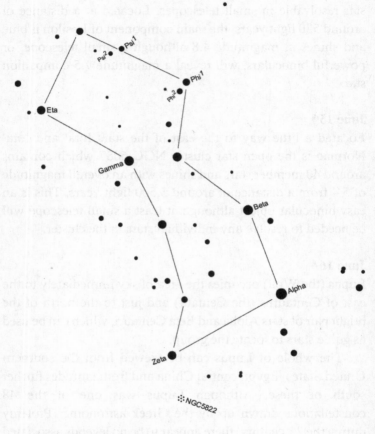

LUPUS

165

June 17th

None of the stars in Lupus are named and none are particularly prominent, the brightest being the magnitude 2.30 Alpha Lupi, a blue star located near the western borders of the group and which shines from a distance of around 460 light years. Located a little way to the north east of Alpha is magnitude 2.68 Beta Lupi, another blue star whose light has taken 382 years to reach us. Yet another blue star is Gamma Lupi which shines at magnitude 2.80 from a distance of a little over 400 light years.

June 18th

Although not awash with prominent stars, Lupus does at least contain a trio of double stars which are worth seeking out. The orange tint of magnitude 3.57 Phi[1] contrasts nicely with the nearby magnitude 4.54 white Phi[2] which lies immediately to the southeast. These two stars form an optical double in that they are not physically related. Phi[1] lies at a distance of 275 light years, a little over half the distance of Phi[2] whose light has taken around 520 years to reach us.

Another pretty optical pair are Psi[1] and Psi[2] located nearby. Psi[1] is a yellow magnitude 4.66 star lying at a distance of 219 light years, somewhat closer than bluish Psi[2] which shines at magnitude 4.75 from a distance of around 360 light years.

Both of the above doubles are resolvable with the naked eye providing the sky is dark, clear and moonless, and are particularly attractive when seen through binoculars. If you have a small telescope you might like to check out the binary star Eta Lupi which lies at a distance of around 440 light years and has a blue-white magnitude 3.6 primary and a much fainter magnitude 7.8 secondary. The fainter component has been described as having an ashy tint.

*

June 19th

The open star cluster NGC 5822 lies a little way to the south of Zeta Lupi and shines with an overall magnitude of around 7. You should pick it up fairly easily in binoculars providing the sky is reasonably dark and clear. NGC 5822 contains around 100 stars ranging from around 9th to 12th magnitude, some of the brightest of which can be resolved in small telescopes or good binoculars.

June 20th

Though at half-past nine it is still light enough for a book to be read out in the open, I look around and see

> *The stars emerging from their secret cell,*
> *A silent night-watch o'er the world to keep.*

(From the poem 'Morn and Even' by Lydia Howard Sigourney)

Vega peers down from the giddy slopes of the eastern sky; Arcturus languidly winks beyond the meridian; Deneb, chief of the Swan stars, makes occasional appearances among the flying clouds that are hastening to form themselves in a blue-gray mass in the north-east. I can just faintly trace the stars of the Plough – which are now beginning their descent to the north-west horizon – and the tail being farthest from the sunglow is much more distinct than the rest of the figure. The Pointers, indeed, are rather difficult to see, they being high up in the west-nor'-west, and just on the fringe of the glow. Megrez is the only one of the seven that I cannot see at all. The Pole Star shines very feebly, and it is only because of my knowing its exact position that I am able to detect it.

Between the sou'-west and south is Virgo's lucida, Spica, full of bluish fire. It, too, is inconstant of apparition, for the Virgin hides her face with tantalising coquetry behind the torn veil of streaming clouds.

June 21st

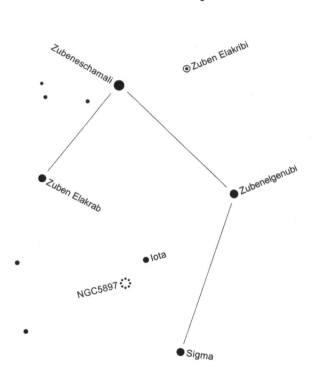

LIBRA

We now turn our attention to the constellation Libra (the Scales) which borders Lupus to the north and is flanked by Virgo (the Virgin) to the north west and Scorpius (the Scorpion) to the south east. Parts of Libra are visible worldwide, the whole of the constellation being observable from anywhere south of latitude 60°N.

Libra is the only constellation in the Zodiac (see Glossary) which represents an inanimate object, the rest of the zodiacal groups depicting people or animals. The stars in Libra were once known as *Chelae* meaning 'The Claws of the Scorpion' and represented the claws of the neighbouring Scorpius, this being reflected in the names of some of the stars in Libra. The early Greeks did not identify the constellation with a Balance, this association being introduced by the Romans during the 1st century BC.

Libra is slightly larger than Scorpius, although it is by no means as prominent, and contains no stars brighter than 2nd magnitude. Consequently the constellation may be a little difficult to pick out for observers at mid-northern latitudes unless the sky is fairly dark and clear. If this is the case, carefully sweeping the area of sky to the south east of the neighbouring constellation Virgo should lead you to the quadrilateral of stars that form the main section of Libra.

June 22nd
Midnight! The first night sky of summer is winter-black. Nowhere – north, east, south, west – does the sky indicate that the sun is but twelve-and-a-half degrees below the horizon, or five-and-a-half degrees within the twilight limit. The relief in the gloom is not afforded by the glow of the midnight sun, but by the beams from the brightly shining moon in a cloud-break yonder in the opposite quarter of the heavens. There was not even this relief up to half-an-hour ago, for rain was then

descending in torrents, and blowing hither and thither.

Thus has the summer season come joyless, and the midnight too – nocturnal noon – broods heavy on my soul.

June 23rd

The brightest star in Libra is Zubeneschamali, its name derived from the Arabic for 'the Northern Claw'. Shining with a magnitude of 2.61, Zubeneschamali is a blue star whose light has taken 185 years to reach us. Zubenelgenubi, derived from the Arabic for 'the Southern Claw', is a double star which lies at a distance of 76 light years. The blue-white magnitude 2.7 primary and yellowish magnitude 5.2 secondary are far enough apart to be easily resolved in binoculars.

Zuben Elakrab is a magnitude 3.91 yellow giant star shining from a distance of around 160 light years. Completing the quadrilateral is the red giant star Sigma Librae, which shines at magnitude 3.25 from a distance of approximately 290 light years.

June 24th

The star Delta Librae, also known as Zuben Elakribi, is an Algol-type eclipsing binary (see November 14th) which has a magnitude range of between 4.8 and 5.9 and a period of a little under 2 days and 8 hours. Located at a distance of almost 300 light years, the variability of Delta Librae was discovered by the German astronomer Johann Friedrich Julius Schmidt in 1859. Delta is located a little way to the west of Zubeneschamali and, as with all variables of this type, is worth keeping an eye on in case you manage to detect a dip in its overall magnitude.

* * *

June 25th

Located a little way to the south east of Iota Librae, on a line between Zuben Elakrab and Sigma, is the faint globular cluster NGC 5897 which shines with an overall magnitude of 8.5 from a distance of around 40,000 light years.

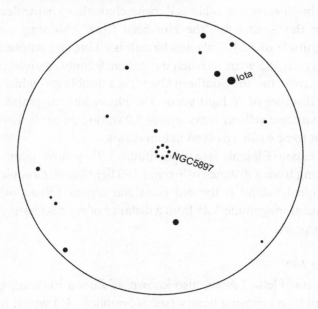

Discovered by William Herschel in 1784, this object can be detected in good binoculars, provided the sky is really dark and clear, although it is somewhat faint and difficult to see. However, if you carefully sweep the area of sky immediately to the south east of Iota, and remember to look for a patch of light rather than a star like point, you should be able to pick it up. The finder chart shows the immediate area around Iota and NGC 5897 and should assist you in your search.

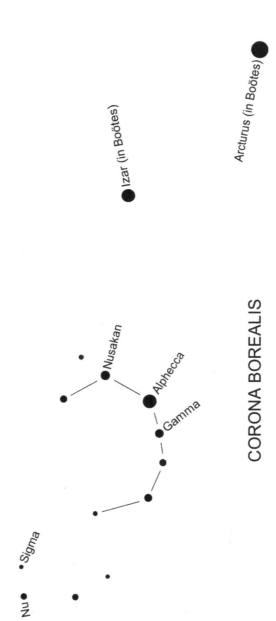

CORONA BOREALIS

Nusakan

Alphecca

Gamma

Zeta

Sigma

Nu

Izar (in Boötes)

Arcturus (in Boötes)

June 26th

Corona Borealis (the Northern Crown) can be found immediately to the east of the constellation Boötes (see May 17th), the chart showing the group along with two guide stars Arcturus and Izar, both of which are in Boötes. Corona Borealis lies not far north of the celestial equator and as a result the entire constellation can be viewed from anywhere north of latitude 50°S, making it a potential target for backyard astronomers in Australia, New Zealand, South Africa and virtually the whole of South America. As you can see, Corona Borealis takes the form of a pretty semicircle of reasonably bright stars and belongs to the somewhat elite number of constellations that actually resemble the object they are supposed to depict!

Different civilizations have identified Corona Borealis in different ways, Arabic astronomers looking upon it as a broken plate (presumably because the stars of the constellation don't form a complete circle). Aboriginal folklore offers us two explanations, one that the group depicts a heavenly boomerang and the other an eagle's nest. However, the oldest story associated with the constellation comes down to us from the Ancient Greeks who said that it was the crown presented by Bacchus to Ariadne, daughter of King Minos of Crete. The crown was made by the supreme goldsmith Hephaestus at his underwater smithy and given to Ariadne after she had been deserted by the unfaithful Theseus. After Ariadne's death, the gods placed her crown in the sky.

June 27th

The brightest star in Corona Borealis is Alphecca, its name derived from the Arabic for 'break' perhaps referring to the fact that the constellation as a whole is an incomplete circle of stars.

The star Alfecca Meridiana in Corona Australis, the southern counterpart of Corona Borealis (see August 10th) derives its name in a similar way. Alphecca shines at magnitude 2.22 and lies at a distance of around 75 light years. Slightly further away is the magnitude 3.66 white star Nusakan, the light from which set off towards us around 115 years ago. Gamma Coronae Borealis is a white star shining at magnitude 3.81 from a distance of around 150 light years.

June 28th
Those of you with small telescopes may like to try their hand at resolving a couple of double stars in Corona Borealis. Both are binary stars in which the two components are actually orbiting each other. The first is Sigma, which hovers on the edge of naked-eye visibility although, once located, its magnitude 5.7 and 6.7 yellowish components are easily resolved through a small telescope. Slightly brighter is Zeta, a system containing two blue-white companion stars of magnitudes 5.1 and 6.0 located at a distance of 470 light years. The accompanying chart should guide you to these two double stars.

June 29th
Nu is an optical double star, the two components lying at different distances. The brightest of these is a magnitude 5.20 red giant shining from a distance of around 640 light years, somewhat further away than its slightly-fainter companion, an orange giant star with a magnitude of 5.40 and whose light has taken around 590 years to reach us. Both components of Nu are far enough apart to be easily resolvable through binoculars. Wide double stars like this are definitely best seen either through binoculars or a telescope finder, both of which have

relatively wide fields of view.

Another exercise for binocular users is to try and count the number of stars visible inside the 'bowl' formed by Corona Borealis. If you can spot a dozen or more then you are doing quite well.

June 30th

The constellation of Hercules is large and sprawling, covers quite a large area of sky, but contains no really bright stars. This is the 5th largest constellation in the sky and the fact that it covers such a large area ensures that portions of Hercules can be seen from almost every inhabited part of the world, the entire group being visible to observers north of latitude 39°S.

Hercules is bordered to the west by Corona Borealis (see June 26th) while still further to the west we find the brilliant star Arcturus in Boötes (see May 18th). A line taken from Arcturus, passing through Alphecca in Corona Borealis and on roughly as far again will lead you to the 'Keystone', the conspicuous quadrilateral of four stars – Epsilon, Pi, Eta and Zeta – marking the central region of Hercules. Once the Keystone has been identified the rest of the stars of Hercules can be traced out around it. The brilliant star Vega in the constellation Lyra (see September 16th) lies on the opposite side of Hercules to Alphecca. The three stars Arcturus, Alphecca and Vega are included on the chart to help you locate the Keystone of Hercules.

HERCULES

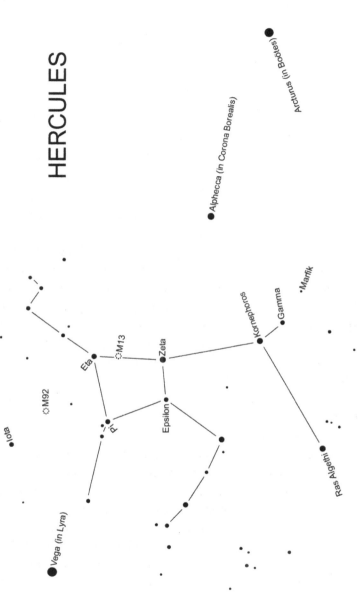

Arcturus (in Boötes)

Alphecca (in Corona Borealis)

M13

Zeta

Eta

Kornephoros

Gamma

Marfik

M92

Epsilon

Iota

Pi

Ras Algethi

Vega (in Lyra)

JULY

July 1st

The origins of this ancient constellation are uncertain. The Greeks knew it as *Engonasin*, meaning 'the Kneeling One' and it wasn't until the third century BC that the Greek astronomer Eratosthenes of Cyrene identified it as representing Hercules, the legendary character who carried out twelve labours at the command of Eurystheus, King of Argos. Hercules was the son of Jupiter and Alcmene, a wise and beautiful mortal princess. He was possessed of great strength and courage and was known far and wide for his exploits, a reputation that was enhanced by the effective way he carried out the dangerous tasks given to him by Eurystheus which included slaying the Nemean lion (see April 1st) and destroying the fearsome multi-headed Lernaean Hydra (see April 15th).

July 2nd

The two brightest stars in Hercules are the magnitude 2.78 yellow giant Kornephoros, the light from which has taken around 140 years to reach us, and Ras Algethi, located a little way to the south east of Kornephoros. The star Kornephoros derives its name from the Greek for 'the Club Bearer' while that for Ras Algethi is taken from the Arabic *'ra's al-jathi'* meaning 'the Kneeler's Head'. The huge red supergiant Ras Algethi shines from a distance of around 350 light years and has a distinct orange-red tint which should be visible in binoculars.

July 3rd

As we have seen, the Keystone of Hercules is formed from the four stars Epsilon, Pi, Eta and Zeta which together, although not very bright, form a fairly distinctive shape. However, the Keystone's main claim to fame is that it plays host to Messier 13, a globular cluster considered to be the finest example of this type of object in the northern sky. With an overall magnitude of 5.8 this celestial showpiece may be discernible to the naked eye providing the sky is exceptionally dark, clear and free of moonlight. To locate it follow an imaginary line from Eta towards Zeta. Roughly a third of the way between these two stars you may glimpse M13 as a faint, misty patch of light.

If you search with binoculars or a small telescope you should have little trouble picking out the faint glow from M13, the view you will get being that of a fuzzy, circular patch of light. In order to resolve individual stars within the cluster you will need a larger telescope.

Globular clusters, as their name suggests, are huge spherical collections of stars which lie in the region of space around our Galaxy (see Glossary). Also known as the Great Hercules Cluster, M13 was discovered by the English astronomer Edmund Halley in 1714 and catalogued by Charles Messier in 1764. Neither Halley nor Messier knew the true nature of this object and it wasn't until later that its true splendour was revealed. M13 measures around 150 light years in diameter and is thought to contain anything up to half a million stars. It shines from a distance of around 25,000 light years which means that the light from M13 we are seeing today actually set off towards us over twice as long ago as the end the Ice Age.

*

July 4ᵗʰ

Another globular cluster in Hercules is M92 which is often overlooked due to the nearby presence of the more impressive M13. Shining at magnitude 6.3, M92 lies below naked eye visibility and therefore requires the use of optical aid to locate it. If you carefully follow a line from Eta in the Keystone towards Iota you should come across M92 lying roughly two-thirds of the way between the two stars.

Visible in binoculars as a non-stellar, fuzzy patch of light, M92 has a diameter of around 110 light years and lies at a distance of just under 27,000 light years. Containing upwards of 250,000 stars, this object was discovered by the German astronomer Johann Elert Bode in 1777 and independently rediscovered by Charles Messier in 1781. However, it was William Herschel who first resolved individual stars within the cluster in 1783.

July 5ᵗʰ

A double star in Hercules worth checking out is Marfik, located a little way to the south west of Gamma. The name of this star is derived from the Arabic *'al-marfiq'* meaning 'the Elbow', its brightest component shining at magnitude 5.3 from a distance of around 365 light years. The yellowish tint of this star contrasts with the bronze hue of the magnitude 6.5 companion. This double is merely a line of sight effect, the light from the fainter star having taken over 450 years to reach us. Both components may just be resolved in good binoculars although a telescope may be needed in order to detect their individual colours.

* * *

July 6th

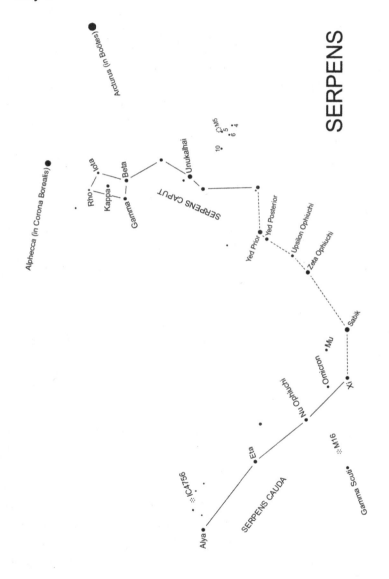

Serpens (the Serpent) is unusual in that it is split into two sections, these being Serpens Caput (the Head) and Serpens Cauda (the Tail), although the two parts are regarded by astronomers as being a single constellation. The group represents a huge snake held by Ophiuchus (the Serpent Holder) (see July 13th), the snake's head held in his left hand while his right hand is gripping the tail. Serpens lies across the celestial equator and the constellation can be viewed in its entirety from all inhabited regions of the world south of latitude 74°N, with at least portions of the constellation being visible worldwide.

July 7th
Serpens and Ophiuchus straddle the celestial equator and are reasonably well placed for observers in both hemispheres at around this time of year. The five stars marking the head of the snake – Beta, Gamma, Iota, Kappa and Rho – form a conspicuous, albeit faint, quadrilateral lying a little way to the east of the brilliant Arcturus in Boötes and immediately to the south of the constellation Corona Borealis (see June 26th). Alphecca, the leading star of Corona Borealis, is included here as a guide along with Arcturus. Once you have identified the five stars marking the head of the snake, the rest of the meandering form of Serpens can be picked out, given reasonably dark and clear skies, and the use of a pair of binoculars to help in tracing out this faint group. The central part of Serpens is depicted by a line of stars which are actually in Ophiuchus and which are also shown on the chart.

The brightest star in Serpens is Unukalhai, a magnitude 2.63 orange giant located a little way to the south of the snake's head and the light from which has taken 74 years to reach us. The name of this star is derived from the Arabic *'unuq al-hayya'* meaning 'the Serpent's Neck' reflecting its position in the constellation. Following the line of stars from Unukalhai takes us across Ophiuchus and on to the snake's tail, the brightest star in which is Eta Serpentis, another orange star shining at magnitude 3.23 from a distance of 60 light years.

July 8th

Eleven o'clock! The piercing light of Vega is disclosed among a mass of broken clouds near the meridian and at a great altitude. A few degrees to the south-eastward is Cygnus, whilst Arcturus is showing in the west-sou'-west.

July 9th

There are a couple of double stars in Serpens worth checking out. One of these is Alya, which marks the tip of the snake's tail. The name of this star is derived from an Arabic word which actually refers to the tail of a sheep. Alya has magnitude 4.62 and 4.98 white components which are easily resolved in a small telescope. The star Nu, which forms a small triangle with Omicron and Xi close to the border with neighbouring Ophiuchus, is another double star with magnitude 4.3 and 8.3 components which can be seen in any telescope.

July 10th

Discovered in 1702 by the German astronomer Gottfried Kirch, the globular cluster Messier 5 is one of the showpieces of Serpens. With an overall magnitude of around 6, this object lies at the threshold of naked-eye visibility and is easily spotted in binoculars. The chart shows the field of stars comprising 4, 5, 6 and 10 Serpentis located a little way to the south west of Unukalhai. The cluster itself can be found immediately to the north west of the star 5 Serpentis.

Located at a distance of 24,500 light years, and with a diameter of around 165 light years, M5 is one of the largest known objects of its type and is thought to contain well over 100,000 individual stars, some estimates putting this at nearer half-a-million. Small telescopes, or even binoculars with magnifications of 12x or more, may just help you to resolve some of the individual stars situated around the edges of this cluster.

July 11th

Lying at a distance of around 1,400 light years, the open star cluster IC 4756 contains around 80 individual stars shining with an overall magnitude of 5.4 a little way to the west of Alya. If the sky is dark, clear and free of moonlight, IC 4756 is easily located in binoculars which will reveal it as a small glowing diffuse patch of light. Small telescopes will resolve individual cluster members.

July 12th

Serpens also plays host to M16, located a little way to the south east of the star Nu Ophiuchi. Also known as the Eagle Nebula, M16 takes the form of a large patch of diffuse nebulosity enveloping a bright open star cluster. Both objects can be seen through binoculars through which will be revealed some of the individual stars within the cluster as well as the nebulosity, which should appear as a faint hazy light surrounding the cluster. A small telescope will increase the number of visible cluster stars and larger instruments should bring out the nebulosity reasonably well.

Lying at a distance of around 7,000 light years, the Eagle Nebula was discovered in around 1746 by the Swiss astronomer Jean-Philippe Loys de Cheseaux, although he only described seeing the star cluster. The object was independently discovered in 1764 by Charles Messier who referred to the cluster being surrounded by a faint glow, an obvious allusion to the nebulosity. Deriving its name from its appearance as seen on photographic images, the Eagle Nebula shines with an overall magnitude of around 6.4 which puts it just below the limits of naked-eye visibility.

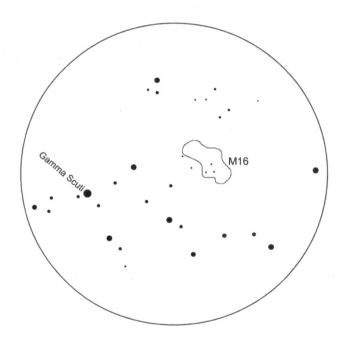

M16 can be found by using the star Gamma in the neighbouring constellation Scutum (see August 27th) as a guide. Gamma Scuti is shown on this finder chart, as well as on the main chart of Serpens, where it is seen to lie to the south east of the three stars Xi and Eta (in Serpens Cauda) and Nu (in Ophiuchus). Once you locate Gamma Scuti within this field of stars, you can use the detailed chart to star-hop your way to M16 via the fainter stars which lie in the immediate area.

July 13th

Now we turn our attention to Ophiuchus (the Serpent Bearer), a constellation depicted as a man grasping the huge snake represented by the adjoining constellation Serpens (see July 6th). Both Ophiuchus and Serpens were among the 48 constellations listed by the Greek astronomer Ptolemy during the 2nd century. Along with the adjoining constellation Serpens, Ophiuchus straddles the celestial equator and the whole of the group can be seen from all inhabited regions south of latitude 60°N, with portions being visible worldwide.

According to legend, Ophiuchus represents Asclepius, the son of Apollo, the god of medicine, and Coronis, the daughter of the Thessalian ruler Phlegyas. Apollo was in love with Coronis who, in spite of this, was unfaithful to him. Coronis took on another lover and, needless to say, this did not please Apollo. When he discovered what was going on, Apollo shot Coronis with his bow and deadly arrows. He instantly regretted his actions although, in spite of trying all his remedies, his efforts to bring Coronis back to life were in vain.

The legacy of this unfortunate state of affairs was their son Asclepius. Apollo took Asclepius to reside with Chiron, the Centaur (see May 2nd), who instructed him in the healing arts. Asclepius soon excelled Apollo in his skills and ultimately became the god of medicine in the place of his father. He even acquired the ability to bring the dead back to life, a talent which did not please Jupiter, who was concerned that people may be inclined to worship their physician rather than him.

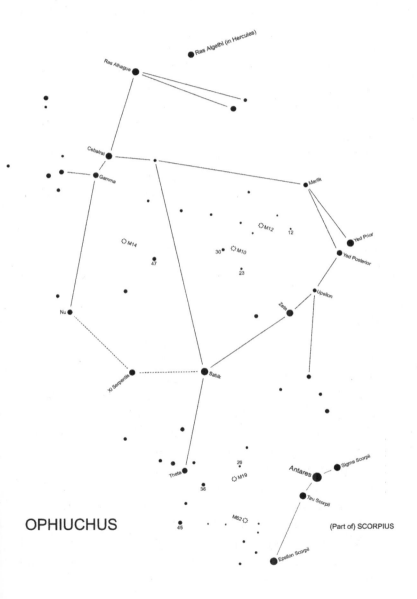

OPHIUCHUS

(Part of) SCORPIUS

Jupiter eliminated this potential challenge to his authority by killing Asclepius with a thunderbolt, following which he placed him in the sky. Because snakes were considered to be a symbol of healing, it is perhaps fitting that Asclepius, represented by the constellation Ophiuchus, is depicted as holding a snake.

July 14th

Nine-thirty! A dark band of cloud, unbroken except in the north-west, envelops the horizon to a height of fully thirty degrees, and thoughts of thunder-storms are raised by the blackness in the south-east and north-east. A gentle air-current floats wisps of cloud with lazy motion to the southward and comes in little eddies of delicious perfumes of flowers and new-mown hay. Fragrance-breathing indeed is this night of mid-July, and thrice welcome is it after the ungenial times through which we have been passing.

July 15th

As we have seen, the constellation Ophiuchus divides Serpens into two separate sections, the main stars that lie between these two sections being Sabik, Zeta, Upsilon, Yed Prior and Yed Posterior. Sabik is the second brightest star in the constellation, shining at magnitude 2.43 from a distance of 88 light years. Slightly fainter is magnitude 2.54 Zeta, the light from which has taken over 350 light years to reach us.

Ophiuchus is shown here alongside a couple of guide stars, these being Ras Algethi in Hercules (see July 2nd) and the brilliant Antares in Scorpius (see July 23rd). A little way to the east of Ras Algethi we find Ras Alhague, the brightest star in Ophiuchus, shining at magnitude 2.08 from a distance of 47 light years. Ras Alhague derives its name from the Arabic for 'the Head of the Serpent Collector'.

To the south of Ras Alhague we find Cebalrai, a magnitude 2.76 orange giant star shining from a distance of 82 light years. The name of this star is taken from the Arabic *'kalb al-ra'i'* meaning 'the Shepherd's Dog'. Slightly more remote than Cebalrai is magnitude 3.75 Gamma, the light from which has taken 103 years to reach us.

The unusually-named Yed Prior and Yed Posterior derive their names from the Arabic *'al-yad'* meaning 'hand', Yed Prior representing the foremost hand and Yed Posterior the hindmost. Yed Prior is a magnitude 2.73 red giant shining at a distance of 170 light years, making it both brighter and further away than Yed Posterior, a yellow giant shining at magnitude 3.23 from a little over 100 light years. Deriving its name from the Arabic *'al-marfiq'*, meaning 'the Elbow', magnitude 3.82 blue giant Marfik shines from a distance of 170 light years.

July 16th

Ophiuchus contains a large number of globular clusters, one of which is M10, located a short way to the east of Yed Prior and Yed Posterior.

Lying in the same binocular field of view as M12 (see July 17th), M10 was discovered by Charles Messier in 1764, who described it as a: *'Nebula, without star in the belt of Ophiuchus.'* It was first resolved into stars by William Herschel, who described it as: *'A beautiful cluster of extremely compressed stars .'*

Located at a distance of around 15,000 light years and glowing at magnitude 6.4, M10 can be tracked down in binoculars, providing the sky is reasonably dark and clear. Start your search by locating the guide star 30 Ophiuchi, which can be found by following a line from Theta northwards through Sabik and on roughly as far again. Once you have located 30 Ophiuchi, look for the triangle formed from 30 and the two nearby stars 12 Ophiuchi and 23 Ophiuchi. You can then use the detailed finder chart to star-hop your way to M10 (and M12 – see July 17ᵗʰ) through the field of faint stars in which these two clusters lie.

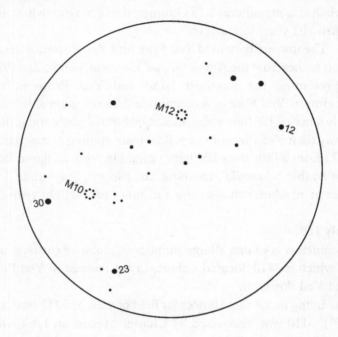

July 17th

The globular cluster M12, located immediately to the north west of M10, was also discovered by Charles Messier in 1764. Messier described it as being a *'...nebula (which) contains no star, round, faint...'* resembling his visual impression of nearby M10. In 1783, the superior telescope of William Herschel allowed him to resolve M12 into individual stars, Herschel describing it as: *'A brilliant cluster...'*

Shining from a distance of nearly 16,000 light years M12 has a magnitude of 6.7, making it slightly fainter than M10, and you will need dark, clear and moonless skies in order to find it. As with all objects of this type, try to look for a patch of light rather than a star like point. Neither M10 nor M12 is particularly prominent so patience may be the order of the day with your efforts to track these two objects down.

July 18ᵗʰ

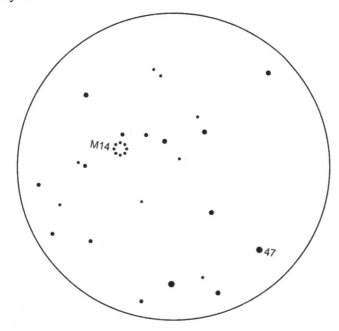

Another of the globular clusters found in Ophiuchus is M14, located just to the north east of the star 47 Ophiuchi and discovered by Charles Messier in 1764. As with the other objects of this type that he discovered in this region of sky, Messier was unable to resolve any individual stars in M14 and it was left to William Herschel to detect stars within this cluster. Herschel described M14 as: *'Extremely bright, round, easily resolvable: with 300x I can see the stars.'*

M14 lies at a distance of around 30,000 light years and is not particularly bright. Shining with an overall magnitude of around 8, this cluster is a difficult object to pick up in binoculars. However, if you like a challenge, first of all locate the guide star 47 Ophiuchi, which is located a little over half way between Sabik and Cebalrai. 47 Ophiuchi is shown on the detailed finder chart and, by using the star-hopping method, you should be able to track down M14 using the pattern of faint stars on the chart as a guide. Clear, dark, moonless skies are essential for your search.

July 19th

Before we take our leave of Ophiuchus, we will check out two more globular clusters, both of which lie near the southern border of the constellation. Neither will be particularly easy to track down for observers at mid-northern latitudes as they both lie fairly close to the horizon. For observers further south, however, these two are more accessible and worth seeking out.

Situated a little way to the west of Theta Ophiuchi is M19 which, like many other globular clusters in this area of sky, was originally discovered by Charles Messier. Locating it in 1764, he described it as a: *'Nebula without a star. Round.'* William Herschel resolved it into stars in 1784 although he appears to have made no additional comment, unlike his son John Herschel, who was impressed enough with this cluster to describe it as being: *'Superb! A globular cluster, very bright, round ...resolved into stars...'* Praise indeed!

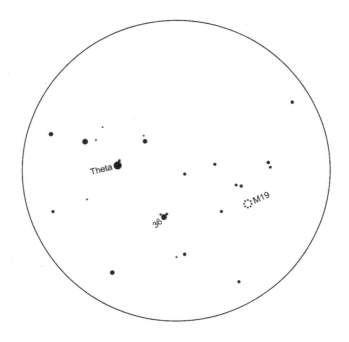

Located at a distance of over 28,000 light years, M19 shines at around magnitude 6.8, putting it within the light grasp of binoculars which will reveal it as a small, fuzzy patch of light. As well as bringing out individual stars within the cluster, closer examination with larger telescopes reveals that M19 is quite elongated and is in fact the most oblate of the known globular clusters. This can be explained by the fact that M19 lies within around 6,000 light years of the galactic centre, the elongation we see being due to the strong gravitational influence of the galactic core stretching the cluster out.

M19 is located near the southern border of Ophiuchus, a short way to the west of the star Theta Ophiuchi, which can be used as a guide. Once you have located Theta, together with the nearby star 36 Ophiuchi, in binoculars, use the detailed finder chart to help you to star-hop your way towards the cluster.

July 20th

Located a little to the south of M19, on the border of Ophiuchus and the neighbouring constellation Scorpius, is the globular cluster M62. It was discovered by Messier in 1771 and, when he observed it again in 1779, described it as: *'A very fine nebula; it resembles a little comet. It is bright in the centre and is surrounded by a faint glow.'* William Herschel first resolved it into stars and seemed to be reasonably inspired by what he saw, pronouncing it as *'...a miniature of M3.'* (M3 is a particularly fine globular cluster in the constellation Canes Venatici – see May 24th).

Shining at around magnitude 6.5 from a distance of 22,500 light years, M62 is well within the light grasp of binoculars which, although not revealing any individual stars within the cluster, will bring it out as a small nebulous object which will be decidedly non-stellar in appearance. Even fairly small telescopes will begin to reveal individual stars. To find M62, first of all locate the guide star Epsilon Scorpii in the neighbouring constellation Scorpius (see July 21st). From here, you can use your binoculars to work your way towards M62 via the patterns of faint stars shown in the detailed finder chart. The two tiny triangles immediately to the east of Epsilon are easily picked up and these can be used as a guide to M62. Alternatively, you can star-hop your way along the line of faint stars extending westwards from the star 45 Ophiuchi.

* * *

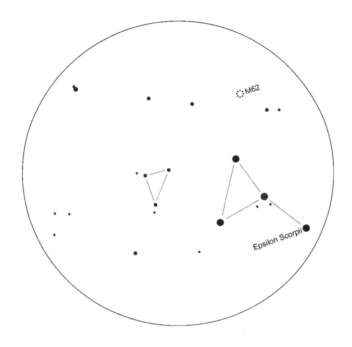

July 21st

The constellation of Scorpius (the Scorpion) depicts the scorpion commanded by Diana, the goddess of the hunt, to sting and kill Orion (see January 2nd) following their hunting match. Because Diana and Orion shared the honours, and the contest between them was declared a draw, Orion bragged of his prowess, his vanity resulting in his demise at the hands (or should that be sting) of the scorpion.

Scorpius is bordered on the west by the constellation Libra. As we have seen (see June 21st) Scorpius was originally much bigger and included stars depicting the scorpion's claws. Known as *Chelae*, meaning 'The Claws of the Scorpion', these stars were removed from Scorpius by the Romans who used them to form the separate constellation Libra.

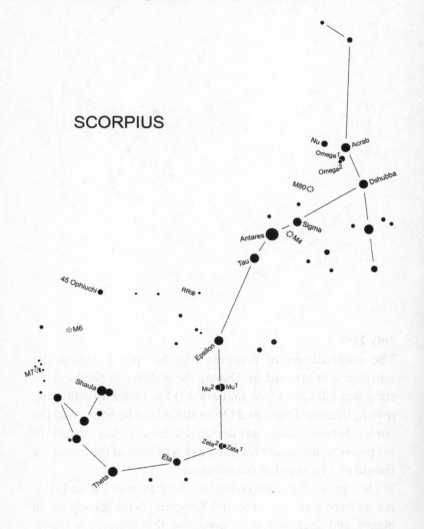

SCORPIUS

July 22nd

Scorpius belongs to that group of constellations that actually resembles the object or character that it is supposed to represent. In the case of Scorpius, the curved line of stars forming the scorpion's tail does indeed bear a resemblance to the sting of a scorpion. The whole of Scorpius can be viewed from the central United States, southern Europe and most of Japan and from latitudes to the south of these areas.

Although not a particularly large constellation Scorpius is very prominent, particularly when viewed from south of the equator from where it will be seen to grace the winter night skies. The brightest star in Scorpius is Antares (see July 23rd), closely followed in prominence by Shaula, a magnitude 1.62 blue star shining from a distance of around 550 light years. Shaula derives its name from the Arabic *'al-shaula'* meaning 'the Scorpion's Sting'.

Located at a distance of around 400 light years, magnitude 2.29 Dschubba takes its name from the Arabic *'jabhat al-aqrab'* meaning 'the Scorpion's Forehead', an appropriate title bearing in mind its location in the scorpion's head. Just to the north of Dschubba is Acrab, a double star shining from a distance of around 400 light years. The name Acrab is derived from the Arabic *'al-aqrab'* meaning 'the Scorpion' and the two components of this double, at magnitudes 2.6 and 4.9, can be resolved even in a small telescope.

July 23rd

The brilliant Antares is the brightest star in Scorpius, this red supergiant shining with a magnitude of around 1.06 from a distance of 535 light years. Its name can be loosely translated as 'rival of Mars' indicative of the fact that, due to its strong red colour, it vies for prominence with the planet Mars (also known as the Red Planet) when the two are seen in the same area of sky.

Antares is flanked immediately to the north west by Sigma Scorpii and to the south east by Tau Scorpii, two blue stars which also share the name Alniyat from the Arabic *'al-niyat'* meaning 'Outworks of the Heart'. They protect Antares, regarded as being the heart of Scorpius. Sigma shines at magnitude 2.90 from a distance of just under 700 light years. Tau is closer, the light from this magnitude 2.82 star having taken only around 450 years to reach us. Sigma, Antares and Tau form a conspicuous trio of stars, one of several in the night sky and which were alluded to by Elgie:

It is of interest that three prominent stars are not infrequently seen in apparent association in the heavens. We have an excellent example of this in the Belt of Orion. The bright star Altair, too... and brilliant Antares, in Scorpio, are each in groups of three.

July 24th
Double stars in Scorpius include Nu Scorpii and Zeta Scorpi. The two components of Nu shine at magnitudes 6.5 and 4.4 from a distance of around 450 light years. Located a little to the east of Acrab, both components are easily resolved in binoculars. Closer examination will reveal that each of the two stars forming Nu is actually double again, the whole system resembling the famous 'double-double' star Epsilon in the constellation Lyra (see September 18th) although, unlike Epsilon Lyrae, fairly large telescopes are needed to reveal all four stars in the Nu Scorpii system.

Zeta Scorpii has a brighter magnitude 3.6 orange component (Zeta^2) and a fainter magnitude 4.7 blue-white companion (Zeta^1), both of which can be seen with the naked eye. Located near the southern border of Scorpius, these two stars are not actually physically related. Zeta² shines from a distance of around 150 light years and is considerably closer than Zeta¹, the light from which has taken around 5,000 years to reach us.

Located a little to the south of Epsilon is Mu Scorpii, another wide double and one which can be resolved with the naked eye. The brightest of the pair is Mu¹ which, at magnitude 3.0, is a little more prominent than its magnitude 3.6 companion Mu². Observation has shown that the association of these two stars is nothing more than a line of sight effect, Mu² having been found to lie at a greater distance from us.

July 25th

Immediately to the south of Acrab are the two stars Omega¹ and Omega² Scorpii. Omega¹ is a blue magnitude 3.93 star shining from a distance of around 470 light years. Somewhat closer to us is the yellowish magnitude 4.31 Omega², the light from which has taken a little under 300 years to reach us. These two stars can be resolved with the naked eye and form a pretty sight in binoculars. Elgie said of Omega Scorpii:

The small star immediately below Beta can just be detected at this moment to be double, but the duplicity can be brought about only by means of averted vision; that is, I look at Beta instead of looking at the star direct. It is distinguished by the numbers 1 and 2 and the letter Omega. The upper star of the two is numbered 1.

July 26th

Located immediately to the west of Antares is the globular cluster M4, discovered in around 1746 by the Swiss astronomer Jean-Philippe Loys de Cheseaux. The French astronomer Nicolas Louis de Lacaille described this object as resembling '...*the small nucleus of a faint comet...* ', he seemingly being unable to resolve any individual stars within the cluster. Charles Messier added it to his catalogue in 1764, his larger telescope revealing it as a: *'Cluster of very small stars; with an inferior telescope it appears more like a nebula...'* Messier's description ties in with the view you would expect through binoculars, which will reveal M4 as a fuzzy ball of light. It is easy to locate, being as it quite close to Antares, and even small telescopes will start to resolve individual cluster stars. With a diameter of around 75 light years, M4 shines at around magnitude 6 from a distance of a little over 7,000 light years.

July 27th

Before the introduction of the telescope several star clusters were recorded, obvious examples being the Pleiades in Taurus (see February 4th) and Praesepe (M44) in Cancer (see March 25th). However, astronomers were not always aware of a star cluster's true nature, as was the case with M7. First recorded by the Greek astronomer Ptolemy in the 2nd century AD, and sometimes known as the Ptolemy Cluster, this magnitude 3.3 object was described by him as being *'...misty...'* And *'...following the Sting (of Scorpius)...'* In reality, M7 is a wonderful cluster of around 80 stars which is easily visible to the naked eye as a hazy patch of light a little way to the north east of the bright star Shaula in the Sting of Scorpius. Referred to by the Persian astronomer Al-Sufi as *'...the cloudiness following the sting ...'* the M7 cluster shines from a distance of around 800 light years.

July 28th

The magnitude 4.2 open cluster M6 lies at a distance of around 1,600 light years and is located a little way to the north of M7 and Shaula. Along with nearby M7, this object may have once formed the termination of the sting of the Scorpion. Visible to the naked-eye, M6 may have been noted by Ptolemy as he was observing the nearby M7 cluster (see July 27th) which lies a little way to the south east. Also known as the Butterfly Cluster, due to its overall shape vaguely resembling that of a butterfly, the M6 cluster was recorded by the Italian astronomer Giovanni Batista Hodierna during the early part of the 17th century. It was also noted by the Swiss astronomer Philippe Loys de Cheseaux around 1746 who described it as: *'A fine cluster between Scorpius, Ophiuchus and Sagittarius.'* M6 contains in the region of 100 stars, many of which can be resolved in binoculars.

Situated fairly low down in the sky as seen from mid-northern latitudes, M6 and M7 are best viewed from the southern hemisphere from where these two fine clusters are well placed, high in the sky and away from any potential horizon glow.

July 29th

The globular cluster M80 can be found a little to the east of the star Dschubba, roughly equidistant between Dschubba and nearby Antares. Shining at around magnitude 7.3, M80 lies at a distance of over 32,000 light years and can be tracked down in binoculars providing the sky is reasonably dark and clear. When seen through binoculars or a small telescope, M80 takes on the appearance of a hairy star. Discovered by Charles Messier in 1781, he described it as a: *'Nebula without star in the Scorpion... round, the centre brilliant... resembles the nucleus of a little comet.'* The English astronomer Thomas William Webb drew similar comparisons when he said it looked: *'Like a comet in a beautiful field...'* Check out this object yourself and see if your view of M80 matches those of Messier and Webb.

July 30th

The long-period Mira-type (see December 4th) variable star RR Scorpii lies a little way to the north of Epsilon Scorpii and can be seen to form a triangle with Epsilon and Tau Scorpii as shown on the chart. Alternatively, you can locate RR Scorpii either by following the line of faint stars westwards from 45 Ophiuchi or by using the triangle of stars east of Epsilon Scorpii as pointers.

RR Scorpii varies in brightness between magnitudes 5.9 and around 11.8 over a period of 281 days and, as with other stars of this type, if you look for the star and have difficulty in finding it, this may well be because it is at or near minimum magnitude. With a little patience you will, over the course of time, eventually see RR Scorpii come into view as it brightens again. Under clear, dark skies, you should be able to follow the star through most of its entire period of variability with binoculars or a small telescope. Remember, though, that variable stars of this type take a long time to undergo their completed cycles of variability, so any observations you start now may not be complete until the following year!

July 31st

Ten o'clock! The twilight is still strong in the nor'-west and nor'-nor'-west and the sky almost everywhere free from cloud. There is a touch of October in the breath of this evening's breeze.

Ten-thirty! Corona Borealis looks quite imposing as it sinks in the west. Its position for the observer is a most favourable one.

AUGUST

August 1st

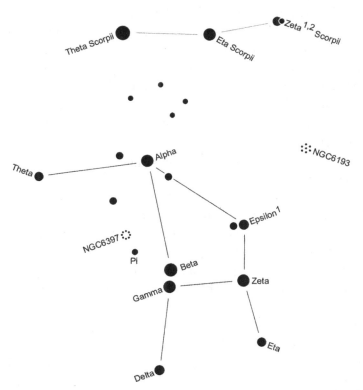

(Part of) SCORPIUS

Theta Scorpii

Eta Scorpii

Zeta 1,2 Scorpii

NGC6193

Theta

Alpha

Epsilon 1

NGC6397

Pi

Beta

Zeta

Gamma

Delta

Eta

ARA

The tiny constellation Ara (the Altar) lies immediately to the south of Scorpius, the stars Theta, Eta and Zeta from Scorpius being included here as a guide. According to legend, Ara represents the altar of the gods and was placed amongst the stars by Zeus following his victory over the Titans and their leader Cronos. Another story has it that the constellation represents the altar on which Centaurus (the Centaur) is offering an animal as a sacrifice to the gods (see June 16th).

The entire constellation can be seen from latitudes south of 22°N, the brightest stars in Ara being Alpha and Beta, both of which shine at around magnitude 2.80. Alpha shines from a distance of 260 light years whilst the light from the orange giant Beta has taken a little over 600 light years to reach us. Delta Arae shines at magnitude 3.60 from a distance of around 200 light years, putting it rather closer to us than the magnitude 3.77 orange giant Eta which lies at a distance of around 300 light years.

Ara plays host to two other orange giant stars, these being magnitude 4.06 Epsilon[1] and magnitude 3.12 Zeta. The light from Epsilon[1] set off towards us around 360 years ago making it somewhat closer than Zeta which shines from a distance of 485 light years. Considerably more remote than either of these, however, is the magnitude 3.31 blue giant Gamma Arae. Located immediately to the south of Beta, Gamma shines from a distance of over 1,100 light years.

August 2nd

Ara plays host to the open star cluster NGC 6193. Located almost on a line from Theta through Alpha Arae, NGC 6193 shines with an overall magnitude of 5.2 and can be glimpsed with the naked eye provided the sky is really dark and clear. This is a straggling cluster with around 30 member stars spread out over a fairly wide area so a wide field of view, such as that obtained with binoculars, helps when checking this object out.

August 3rd

Lying just to the north of Pi Arae, the globular cluster NGC 6397 forms a triangle with Alpha and Beta and is fairly easy to find. This object was discovered by the French astronomer Nicolas Louis de Lacaille who described it as a: *'Faint star in nebulosity'*, a testament, perhaps, to the small size of the telescope he was using. Located at a distance of around 8,400 light years, this is one of the nearest globular clusters and, with a magnitude of 5.7, is an easy object for binoculars.

August 4th

Ten-thirty! The great Cross (Cygnus) is shining from a dizzy height at this hour. It is curious how the centre star (Gamma) – the star immediately below Alpha and midway between Delta and Epsilon – appears to be thrust in advance of the others, giving the head of the Cross a rounded aspect. This optical effect is caused, no doubt, by the slight curvature of the 'upright' formed by Alpha (Deneb), Gamma, Eta and Beta (Albireo), and the curvature also of the 'arms'.

August 5th

The constellation Pavo (the Peacock) can be found immediately to the east of Ara, its westernmost star Eta lying a little to the south east of the three stars Beta, Gamma and Delta Arae (see August 1st) all three of which are shown here for reference. Completely visible from latitudes south of 15°N, the bulk of the constellation Pavo takes the form of an extended oval of stars and is another of the groups introduced following observations made by Pieter Dirkszoon Keyser and Frederick de Houtman (see May 10th) during the 1590s. The constellation depicts a peacock which was rather limited in distribution at the time but which is now found in parks and gardens throughout the world.

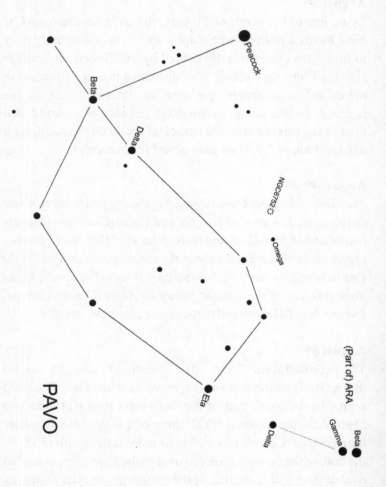

August 6th

The brightest star in Pavo is the appropriately-named Peacock (Alpha Pavonis), situated on the northern border of the constellation and which, at magnitude 1.94, shines from a distance of around 180 light years. Beta Pavonis, located to the south of this star, shines at magnitude 3.42, its light having taken 135 years to reach us. Eta Pavonis, near the western border, is an orange giant star with a magnitude of 3.61 shining from a distance of 350 light years. Delta Pavonis is considerably closer, its magnitude 3.55 glow coming from just 19.9 light years away, making it almost a close stellar neighbour!

August 7th

Held to be one of the finest globular clusters in the sky, NGC 6752 is located immediately to the east of the star Omega Pavonis. Also known as the Great Peacock Cluster, NGC 6752 was discovered by the Scottish astronomer James Dunlop in 1826 and current estimates put its distance at around 13,000 light years. This object is a must for the backyard astronomer! Shining at around magnitude 5.4, NGC 6752 can be glimpsed with the naked eye provided the sky is dark and clear, and binoculars will bring it out quite well. Even small telescopes will reveal individual stars in the outer regions of the cluster.

August 8th

Located just to the north of Pavo, and visible in its entirety from latitudes south of 33°N, is the tiny constellation Telescopium (the Telescope), its easternmost star being magnitude 4.93 orange giant Xi Telescopii which lies just to the north west of Peacock, the brightest star in Pavo. Peacock is shown here as a guide, along with Alpha Indi in the neighbouring constellation Indus (see October 28th).

Telescopium was devised by the French astronomer Nicolas Louis de Lacaille, following his stay in South Africa during 1751 and 1752, to commemorate the invention of the telescope. The constellation takes the form of an extended circlet of faint stars, none of which are named and none of which are at all prominent.

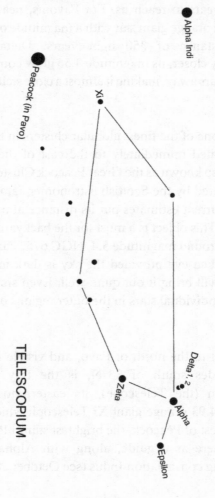

The brightest star in the group is Alpha Telescopii, a magnitude 3.50 blue star shining from a distance of over 250 light years. This is closely followed by magnitude 4.10 orange giant Zeta, the light from which has taken around 125 years to reach us. Epsilon Telescopii is another orange giant star, the magnitude 4.52 glow of which reaches us from a distance of 415 light years.

August 9th

Located immediately to the east of Alpha is Delta Telescopii, an optical double within the reach of binoculars. The two stars forming this double are located at vastly differing distances. Both stars are almost identical in terms of magnitude and both are blue-white, although the colours may not be easily discernible. Delta[1] shines at magnitude 4.92 from a distance of a little over 700 light years, the light from magnitude 5.07 Delta[2] having taken nearly 1,200 years to reach us.

August 10th

Corona Australis (the Southern Crown) takes the form of a small broken circlet of stars to the east of the Sting of Scorpius and to the north of Telescopium. Alpha Telescopii, together with the nearby stars Delta[1,2], Epsilon and Zeta (all in Telescopium) are included on the chart for reference. The whole of Corona Australis is observable from the central United States, southern Europe and from latitudes to the south of these.

As its name suggests, Corona Australis is the southern counterpart of Corona Borealis (the Northern Crown) (see June 26th) and was one of the 48 constellations drawn up by the Greek astronomer Ptolemy during the 2nd century. There appear to be no legends directly associated with Corona

Australis and the stars forming this group are not particularly prominent, although its shape is distinctive in spite of this.

CORONA AUSTRALIS

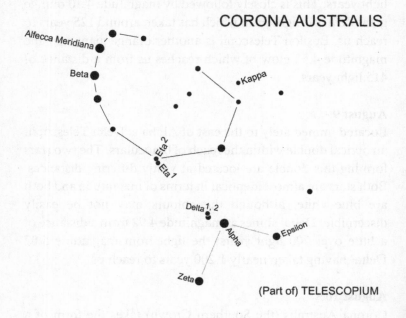

(Part of) TELESCOPIUM

The two brightest stars in Corona Australis have almost identical magnitudes. The brighter of the two is Alfecca Meridiana which, at magnitude 4.10, shines from a distance of 125 light years. The first part of this name is derived from the Arabic for 'break', alluding to the fact that the constellation as a whole takes the form of a broken circle of stars. The second part of the name is loosely derived from the Latin for 'south' or 'southern', perhaps as a contrast to the similarly-named Alphecca in this constellation's northern counterpart Corona Borealis.

Marginally dimmer than Alfecca Meridiana is Beta

Coronae Australis, a magnitude 4.11 orange giant, the light from which has taken 510 years to reach us.

August 11th

The two stars Eta[1] and Eta[2] form an optical double which can be resolved with the naked eye. Both stars are white, Eta[1] shining at magnitude 5.50 from a distance of around 350 light years. Slightly dimmer is Eta[2] which, at magnitude 5.60, is located around 500 light years from us.

Another optical double is Kappa which has components of magnitudes 5.65 and 6.30 which can be resolved in a small telescope. These two stars are located at vastly differing distances, the brighter star shining from around 1,700 light years and the light from its fainter companion having taken just 490 years to reach us.

August 12th

The constellation Sagittarius (the Archer) lies a short way to the south of the celestial equator and, although much of the group is visible from mid-northern latitudes, it is best viewed from the southern hemisphere from where it can be seen high up in the northern sky during the winter months. If you are located anywhere south of latitude 45°N you will be able to see the entire constellation and portions of the group are visible from practically every inhabited part of the world. Bordering Sagittarius is the constellation Scorpius (see July 21st) which, with its brilliant star Antares and the curve of stars marking the Sting of Scorpius, can be seen to the west.

Sagittarius lies immediately to the east of the neighbouring constellation Scorpius (see July 22nd), the stars Shaula, Theta and several others at the end of the 'sting' of Scorpius included here as a guide to locating the group. Sagittarius was one of the 48 constellations drawn up by the Greek astronomer Ptolemy during the 2nd century and, according to legend, represents an archer firing an arrow in the direction of Scorpius. Mythology has it that the archer in question is the satyr Crotus, the son of Pan. Crotus was a skilful hunter and the inventor of archery. His prowess in hunting and skill with a bow and arrow eventually led to him being rewarded by Zeus placing him in the sky.

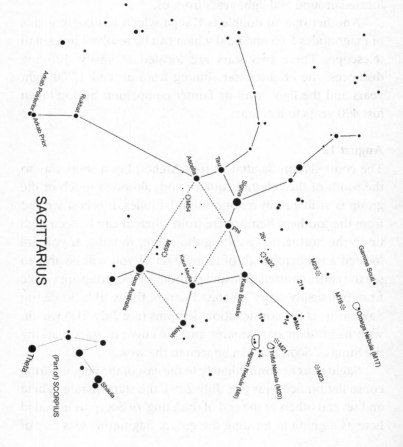

SAGITTARIUS

August 13th

The brightest star in Sagittarius is the magnitude 1.79 Kaus Australis, a white giant shining from a distance of 143 light years. Just to the north is the orange giant Kaus Media which, at magnitude 2.72, lies at a distance of around 350 light years. The light from magnitude 2.82 Kaus Borealis, located slightly further to the north, has taken 78 years to reach us. These three stars derive their names from a mixture of Arabic and Latin meaning the southern, middle and northern part(s) of the bow and together represent the bow held by Sagittarius.

In keeping with this is Nash, the name of which is derived from the Arabic for 'the Point', alluding to its position at the end of the arrow being fired by the archer. Nash is a magnitude 2.98 orange giant shining from a distance of 97 light years.

Arkab Prior and Arkab Posterior, located near the southern border of Sagittarius, derive their names from the Arabic for 'the Tendon' representing as they do the archer's tendons. Arkab Prior is known as such due to the fact that it leads its companion, Arkab Posterior, across the sky. These two stars form a pretty double when viewed through binoculars although even a small telescope will reveal that Arkab Prior is itself a binary star with magnitude 3.96 and 7.40 components. Arkab Prior lies at a distance of around 375 light years, nearly three times the distance of magnitude 4.27 Arkab Posterior, the light from which has taken 134 years to reach us.

A little way to the north of these two is the appropriately-named Rukbat, a magnitude 3.96 star whose name is derived from the Arabic *'rukbat al-rami'* meaning 'the Knee of the Archer'. Rukbat lies at a distance of around 180 light years, roughly twice the distance of magnitude 2.60 Ascella, the light from which has taken just 88 years to reach us. Ascella takes its name from the Latin for 'the Armpit'.

August 14th

Sagittarius contains one of the most famous and well known asterisms, this being the Teapot, a distinctive pattern formed from a group of stars located within the central regions of the constellation. The body of the Teapot is made up from the quartet of stars Ascella, Phi, Kaus Media and Kaus Australis, the tip of the spout being represented by Nash, the handle by Tau and Sigma and the top of the lid by Kaus Borealis. Although the rest of Sagittarius is fairly rambling and has no clear and well-defined shape, the eight stars forming the Teapot stand out quite well and act as a good guide to identifying the constellation as a whole.

August 15th

In the magic hour that follows the sweet mid-August sunset two stars – seen at eight o'clock – send forth their pale fires from out the dusky blue. One – in the south-west – in Arcturus; the other – high up, and a little way east of the meridian – is Vega. Ere half an hour has elapsed Arcturus has deepened into its rich golden hue and Vega into its greenish-blue tint. Polaris, too, shines out modestly, and the stars of the Plough – Megrez alone excepted – are dimly seen.

August 16th

The constellation of Sagittarius contains more Messier objects than any other constellation, and we can take a closer look at a few of them here, starting with M23, an open star cluster discovered by Charles Messier in 1764. Located towards the north western border of Sagittarius, M23 lies at a distance of 2,150 light years and has an overall magnitude of 6.9 making it a fairly easy binocular object providing the sky is dark and clear. It can be tracked down by first of all locating the guide star Mu Sagittarii and then following the trail of stars shown on the finder chart. The English astronomer William Henry Smyth described M23 as: *'A loose cluster: an elegant sprinkling of telescopic stars over the whole field under moderate magnification.'* Low magnifications, such as those available with binoculars or a small telescope, are best for this object. Seek M23 out and see if your impression matches that of Smyth.

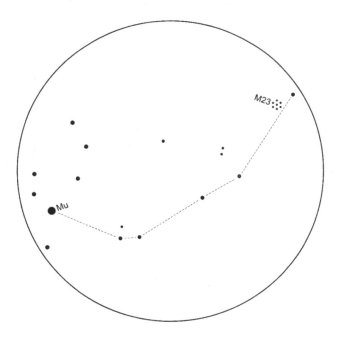

August 17th

Possibly discovered by the rather grandly-named French astronomer Guillaume-Joseph-Hyacinthe-Jean-Baptiste Le Gentil de la Galazière sometime before 1750, and independently discovered by Charles Messier in 1764, the gaseous nebula M20, also known as the Trifid Nebula, can be found a little way to the south of the open cluster M23 and to the south west of the star Mu Sagittarii. Located at a distance of around 5,000 light years, this object shines with an overall magnitude of 6.3 putting it within the light grasp of binoculars or a small telescope.

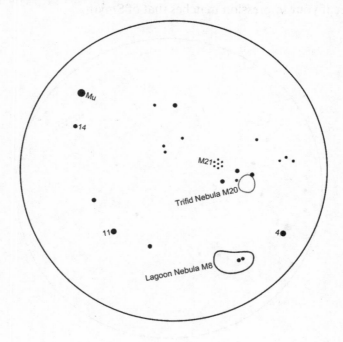

M20 is known as the Trifid Nebula due to the fact that, when seen through larger telescopes, the bright nebula appears to be divided into three distinct sections. This apparent division is due to lanes of dark dust superimposed against the brighter backdrop of nebulosity. The name was probably first applied to the nebula by John Herschel who described it as: *'... consisting*

of 3 bright and irregularly formed nebulous masses ...surround(ing) a sort of 3-forked rift... quite devoid of nebulous light.'

The main section of the Trifid Nebula consists of a characteristically coloured red area of emission nebulosity (see Glossary) against which are seen the lanes of dust. Adjoining this main section is a smaller patch of blue reflection nebulosity. This object can be found by locating the guide star Mu and working your way through the field of faint stars which lie between Mu and the nebula. The finder chart, which also shows the locations of the Lagoon Nebula (see August 18th) and the open cluster M21 (see August 19th) should help you track it down. Clear, dark and moonless skies are essential, however, as it can be somewhat elusive. As is the case with all objects of this type, make sure you look for a patch of light rather than a star like point. It is also worth remembering that the different colours of the nebulosity may not be particularly evident when viewed through binoculars or small telescopes.

August 18th

A little to the south of M20 we find another gaseous emission nebula. This is M8, also known as the Lagoon Nebula which, with a magnitude of around 6, can be glimpsed with the naked eye under really dark, clear skies. Binoculars will show this object quite well, revealing it as a roughly-oval colourless patch of light surrounding a bright star cluster. Under favourable conditions, even a small telescope will reveal a dark dust lane separating this region from a second area of nebulosity.

Located at a distance of around 5,000 light years, the Lagoon Nebula is regarded as one of the finest nebulae in the sky. It was originally discovered by the Sicilian astronomer Giovanni Battista Hodierna sometime before 1654, following which it was noted by several astronomers prior to Charles

Messier cataloguing it in 1764.

Long-exposure photographs are needed in order to reveal the full glory of the Lagoon Nebula, and to bring out its characteristic reddish colour. However, this splendid object is definitely worth the attentions of the backyard astronomer and can be tracked down by using the finder chart. Working your way through the field of faint stars that lie between the guide star Mu Sagittarii and the Lagoon Nebula, look carefully for the tiny triangle the nebula forms with the nearby Trifid Nebula and the faint star 4 Sagittarii.

August 19th

Located within the same field as the Trifid Nebula and Lagoon Nebula is the open star cluster M21 which, with an overall magnitude of around 7, is fairly easy to locate with binoculars or a small telescope. This cluster contains over 50 individual stars and lies at a distance of 4,250 light years. Discovered by Charles Messier in 1764, it was described by William Henry Smyth as: *'A coarse cluster of telescopic stars... near the upper part of the Archer's bow...'* Although not the most impressive of the Messier objects to be found in Sagittarius, it is worth while tracking down if only for the fact that it lies in the immediate area of the Trifid and Lagoon, all three objects being depicted on the same finder chart.

August 20th

Located a little to the south west of the star Gamma Scuti, close to the border between Sagittarius and the neighbouring constellation Scutum (see August 27th), we find another gaseous emission nebula. Also known as the Omega Nebula or Horse-shoe Nebula, M17 shines at around magnitude 6 and is therefore just visible to the naked eye provided the sky is exceptionally dark and clear. The Omega Nebula is smaller and more concentrated than the Lagoon Nebula and is consequently that little bit easier to see. Binoculars or a small telescope will show this object reasonably well, although they will not reveal its characteristic reddish colour.

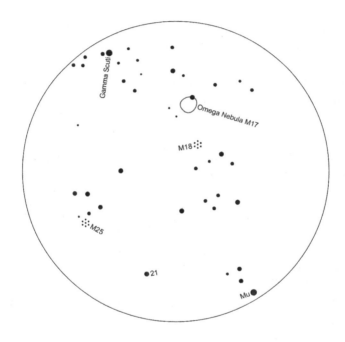

The Omega Nebula was discovered by Philippe Loys de Cheseaux in 1746 and was described by him as: *'A nebula which has never been discovered... it has the perfect form of a ray or the tail of a comet.'* When Messier added it to his catalogue in 1764 he described it as being: *'A train of light without stars... in the shape of a spindle... light very faint.'* Somewhat more dramatic was the description given by the French astronomer Nicolas Camille

Flammarion who likened it to: '...a smoke-drift, fantastically wreathed by the wind.'

The Omega Nebula can be tracked down with the finder chart by first of all locating the star Mu Sagittarii and then star hopping your way northwards. Alternatively, you can find it by using the star Gamma in the neighbouring constellation Scutum (see August 27th) as a guide. Both stars are shown on the finder chart. As with most objects of this type, each observer forms his or her own opinion as to what they see when they turn their attentions towards them. Do your impressions of the Omega Nebula match those of past astronomers?

August 21st
Located immediately to the south of the Omega Nebula is M18, an open star cluster shining at magnitude 7.5 from a distance of 4,900 light years. It was discovered by Charles Messier in 1764 who described it as: 'A cluster of small stars, a little below M17...' Although M18 is only a small cluster containing no more than around 20 stars or so, this is more than made up for by the fact that we see it against the backdrop of the Milky Way. The English astronomer Thomas William Webb, when describing M18, alluded to the area around it as a: 'Glorious field in a very rich vicinity. South, lies a region of surpassing splendour.'

Shown here on the same finder chart as the Omega Nebula and M25 (see August 22nd), M18 can be found by carefully star-hopping your way either northwards from Mu Sagittarii, or southwards from Gamma Scuti, through the surrounding field of faint stars. Binoculars will enable you to track this cluster down and a small telescope will resolve a dozen or so of its member stars. Perhaps more alluring, however, are the surrounding star fields described so inspiringly by Webb.

August 22nd

Another of the open star clusters found in Sagittarius is M25, a magnitude 6.5 object located at a distance of around 2,000 light years. It was discovered by Philippe Loys de Cheseaux in 1746, who described it as: *'A star cluster between the bow and head of Sagittarius.'* In 1764 Messier added it to his catalogue, referring to it as: *'A cluster of small stars... The nearest star is 21 Sagittarii... No nebulosity seen.'*

M25 can be located via the finder chart and can be seen to form a triangle with the guide star Mu Sagittarii and M18. Once you've got Mu in your field of view, carefully take your gaze towards the star 21 Sagittarii, mentioned by Messier, and then veer very slightly northwards and go almost as far again. M25 should come into view as a patch of light with a few individual stars visible, providing the sky is dark and clear. A small telescope will resolve more cluster members.

August 23rd

The globular cluster M22, located a short way to the east of the star Kaus Borealis, was discovered by the German amateur astronomer (and postman) Abraham Ihle in 1665, although it may have been spotted earlier by the Polish astronomer Johannes Hevelius. M22 appears to be the first ever globular cluster to be discovered and is regarded as being one of the finest objects of its type in the sky. John Herschel described it as: *'A magnificent globular cluster...'*, a sentiment echoed by many astronomers since, including Thomas William Webb who recorded it as being a: *'Beautiful bright cluster...'*

Containing upwards of 70,000 individual stars, M22 shines at magnitude 5.9 from a distance of around 10,500 light years and can be found quite easily in binoculars through which it will appear as a prominent but fuzzy patch of light a little way from Kaus Borealis. If the sky is really dark, clear and moonless, M22 can be seen with the naked eye. The finder chart should enable you to star hop your way towards the cluster which, even when viewed through small telescopes, will reveal a number of its individual member stars.

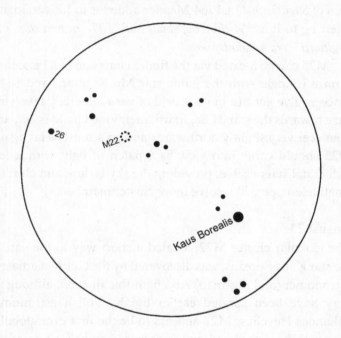

August 24th

Before we take our leave of Sagittarius, we should check out two more globular clusters, both of which are located within the triangle of sky formed by Kaus Media, Kaus Australis and Ascella.

Discovered by Charles Messier in 1778, M54 can be seen a little to the west of Ascella and has been found to lie at a distance of almost 90,000 light years. Research has shown that M54 is not associated with our own Milky Way Galaxy but actually belongs to the Sagittarius Dwarf Elliptical Galaxy, a recently-discovered member of the Local Group of Galaxies (see Glossary).

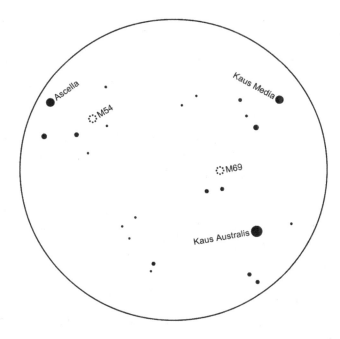

Shining at around magnitude 7.5, M54 is fairly bright, although quite small and can, at first sight, resemble a star in appearance. Consequently, it can be difficult to pick up in binoculars or small telescopes and offers a bit of a challenge to the backyard astronomer armed with only modest optical aid. However, if you use the finder chart and look very carefully, M54 will appear as a tiny nebulous object, brighter in the middle and fading towards the edges. This description echoes those of earlier astronomers, including John Herschel who described M54 as being: *'A globular cluster, very bright... at first gradually, then suddenly much brighter in the middle...'* Check M54 out for yourself and see what your impressions are.

August 25th

A quarter to ten! A cloud-opening in the north-east allows of a find view of Algol and the other Perseus stars. Algol is, of course, Beta Persei. The other bright stars of the constellation – Alpha, Gamma, and Delta – will be seen to be formed in a graceful curve, at almost equal distances from one another.

Ten-thirty! A word of welcome to the Pleiades which now glitter in the north-east sky. The ghost of a summer is passing and thoughts of winter arise when the Seven Sisters – the vanguard of the winter starry host – appear.

The cluster is sunk to a profound depth in the silent solitudes of space, and there are those who consider that it is even larger than the Great Bear. It is a twinkling mystery, and not its least mysterious feature is the fact of it being immersed in a sea of nebulous matter.

August 26th

Our final port of call in Sagittarius is the globular star cluster M69, discovered by Nicolas Louis de Lacaille in 1751-52. Charles Messier added it to his catalogue in 1780, describing it as a: *'Nebula without a star in Sagittarius... very faint... position determined from Epsilon Sagittarii...'* The finder chart depicting M69 (and M54) included here shows Kaus Australis (which has the alternative name Epsilon Sagittarii used by Messier in his description) as one of the two guide stars.

M69 lies at a distance of around 30,000 light years and, like nearby M54, hardly rises above the horizon as seen from mid-northern latitudes. It is best observed from more southerly locations, from where Sagittarius can be found higher up in the sky. Shining at around 8th magnitude, M69 is fairly faint and can, initially at least, be difficult to track down. The finder chart, which shows the positions of M54 and M69 relative to the guide stars Kaus Media, Kaus Australis and Ascella together with other fainter stars in the immediate area, should help you pin point these two clusters.

When seen through binoculars or a small telescope, M69 should resemble a faint, hairy star and be similar in appearance to M54. Dark, clear and moonless skies are needed for these two elusive objects although, with a little patience and suitably-dark skies, your efforts should be rewarded.

August 27th

Our next destination is the constellation Scutum (the Shield) which can be found bordering Sagittarius and Aquila.

The stars Lambda and 12 in Aquila (see September 2nd) are included here as a guide. Scutum was originally introduced in 1684 by Johannes Hevelius in honour of King John III Sobiesci of Poland, a distinguished warrior, the original name for the constellation being Scutum Sobiescianum (Sobiesci's Shield). The name has since been shortened to Scutum.

The entire constellation of Scutum is visible from latitudes south of 74°N and portions can be seen worldwide, apart from some regions in the Arctic, which should not pose too many problems for the average backyard astronomer! None of the stars in Scutum are particularly prominent, the brightest being Alpha, a magnitude 3.85 orange giant shining from a distance of around 200 light years. The northern tip of the constellation is depicted by the magnitude 4.22 yellow supergiant Beta, the light from which has taken 900 years to reach us. Magnitude

4.88 Epsilon is a yellow giant shining from a distance of 530 light years, somewhat more distant than Delta, a magnitude 4.70 star situated around 200 light years away.

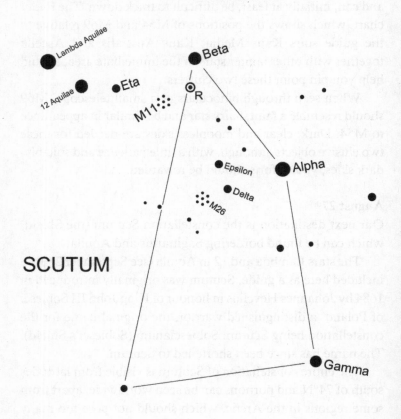

SCUTUM

Located at the south western corner of Scutum is Gamma, a white star with a magnitude of 4.67 located at a distance of 320 light years. Gamma is one of the guide stars for locating the Eagle Nebula in the neighbouring constellation Serpens

Cauda (see July 12th) and the Omega Nebula in Sagittarius, which also borders Scutum (see August 20th).

August 28th

Although fairly small and relatively obscure, Scutum lies within a rich and star-packed region of sky. The constellation plays host to a large, bright section of the Milky Way, which is a wonderful target for the naked-eye backyard astronomer. This area is known as the Scutum Star Cloud and is one of the richest regions of the Milky Way. Here, no interstellar dust blocks out the light from the star fields beyond, and when viewed under dark, clear skies and from areas unspoiled by light pollution, this region of the Milky Way stands out well.

In his book *'Star Lore: Myths, Legends, and Facts'* the American astronomy writer William Tyler Olcott tells us that: *'...it is said that within the boundaries of Scutum, in a space five degrees square, Sir Wm. Herschel estimated that there were 331,000 stars.'* Although the number of stars alluded to seems a little precise, this entry does highlight the richness of the Milky Way in Scutum. Indeed, the American astronomer Edward Emerson Barnard described this region as being a: *'Gem of the Milky Way'*. Check out the Scutum Star Cloud for yourself and see if you agree with Herschel and Barnard!

August 29th

Situated at the northern edge of the Scutum Star Cloud is the prominent open star cluster M11. Also known as the Wild Duck Cluster this object was discovered in 1681 by the German astronomer Gottfried Kirch who described it as: *'A small obscure spot...'*. It was first resolved into stars by the English astronomer William Derham. This cluster derives its popular name from comments made about it by William Henry Smyth who likened its appearance to '...*a flight of wild ducks*... *a gathering of minute stars*...'

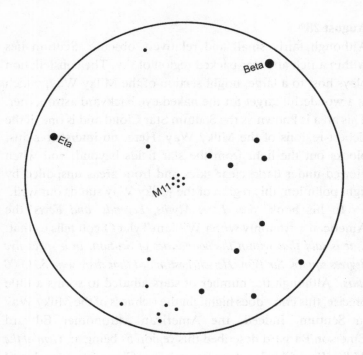

Located at a distance of around 6,000 light-years, M11 contains almost 3000 stars and shines with an overall magnitude of 6.3 making it an easy target for binoculars. However, you'll need a small telescope in order to resolve any individual members of the cluster. M11 forms a small triangle with the nearby stars Beta and Eta, as shown on the finder chart, and you should have little trouble tracking this one down.

*

August 30th

Located in same binocular field as Delta, and lying a little way to the east of that star, is the open star cluster M26. Discovered by Charles Messier in 1764, although possibly seen by the French astronomer Le Gentil prior to then, this cluster shines with an overall magnitude of around 8 and lies at a distance of 5,000 light years.

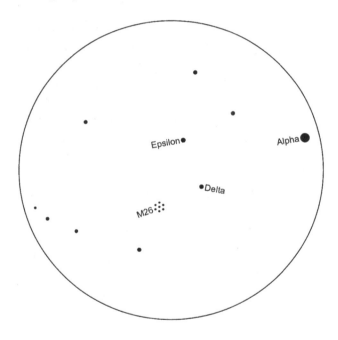

M26 is seen against the backdrop of the Milky Way and, as a consequence, can be difficult to make out against the background star fields, against which it will be seen as a small concentration of stars. As shown on the finder chart, a line drawn from Alpha through Delta and on roughly half as far again will lead you to this cluster. Provided the sky is reasonably dark and clear, binoculars should help you track it down and a small telescope should bring out some of the individual stars within the cluster. Unlike the nearby Wild Duck Cluster, M26 presents something of a challenge to locate.

August 31st

Located just to the south of Beta is the variable star R Scuti, the variations in brightness of which are somewhat unusual. Generally speaking, the magnitude of R Scuti varies between around 5 and 6 over a period of 140 days or so. However, neither the period of variability nor the magnitude range are constant. Occasionally R Scuti can drop to 8th or 9th magnitude, putting it at the threshold of binocular visibility. The variability of R Scuti was first noted by the English astronomer Edward Pigott in 1795 and this star is always within the light grasp of either binoculars or a small telescope. The somewhat erratic behaviour of R Scuti makes it worth keeping an eye on!

SEPTEMBER

September 1st

During September evenings, from mid-northern latitudes, once the sun has set and the stars become visible, you should see the prominent constellation Aquila (the Eagle), its brightest star Altair visible fairly high up in the southern sky. Observers in the southern hemisphere should look high up towards the north. Aquila lies on the celestial equator and as a consequence the whole constellation is visible from almost every inhabited part of the world.

Altair is flanked by two fainter stars, Tarazed and Alshain, which together form a distinctive trio. The rest of Aquila can be seen extending to the south west of these three stars, the group taking the form of a large cross which can be easily likened to a bird in flight. The constellation is shown here along with the main stars in Scutum (see August 27th) as a guide.

Aquila depicts the eagle which, according to Greek and Roman legend, carried the thunderbolts of Zeus. The constellation was important to the Romans and was portrayed on many Roman coins. The Roman poet Caesius, who lived during the reign of Nero, referred to the group as the Eagle of Military Rome or the Eagle of St John.

If the night is dark and clear you may see the Milky Way running from roughly north to the south, passing through Aquila on its way. As a result, the area of sky around Aquila is rich in star fields and will repay sweeping with binoculars on really dark, clear nights.

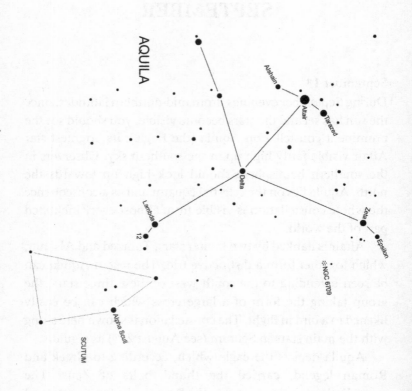

AQUILA

Altair

Tarazed

Alshain

Delta

Lambda

12

Zeta

Epsilon

NGC 6709

Alpha Scuti

SCUTUM

September 2nd

Magnitude 0.76 Altair, shining from a distance of a little under 17 light years, is the brightest star in Aquila. Altair derives its name from the Arabic *'al-nasr al-ta'ir'* meaning 'the Flying Eagle'. Immediately to the north of Altair is Tarazed, a magnitude 2.72 orange giant star located at a distance of almost 400 light years. Binoculars reveal the orange tint of Tarazed quite well. Altair is also flanked by Alshain, a yellow star of magnitude 3.71, the light from which has taken 45 years to reach us. This prominent trio of stars ensures that Altair, and the constellation Aquila in general, is fairly easy to recognise.

Altair is the southernmost of the three bright stars that make up the Summer Triangle, the others being Deneb in Cygnus (see September 4th) and Vega in Lyra (see September 16th).

Marking the central point of Aquila is Delta, a white star of magnitude 3.36 located some 50 light years away. The tail of the eagle is represented by the two stars Zeta and Epsilon, the yellow-orange tint of Epsilon contrasting with the blue-white Zeta. Many of these colour comparisons should be seen in binoculars given clear and transparent skies.

Situated near the south western corner of Aquila is Lambda Aquilae, a blue star of magnitude 3.43 shining from a distance of 125 light years. Close by is the orange giant star 12 Aquilae which, with a magnitude of 4.02 is located around 145 light years away. Together, these two stars are a useful location guide to the tiny constellation of Scutum (see August 27th) which borders Aquila and which is also shown on the chart with Alpha Scuti, its brightest star, named.

September 3rd

Zeta and Epsilon act as guide stars for the faint open star cluster NGC 6709. This cluster lies around 3,500 light years away and can be found to the southwest of Zeta and Epsilon near the western border of Aquila. Shining at magnitude 6.7, NGC 6709 contains around 50 member stars. This object may be difficult to pick out against the background of star fields in the Milky Way. However, if you use binoculars to carefully search the sky a little way to the south west of the two stars Zeta and

Epsilon you might be able to pick out the cluster as a faint nebulous patch of light providing the skies are dark, clear and moonless.

September 4th

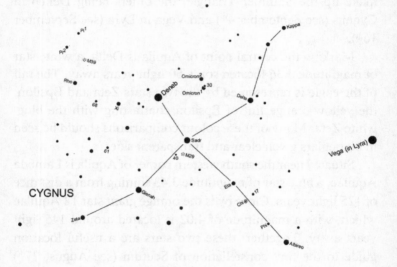

During September evenings at mid-northern latitudes, the constellation of Cygnus (the Swan), known also as the Northern Cross, can be seen at or near the overhead point, straddling the Milky Way. Those living south of the equator will see the cruciform shape of Cygnus above the northern horizon with brilliant Vega in Lyra (see September 16ᵗʰ) to its west and Altair, the leading star in Aquila (see September 1ˢᵗ) higher up and to the south of this pair. The whole of Cygnus can be seen from latitudes north of 29°S with portions of the constellation being visible from anywhere to the north of latitude 62°S. The chart shows Cygnus together with the two nearby bright stars Vega (in Lyra) and Altair (in Aquila) which, along with Deneb, make up the conspicuous asterism known as the Summer Triangle.

It seems that the group has nearly always been associated with a bird, and records show that ancient astronomers have likened it to a flying eagle, a hen, a partridge and even a pigeon! However, the title that we now have for the constellation as a whole was first adopted by the Romans who linked the group with the mythical swan identified with *Cycnus*, the son of Mars.

Deneb depicts the tail of Cygnus and marks the northern end of the constellation and from Deneb the rest of Cygnus can be picked out easily, the swan's outstretched wings and characteristic long neck prominent. Cygnus spans the Milky Way and conjures up the image of a huge celestial bird flying southwards. An old Polish hymn talks of '...*a sleeping swan's white plumage fringed with gold*' – the glow of the Milky Way surrounding the heavenly bird. On a clear, dark, moonless night the effect is striking. In 1844 the American astronomer Percival Lowell wrote of the constellation Cygnus that the countless splendours in the sky were '...*crowned by the blazing Cross hung high o'er all*' – praise indeed!

September 5th

The constellation Cygnus represented a hen to the astronomers of Ancient Greece and Arabia, Deneb deriving its name from the Arabic *'dhanab al-dajaja'* meaning 'the Hen's Tail'. Deneb is the brightest star in Cygnus, this magnitude 1.25 white supergiant shining from a distance of 1,380 light years. In keeping with the theme of a hen's anatomy is magnitude 2.23 Sadr, another white supergiant, the light from which has taken around 1,800 years to reach us. Sadr derives its name from the Arabic *'sadr al-dajaja'* meaning 'the Hen's Breast'.

Gienah takes its name from the Arabic *'janah'* meaning 'wing' (as does the star in Corvus which bears the same name - see June 5th). Magnitude 2.48 orange supergiant Gienah is located 73 light years from us, less than half the distance of Delta, a white star of magnitude 2.86 shining from around 170 light years away.

The tips of the swan's wings are marked by Zeta and Kappa Cygni. Both these stars are yellow supergiants, Zeta shining at magnitude 3.21 from a distance of 143 light years, slightly further than magnitude 3.80 Kappa, the light from which has taken just 124 years to reach us.

September 6th

Truly, do the days shorten! It is now but twenty minutes after seven and there, solitary and silvery, twinkles the North Star among some broken clouds, themselves almost as silvery as the star. And there, too, is Arcturus, splintering its golden light against an opal sky in the west. A delightful evening of early September... gently breezy, with luminous patches of sky west and north, and a mottling of cloud elsewhere. A twilight atmosphere; pre-autumn mists softening the features of fields and woods and houses in the distant hollow and on the picturesque slope that rises to the north-east sky-line.

September 7th

The beak of the swan is marked by Albireo which is recognised as being one of the most beautiful double stars in the sky, the description given to it by Thomas William Webb of it being: *'One of the finest in the heavens'* typifying the esteem that Albireo is held in by star gazers. To the naked eye, Albireo shines at around 3rd magnitude, its true beauty being revealed even when viewed through a small telescope. The brightest component, Albireo A, shines at magnitude 3.05 from a distance of around 430 light years. The yellowish tint of this star contrasts wonderfully with its bluish fainter companion, Albireo B which, at magnitude 5.10, is a little closer, its light having taken just 400 years to reach us.

Albireo has been described as a showpiece for small telescopes, a sentiment echoed by Joseph Henry Elgie when he said of the star: *Of Beta Cygni (Albireo), its chief interest consists in it being a very beautiful double. The component star... is an easy object in a small telescope. Webb... describes Albireo as topaz yellow in colour and the component as sapphire blue. He thinks the double to be one of the finest in the heavens...*

September 8th

The trio of stars Omicron[1], Omicron[2] and 30 Cygni form a pretty sight in binoculars. Both Omicron[1] and Omicron[2] are orange super giants, the latter shining at magnitude 3.96 from a distance of a little over 1,000 light years. Although estimates as to the distance of magnitude 3.80 Omicron[1] vary, the generally accepted value is around 800 light years. Shining from a distance of around 600 light years, and located in virtually the same line of sight as seen from our location in space, is the magnitude 4.80 white star 30 Cygni, which can be seen lying close to Omicron[1].

September 9th

The discovery of the open star cluster M39 is usually credited to Charles Messier who described it in 1764 as a: *'Cluster of stars near the tail of Cygnus…'* However, this object may have been seen earlier by the French astronomer Le Gentil who, in 1750, noted: *'At the tip of the tail of Cygnus… a large cloud, bigger at one end than the other… can be seen without the telescope.'*

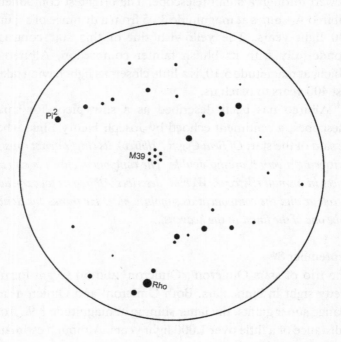

M39 is a large but fairly loose gathering of stars located a short way to the north east of Deneb. This cluster lies at a distance of 825 light years and has an overall magnitude of around 5.5, making it just visible to the naked eye under really dark and clear skies. Because of its large apparent size, M39 is best seen in the wide field of view of binoculars, or telescopes using the lowest magnification possible. When seen through either, the overall triangular shape of this cluster, apparently alluded to by Le Gentil in 1750, should be evident.

The wide field of view of binoculars probably make them the best instrument to use for your initial search for M39. The cluster can be tracked down by first of all following the line of faint stars Xi, 68, Rho, Pi^2 and Pi^1 away from Deneb. Once you have the star field between Rho and Pi^2 in your field of view, M39 can be seen to form a small triangle with these two stars, as depicted on the finder chart. Some individual stars in the cluster will be seen through binoculars, and even a small telescope will bring out a handful of cluster members.

September 10th

The open star cluster M29 was discovered by Charles Messier in 1764, at which time he noted it as a: *'Cluster of seven or eight very small stars which are below (Sadr)...'* Shining with an overall magnitude of 7.1 and containing around 50 member stars, M29 lies at a distance of around 4,000 light years and is a fairly easy target for the backyard stargazer. The French astronomer Nicolas Camille Flammarion must have thought highly of this cluster, describing it as resembling *'...a miniature archipelago in this opulent stellar region.'* The region of the sky in which M29 lies is indeed rich in stars, and Flammarion's comments echo this.

When viewed through a small telescope, M29 takes on a box-like shape and the appearance of the cluster has been likened to a smaller and somewhat stunted version of the Plough. M29 is located immediately to the south east of Sadr and can be found by first of all locating the nearby guide star

40 Cygni and then star hopping your way to the cluster using the finder chart. This object is somewhat fainter than M39 and may require a little patience during your search. However, binoculars will show the cluster as a distinct fuzzy patch of light, small telescopes bringing out some individual cluster members.

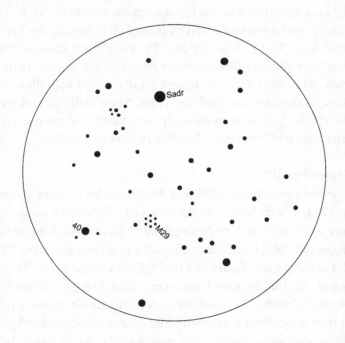

Located a little over half way between Phi and Eta Cygni, and just to the south east of 17 Cygni, is the Mira-type variable star Chi Cygni, the changes in brightness of which were first noted in 1686 by the German astronomer Gottfried Kirch. Chi Cygni is unusual in that it undergoes one of the largest variations in brightness known, ranging between around 5th and 13th magnitudes over a period of 407 days. What makes this star even more remarkable, however, is that it can be anything up to two magnitudes brighter when at maximum, peaks in magnitude of 4.6 and even 3.3 having been recorded.

There are potential problems as far as checking out Chi Cygni is concerned due to the fact that, when the star is at or near minimum brightness, you would need a telescope to see it. In any case, it would be difficult to pick out from the surrounding field of faint stars. The best idea would be to keep an eye on the location and await the time when the star is near maximum. The typically reddish tint of stars of this type should help you pick it out and, once you have identified it, comparing its brightness to nearby stars will reveal its subsequent decline in magnitude. You should be able to follow the star with binoculars or a small telescope through most, but not all, of its entire period of variability. Remember, though, that variable stars of this type take a long time to complete a full cycle, so observations you start now may not be completed until the following year!

September 12th

The star 61 Cygni, located to the south east of Deneb, is notable in that this was the first star to have its distance measured, this by the German astronomer Friedrich Bessel in 1838. Stars were once thought to be fixed in space, although observations carried out by the English astronomer Edmond Halley revealed that a number of bright stars had changed position over the centuries since star catalogues were first drawn up. It was logical to assume that the closer a star was to us, the greater would be its observed shift across the sky, this shift being due to the actual movement ('proper motion') of that star through space.

Bessel noticed that the star 61 Cygni had a comparatively large proper motion and he selected it as the star whose distance he would estimate using a method called trigonometrical parallax. The principle behind this is easy to demonstrate. Close one eye and hold up a finger at arm's length, lining it up with a suitable reference point, such as a distant tree. Now, keep your finger in the same position but look at it with your other eye. This will produce an apparent motion, or shift, of your finger in relation to the tree. This is because you are viewing it from a slightly different direction. By knowing the distance between your eyes, and the angle by which your finger appears to shift, the distance to your finger can be worked out by using simple trigonometry.

Astronomers apply the same principles to the measurement of stellar distances. Just as your finger appears to shift against the background when viewed alternately with each eye, a nearby star will undergo a shift against the background of more distant stars when observed from opposite points in the Earth's orbit around the Sun. By measuring the angular shift of the star, and knowing the diameter of the Earth's orbit, the distance to the star can be calculated.

Bessel had access to good quality telescopes and equipment, which allowed him to measure the tiny parallax shift of 61 Cygni. Application of trigonometry enabled him to work out that 61 Cygni was located at a distance of just over 10 light years. Comparison with the currently accepted value of 11.4 light years is testament to Bessel's skills as an observer, his efforts finally giving astronomers an idea of the distribution of stars in the solar neighbourhood, and the potentially vast distances involved.

September 13th

The small but conspicuous constellation of Lyra (the Lyre) is one of the most prominent groups in the night sky.

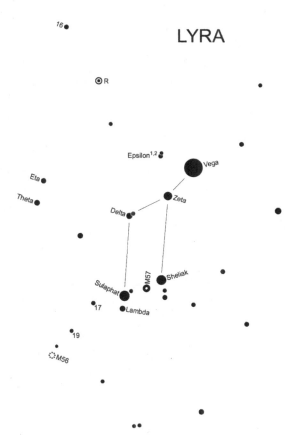

For observers at mid-northern latitudes, Lyra is easy to locate, its brightest star Vega conspicuous just to the west of the overhead point during September evenings shortly after sunset. The entire constellation is visible from latitudes north of 42°S and backyard astronomers observing from central South America, South Africa and Australia will see Vega low down in the northern part of the sky.

This group was known to the North American Indians as a Vulture, to the Arabs as an Eagle of the Desert and to the Romans as a Harp, although the most famous legend attached to Lyra is that told by the Ancient Greeks who identified the group with the lyre given by Apollo to the musician and poet Orpheus to accompany his songs.

Vega also features in a Japanese legend which tells the story of two lovers – the beautiful Orihime and the shepherd Hikoboshi. After their marriage, they began to neglect their work to be with each other. This angered the gods who punished the couple by sending them to opposite banks of the heavenly river. They are only allowed to meet on one night – July 7th – which is celebrated as a holiday by children in Japan.

Orihime is represented by Vega and Hikoboshi by Altair (in Aquila). If the night is dark and clear you may see the heavenly river, represented by the pearly light of the Milky Way, stretching between them, running from the north, extending across the sky and meandering down towards the south. When you do, perhaps you can spare a thought for the two lovers Orihime and Hikoboshi.

September 14th

Ten! In the words of eloquent Michael Fairless there is a 'blue-black sky ablaze with stars'. And the brave, noble-hearted author of 'The Roadmender' might have added that though it be night the heavens are aglow with sunlight – the light of a host of suns.

Michael Fairless was the pseudonym of the English

Christian writer Margaret Fairless Barber. Her book of meditations, The Roadmender (published in 1902) was hugely popular at the time.

September 15th

May I hope to be forgiven for interposing a purely meteorological note bearing on the brilliance of Fomalhaut last night. When a star of such low altitude is seen so distinctly it must mean an unusually clear state of the atmosphere. Be that as it may, this has been a glorious day of sunshine and warmth, though not without that touch of melancholy with which the year parts with the summer.

September 16th

The leading star in Lyra is the brilliant blue-white Vega which shines at magnitude 0.03 from a distance of around 25 light years. Vega is the 5th brightest star in the sky and one of the Sun's closest stellar neighbours, and is destined to play an important role in the distant future, at least as far as Earth-based observers are concerned.

The north celestial pole is currently marked by the star Polaris, which is situated in the constellation of Ursa Minor (see March 12th and 13th). The Earth's axis is currently pointing towards Polaris, which means that if you were stood at the North Pole, Polaris would be located directly overhead. The daily rotation of our planet on its axis makes the rest of the stars in the sky appear to travel around Polaris, their paths through the sky being centred on the Pole Star.

However, the position of the north celestial pole is slowly changing, this because of a 'wobble' in the Earth's axis of rotation. This wobble is known as 'precession' and is similar to that of a spinning top which is slowing down. Precession is caused by the combined gravitational influences of the Sun and

Moon on our planet. Each resulting wobble of the Earth's axis takes nearly 26,000 years to complete, the net effect of precession being that, over this period, the north celestial pole traces out a large circle around the northern sky. For northern hemisphere observers, this results in a slow change in the apparent location of the north celestial pole. Polaris will eventually relinquish its position and Vega will become the Pole Star some 11,500 years from now.

September 17th
Located a little way to the south east of Vega is Sulaphat, a magnitude 3.25 white giant star shining from a distance of a little over 600 light years. This star derives its name from the Arabic *'al-sulahfat'* meaning 'the Tortoise'. Magnitude 3.52 Sheliak takes its name from the Arabic *'al-salbaq'* meaning 'the Harp', the light from this star having set off towards us around 950 years ago. Just to the south of Sulaphat is the magnitude 4.94 orange giant star Lambda Lyrae which lies at a distance of around 1,100 light years.

September 18th
Lyra plays host to several double stars, one of which is Zeta Lyrae. The magnitude 4.34 and 5.73 components of Zeta are easily seen in a small telescope, although you may have difficulty resolving this pair in binoculars.

Another double is Delta Lyrae which has widely-separated components of magnitudes 4.22 and 5.58 which are clearly resolved in binoculars. The brightest component is a red giant shining from a distance of around 850 light years. The ruddy glow from this star contrasts nicely with the blue-white tint of its companion, the light from which has taken 870 years to reach us.

One of the most famous objects in Lyra is the Double-Double star Epsilon Lyrae, located immediately to the north west of Vega. At first glance, Epsilon appears to be a single star, although those with really keen eyesight may be able to identify it as a double. The magnitude 4.59 and 4.62 components are easily resolved with any form of optical aid, and closer inspection with a telescope will show that each of these two stars is double again, making Epsilon Lyrae a quadruple star system, although neither of these two closer pairs will be resolvable with small telescopes

September 19th
Discovered by Charles Messier in 1779, the globular cluster M56 shines at magnitude 8.2 from a distance of 32,900 light years.

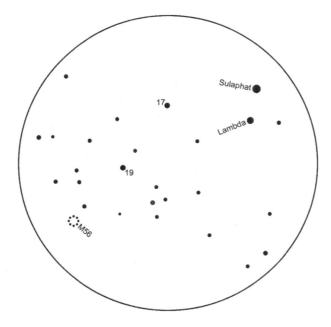

It can be located fairly easily in binoculars or a small telescope which will show it as a fuzzy patch of light. M56 can be found by following a line from Sulaphat through the stars 17 and 19 Lyrae. Extending this line a little further, as shown on the finder chart, should lead you straight to it. William Henry Smyth described M56 as: *'A globular cluster in a splendid field.'* echoing the fact that this object can be seen against the star-filled backdrop of the Milky Way. Check it out yourself and see if you agree with him.

September 20th

The Milky Way was overhead at half-past nine this evening, stretching in one mighty bow of star-mist from north-east to south-west. Cassiopeia and Perseus were mounting its north-eastern span, and Cygnus – where the Galaxy is of marvellous richness – was descending it, tail first, to the south-west.

September 21st

Another of Lyra's showpieces is the planetary nebula M57, discovered in 1779 by the French astronomer Antoine Darquier and described by him as: *'A very dull nebula, but perfectly outlined; as large as Jupiter and looks like a fading planet.'* Indeed, planetary nebulae derive their name from their normally disc-like appearance when viewed through small telescopes, the description first being coined by William Herschel in 1785.

M57 is also known as the Ring Nebula and, as is the case with other planetary nebulae, consists of material thrown off a star during the latter stages of its evolution. In the case of M57 the ejected material has formed a shell which surrounds its parent star, a dim 15th magnitude object which cannot be seen without a large telescope. As we gaze at M57 we are looking through the nearest wall of the shell of gas, around the edge of which is a more opaque concentration of material which appears as a ring. The same general effect would no doubt be noticed by observers looking at M57 from other positions in space. The neat, well-contained shape of M57, which led to it being christened the Ring Nebula, is not typical of planetary nebulae as a whole, most of the other known examples having comparatively irregular forms.

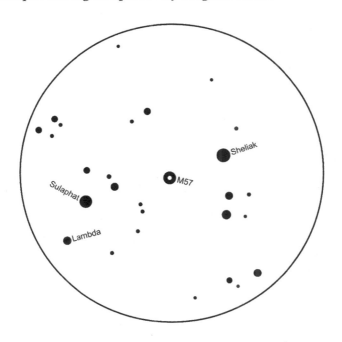

Darquier's description indeed matches the visual appearance of M57 when seen through a small telescope. Shining at magnitude 9.3 from a distance of 2,300 light years, M57 can be seen a little less than half way along a line from Sheliak to Sulaphat, as shown on the finder chart. Because this object is quite small and faint it may be difficult to see unless the sky is really dark and clear, although if you do track it down you will have the satisfaction of looking at what is probably the most famous of the planetary nebulae.

September 22nd

The semi-regular variable R Lyrae is located a little way to the north east of Vega and you should have no problem finding it, its characteristic reddish tint being fairly evident. Semi-regular variables are large, red stars with ranges in magnitude and periods of variability that are not as regular as those of Mira-type variables.

The variability of R Lyrae was discovered by the English astronomer Joseph Baxendell in 1856. R Lyrae is suitable for binocular observation, its brightness varying between magnitudes 3.9 and 5 over a period of around 46 days. The nearby star 16 Lyrae, which shines at magnitude 5.00, can be used to compare the brightness of R Lyrae, as can Eta (magnitude 4.43) and Theta (magnitude 4.35), although this latter pair is slightly awkwardly-placed, being outside the binocular field of view of R Lyrae.

September 23rd

The Polish astronomer Johannes Hevelius introduced a number of new constellations, many of which are still in use today, including the small and relatively faint Vulpecula (the Fox). The zig-zag line of stars forming Vulpecula is located immediately to the south of the constellation Cygnus and is shown here along with the bright star Albireo (in Cygnus) as a guide. Because the brightest stars in this group are by no means conspicuous, you may need a little patience picking Vulpecula out against the background star fields.

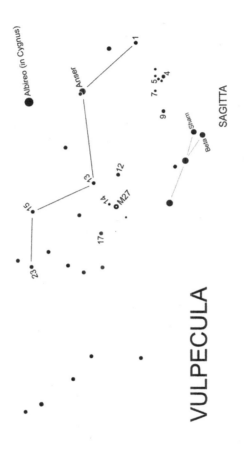

Hevelius originally named this group Vulpecula et Anser ("the Little Fox and the Goose") and depicted it as a fox holding a goose in its jaws. The Fox and the Goose were then split into separate groups, but later reunited into a single constellation. The Goose is now represented by Anser, the brightest star in Vulpecula. Vulpecula lies a little to the north of the celestial equator, the whole of the constellation being visible from all inhabited parts of the world north of latitude 60°S.

September 24th

This is the day of the Autumn equinox. Autumn began at nine minutes past five this morning, and the sun, which has not been over kind during his stay in the northern hemisphere, has now crossed the equator on his journey southward. For our South African kinsfolk Winter has departed and Spring begun. Let us hope that their Spring will be of more genial nature than was ours. And surely consternation would reign among them were their summer even as sunless as ours has been. I have sometimes sung with Christina Rossetti, in her 'Seasons':-

> *O sweet summer, pass not soon,*
> *Stay awhile the harvest moon;*
> *O sweetest summer, do not go,*
> *For Autumn's next, and next the snow.*

But who could bid tarry a summer such as this one just passed! An impostor of a summer, not fit to be classed with genuine seasons.

September 25th

The brightest star in Vulpecula is Anser. Shining from a distance of 297 light years, the colour of this magnitude 4.44 red giant can be distinguished in binoculars, which will also show a magnitude 5.82 orange star lying very close by. Together, Anser and its companion make an easy double-star target for binoculars, although the lining-up of these two stars occurs only by chance. They both happen to lie in roughly the same line of sight as seen from our planet, the fainter of the two being situated nearly twice as far away as Anser.

To the south west of Anser is 1 Vulpeculae, a magnitude 4.76 star whose light has taken just over 800 years to reach us. The magnitude 4.57 blue giant 13 Vulpeculae is somewhat closer, shining from a distance of 333 light years. Completing Vulpecula's zig-zag pattern are the magnitude 4.66 white giant 15 Vulpeculae which, at a distance of 236 light years, is a little closer than magnitude 4.50 orange giant 23 Vulpeculae, the light from which has taken around 340 years to reach us.

September 26th

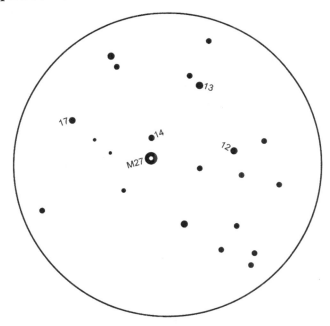

The Dumbbell Nebula, or M27, was the first planetary nebula to be discovered, this by Charles Messier in 1764. Located at a distance of around 1,350 light years, M27 shines with an overall magnitude of 7.4 and is a fairly easy target for binoculars. The Dumbbell Nebula derives its name from its appearance when seen through a telescope, the English astronomer Edwin Dunkin describing it as a '...*nebula shaped like a dumb-bell or hour-glass in the constellation Vulpecula... consist(ing) of two luminous symmetrical patches, joined together by a narrow isthmus...*', a description which illustrates it very well.

Situated a little way to the south east of the star 13 Vulpeculae, M27 is considered as being the finest object of its type in the sky and is well worth seeking out. If you locate the two stars 13 and 14 Vulpeculae, the Dumbbell Nebula will be seen immediately to the south of 14, as shown on the finder chart. Providing the sky is dark and clear, you should have no trouble at all picking this object out in binoculars, which should reveal the nebula as a small, fuzzy patch of light. A closer examination with even a small telescope should start to reveal the unusual shape for which this object is famous.

September 27th
Perhaps the most distinctive object in Vulpecula is the cluster of stars known as the Coathanger which lies on the edge of Vulpecula, a little to the north of the two end stars in the neighbouring constellation Sagitta (see September 28th). This object was first seen and catalogued by the Persian astronomer Al Sufi in the 10th century who described it as '...*a little cloud situated to the north of the two stars of the notch of Sagitta*'. Al Sufi saw the cluster with the naked eye and, if the sky is really dark, clear and moonless, you might also be able to make out the Coathanger with the unaided eye as a tiny fuzzy patch of light.

To see the Coathanger in all its glory you will need some form of optical aid, such as a pair of binoculars. To find it, first of all locate the tiny constellation Sagitta, the main outline of which is shown here, and follow a line from Beta, through Sham, to the star 9 in Vulpecula. Then turn to the west and move a short way until you come across the distinctive shape of the Coathanger, the main members of which are depicted on the chart.

The Coathanger is arranged around the stars 4, 5 and 7 in Vulpecula and is definitely well worth seeking out. The wide field view of binoculars brings out the cluster's distinctive shape quite well, revealing a row of six stars forming the 'bar' of the Coathanger and four more stars forming the 'hook'. Although impressive, the Coathanger is not a true star cluster, but rather a chance alignment of stars whose true distances range from a little over 200 light years to nearly a thousand light years from us. However, this does not make it any the less interesting to look at, and observers who see the Coathanger for the first time seldom fail to be impressed and delighted by its somewhat unusual appearance.

September 28th

The constellation Sagitta (the Arrow) is quite small and faint, but does have a distinctive shape, taking on the appearance of a tiny dart. It is one of the few groups of stars that actually resemble the object that it is supposed to depict and, as it is located a little way to the north of the celestial equator, you can check the whole of this tiny constellation out from any inhabited part of the world.

Sagitta can be found to the north of the bright trio of stars Alshain, Altair and Tarazed in the neighbouring constellation Aquila (see September 2nd) as shown here. If you have trouble picking out Sagitta, a pair of binoculars will be a help.

*

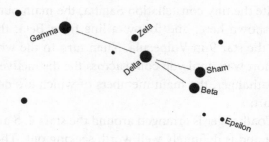

SAGITTA

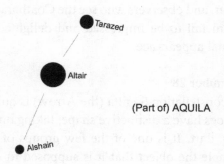

There are a number of legends attached to Sagitta, one of these identifying it as the arrow with which Hercules slew the Stymphalian vultures. Stymphalus was a lake upon whose banks lived a flock of dangerous brazen-clawed birds. Hercules managed to wipe out the entire flock with the help of a number of arrows which had been dipped in the venomous blood of Hydra, whom Hercules had slain as his second labour (see April 15th).

September 29th
The brightest star in Sagitta is Gamma Sagittae, a magnitude 3.51 red giant located at a distance of 258 light years. Another red giant is Delta Sagittae which, at magnitude 3.68, is slightly fainter than Gamma. The light from Delta has taken 580 years to reach us. Both Sham and Beta Sagittae shine at magnitude 4.39 and lie at roughly equal distances. Yellow giant Sham, the name of which is derived from the Arabic *'al-sahm'* meaning 'the Arrow', shines from a distance of 425 light years, marginally closer than Beta, the light from which set off on its journey towards us 439 years ago. Zeta Sagittae, located immediately to the north east of Delta, is a magnitude 5.01 white star located around 250 light years away.

September 30th
Located on the southern border of Sagitta is the wide optical double star Epsilon Sagittae. This pair is easily resolved in binoculars, the primary component being a magnitude 5.70 bluish star, which is accompanied by an 8th magnitude yellow giant companion.

OCTOBER

October 1st

The small but very distinctive diamond-shaped constellation Delphinus (the Dolphin) can be found a little way to the east of the trio of bright stars Alshain, Altair and Tarazed in the neighbouring constellation Aquila as shown here and can be viewed in its entirety from all inhabited parts of the world.

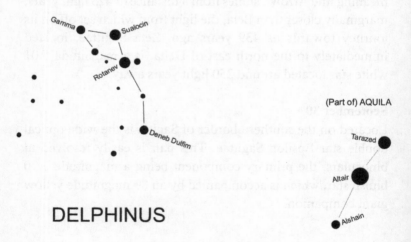

DELPHINUS

The presence of the dolphin in the sky is explained by a Greek legend which relates to Arion, the talented poet and musician. Arion had made his fortune playing music in Sicily and eventually decided to return to Greece, although the sailors on board the ship taking him home plotted to kill him and steal his wealth. They did allow Arion one last wish, letting him play some of his favourite music before he died. However, before he had finished playing, the sailors noticed that a school of dolphins had been attracted to the ship by Arion's harp. Terrified by the apparent power of his music, the sailors threw him overboard. Luckily, Arion landed on the back of one of the dolphins and was eventually carried to the safety of land. To honour the dolphin for his efforts Apollo placed the creature up among the stars where he can be seen to this day.

October 2nd

The brightest star in Delphinus is magnitude 3.64 Rotanev which shines from a distance of a little over 100 light years, somewhat closer than magnitude 3.77 Sualocin, the light from which has taken around 250 years to reach us. A degree of controversy surrounds the origin of the names given to these two stars. When spelled backwards, Sualocin and Rotanev read as Nicolaus Venator, which is the Latinized version of Niccolo Cacciatore. This gentleman was the assistant to Guiseppe Piazzi, the director of the Palermo Observatory in Sicily during the early 19th century. Cacciatore succeeded Piazzi as director and these two names first appeared in the observatory's 1814 star catalogue. To say that this is a rather unusual origin for star names is something of an understatement.

Sualocin is blue-white in colour while Rotanev has a yellowish tint. Binoculars, and really clear skies, will show this colour difference. Shining from a distance of around 100 light years, Gamma Delphini is a pretty double star with components of magnitudes 4.27 and 5.15 which can be resolved in a small telescope. Both components of this binary system have yellowish tints.

Deneb Dulfim shines at magnitude 4.03 from a distance of around 350 light years, the name of this star being derived from the Arabic for 'the Tail of the Dolphin'. Deneb is a common star name and crops up in many other constellations in one form or another, including Deneb in Cygnus (see September 5th) and Deneb Algiedi in Capricornus (see October 5th).

October 3rd

The constellation Capricornus (the Goat) lies to the south east of Aquila, a line drawn through Tarazed, Altair and Alshain in Aquila and projected southwards leading to the two stars Giedi and Dabih in Capricornus, from where the rest of Capricornus can be traced out.

This constellation is visible in its entirety from anywhere south of latitude 62°N but is always low down in the southern sky as seen by those at mid-northern latitudes. Those south of the equator will see Capricornus high in the north western sky during October evenings, the three above-mentioned guide stars in Aquila, themselves visible low in the north west, pointing the way.

Although none of the stars in Capricornus are particularly bright, the constellation is one of the oldest, depictions and accounts of it going back well before 1,000 BC. Capricornus was one of the 48 star groups drawn up by the Greek astronomer Ptolemy during the 2nd century. Greek mythology identifies Capricornus as Pan, the god of the countryside and personification of nature, and who had the hindquarters, legs and horns of a goat and the tail of a fish. Pan assisted Zeus in his battle with the monster Typhon, during which events Pan hid from Typhon by giving himself a fish's tail and diving into a river. To show his gratitude to Pan for his services, Zeus placed him in the sky where we see him today in the form of Capricornus.

*

(Part of) AQUILA

CAPRICORNUS

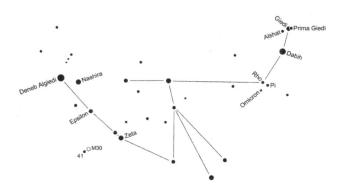

October 4th

A June-like warmth in the daytime is now, at a quarter-past ten, responsible for a night of haze. But some of the more familiar star groups can be traced with fair distinctness. There is, for instance, Cygnus, which leans from its elevated position in the west towards the north-west horizon, as though it were about to topple over on to Vega. That brilliant star is but little bedimmed by the brooding mist; indeed

its prominence in the sky, to the right of and on a level with Albireo,
the lowermost star of the Cross – as we may continue to call Cygnus
– seems as noteworthy as on an ordinarily clear night.

October 5th

The brightest star in Capricornus is Deneb Algiedi, a name derived from the Arabic *'dhanab al-jady'* meaning 'the Kid's Tail'. Located at the eastern end of the constellation, this star shines at magnitude 2.85 from a distance of 39 light years. Situated just to the west of Deneb Algiedi is Nashira, a magnitude 3.69 white giant star whose light has taken just over 150 years to reach us.

With a name taken from the Arabic *'al-jady'* meaning 'the Kid', the magnitude 3.58 yellow giant Giedi shines from a distance of 106 light years. Giedi actually forms a wide double with the nearby Prima Giedi, a yellow magnitude 4.30 supergiant situated immediately to its north west. This pair can be split with the naked eye and binoculars bring them out well. However, these two stars are not actually related, Prima Giedi shining from a distance of over 550 light years. Just to the east of Giedi is magnitude 4.77 Alshat, the light from which set off towards us around 250 years ago.

October 6th

The orange giant Dabih, a magnitude 3.05 star shining from a distance of 340 light years, can be found a short way to the south of Alshat and Giedi. Dabih is actually a binary star with components of magnitudes 3.05 and 6.10, both of which are easily seen in binoculars. The brightest of the stars is white and its fainter companion blue. Comparing the two may help you detect the bluish tint of the fainter component.

Another double worth checking out is Omicron Capricorni,

which forms a tiny triangle with Rho and Pi, a little to the south east of Dabih. Omicron has white components of magnitude 5.94 and 6.74 which are far enough apart to be seen in a small telescope.

October 7th

A peaceful, starlit evening, of autumnal keenness; sounds come up from the city below clear and distinct, and the lights scattered among the houses on the eastern slope shine unwontedly vivid.

October 8th

Discovered by Charles Messier in 1764 and described by him as: *'Nebula discovered near 41 Capricorni. Round, contains no star. Found from (Zeta) Capricorni'* the globular cluster Messier 30 lies near the south eastern corner of Capricornus. Although Messier's small telescope revealed little in the way of detail for M30 (as was the case for many other objects that he discovered), later observers were better equipped and more impressed, including William Henry Smyth who described M30 as: *'A fine, pale white cluster'* and Thomas William Webb who recorded M30 as being: *'Moderately bright, beautifully contrasted... comet-like... with higher powers, resolvable.'*

Located at a distance of around 26,000 light years, M30 shines with an overall magnitude of 7.2 and will appear as little more than a diffuse ball of light in binoculars or a small telescope. Slightly larger telescopes, or very powerful binoculars, should enable you to resolve some of the individual stars within the cluster. Finding M30 can be a little difficult, although two of the guide stars used by Messier appear on the finder chart. M30 forms a triangle with Zeta and Epsilon Capricorni and appears immediately to the west of the faint star 41 Capricorni. Once you have identified either Zeta or

Epsilon, you should be able to star hop your way to the cluster fairly easily. Dark, clear skies are probably necessary when tracking this object down for the first time.

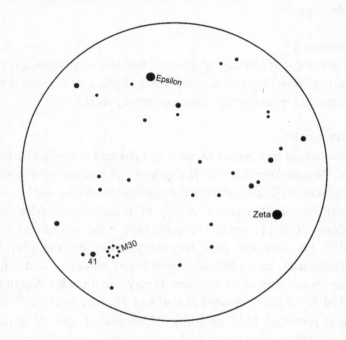

October 9th

The constellation of Draco (the Dragon) lies in the far-northern sky and winds its way around Polaris, the Pole Star. Although the group itself is quite large (the eighth largest of all the constellations) it isn't particularly prominent. However, it can be spotted fairly easily by using the stars of Ursa Minor as a guide, as shown here. Ursa Minor can be located by using two of the stars in the nearby Plough as direction finders (see March 12th), Ursa Major itself being located over the northern horizon during October evenings as seen from mid-northern latitudes. The main stars of Ursa Minor, as well as Benetnash, the end star in the Plough 'handle' and the brilliant Vega in Lyra are also shown here as a guide to locating Draco.

Because of its location, winding around the north celestial pole, Draco is effectively lost to view for astronomers in the southern hemisphere, being completely invisible from latitudes south of 42°S and only visible in its entirety north of latitude 4°S. The best time to view this group is actually around July and August during which period it is located at or near the overhead point when viewed from mid-northern latitudes. During October evenings, observers in the northern United States, northern Europe and similar latitudes will see Draco high in the north western sky.

The stars that form the 'tail' of Draco lie in the area of sky adjoining Ursa Minor, while the 'head' of Draco can be found near the brilliant star Vega in the constellation Lyra which, for observers at mid-northern latitudes, can be seen high up in the north western sky during October evenings. If the sky is fairly dark and clear you should have little difficulty in tracing out this meandering constellation as it winds its way around the northern sky.

Draco appeared in the star catalogues of astronomers over two thousand years ago and depicts the dragon slain by Hercules during one of his twelve labours, the task set for Hercules being to steal some of the fruit from the golden apple tree gifted to Hera following her marriage to Zeus. The tree was planted on the slopes of Mount Atlas and was guarded by the Hesperides, the daughters of Atlas. However, as guardians they proved to be somewhat untrustworthy. They kept picking and eating the apples themselves, so a replacement guard was installed in the form of a dragon named Ladon. According to one legend, Ladon had a hundred heads and presented a rather fearsome sight to onlookers. Hercules was undaunted, however, and promptly killed the dragon with poisoned arrows before making off with several apples for himself! Hera placed the unfortunate dragon in the sky where it can be seen to this day in the form of the constellation Draco.

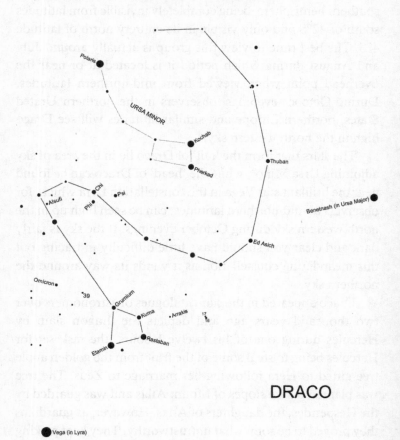

DRACO

October 10th

As we have seen (see September 16th) the position of the north celestial pole (currently marked by Polaris in Ursa Minor) is slowly changing, due to the fact that the Earth's axis of rotation is 'wobbling'. A consequence of this wobbling motion, known as precession, is that the north celestial pole was marked by the star Thuban at around the time the Egyptians were building the Pyramids. In other words, Thuban was the 'Pole Star' of the Ancient Egyptians. Shining at magnitude 3.67 from a distance of just over 300 light years, Thuban derives its name from the Arabic *'ra's al-tinnin'* meaning 'the Serpents Head'.

The brightest star in Draco is Etamin, a magnitude 2.24 orange giant whose light has taken 154 years to reach us. Etamin is one of the four stars forming the head of Draco, another being magnitude 2.79 Rastaban, a yellow supergiant located at a distance of 380 light years. The other two stars in the Dragon's head are Kuma (see October 11th) and the orange giant Grumium, which shines at magnitude 3.73 from a distance of 113 light years.

Deriving its name from the Arabic *'al-raqis'* meaning 'the Trotting Camel', the magnitude 4.97 Arrakis can be found close to the Dragon's head, its light having taken around 90 years to reach our planet. Shining from a distance of just 18.7 light years, making it one of the closer stars to us, is the magnitude 4.67 yellow star Alsufi. The magnitude 3.29 orange giant Ed Asich, lying at a distance of 101 light years, takes its name from the Arabic *'al-dhikh'* meaning 'the Male Hyena'.

October 11th

The faintest of the four stars forming the head of Draco is Kuma, one of the most easily-resolved double stars in the northern skies. Those with really keen eyesight may be able to split this pair with the naked eye, and binoculars bring them out well. At magnitudes 4.86 and 4.89, the two stars forming the Kuma system are almost identical in brightness.

Located on a line taken from Kuma, through Grumium and 39 Draconis, is Omicron Draconis, another double star which can be resolved in binoculars. The brighter magnitude 4.7 component has an orange tint which contrasts nicely with the blue of its magnitude 7.5 companion.

October 12th

Amongst the other binocular double stars in Draco which are worth checking out is Psi Draconis which is located near the middle of the Dragon's back, and forms a tiny triangle with the nearby Chi and Phi. Psi Draconis is formed from magnitude 4.6 and 5.8 yellowish and bluish stars which are easily resolved in binoculars, although a telescope may be needed to bring out their individual colours.

Our final port of call in Draco is the pretty, widely-spaced binocular double formed from the two stars 16 and 17 Draconis, located near the border of the constellation a little way from the Dragon's head. To locate this pair follow a line from Kuma, through Arrakis and on roughly as far again. The light from magnitude 5.53 star 16 Draconis has taken around 425 years to reach us, making it slightly more remote than 17 Draconis which, at magnitude 5.07, shines from a distance of 411 light years.

October 13th

Next we come to Pegasus (the Winged Horse), which is regarded as being the main autumnal constellation as seen from northern latitudes. According to legend Pegasus was the son of Neptune and Medusa. When Perseus slew Medusa (see

November 12th), Pegasus sprang from her decapitated body and flew away, eventually reaching Corinth where he was found by Bellerophon, the son of Glaucus. Bellerophon tamed Pegasus and used him in his fight against the fire-breathing monster Chimaera. After enjoying many other adventures with Pegasus, Bellerophon eventually decided to try and fly to Olympus, the home of the gods. On the way, Pegasus threw Bellerophon and completed the journey alone. Zeus, the ruler of Olympus and god of sky and thunder, eventually placed the winged horse in the heavens where we see him today.

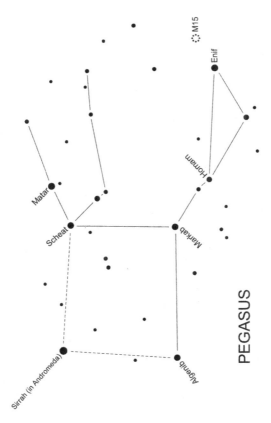

The constellation contains no really bright stars although, being located just to the north of the celestial equator, the Square of Pegasus is fairly easy to locate from almost anywhere. Pegasus is best placed for observation around October, at which time those at mid-northern latitudes can see the Winged Horse roughly two-thirds of the way up from the southern horizon to the overhead point. Backyard astronomers in the southern hemisphere need to look towards the north where they will see the Square above the northern horizon. The entire constellation can be seen from latitudes north of 54°S and, once the Square of Pegasus has been identified, the rest of the group can be picked out trailing away towards the west.

October 14th

The first interesting point to note is that Sirrah, the star marking the north-eastern corner of the Square, is actually a member of the adjacent constellation Andromeda (see October 31st), and is only 'borrowed' to complete the Square of Pegasus on star charts.

To the south of Sirrah, and denoting the south-eastern corner of the Square, can be found the magnitude 2.83 star Algenib, the name of which is derived from the Arabic *'al-janb'* for 'wing' or 'side'. Algenib shines from a distance of around 390 light years. Marking the south-western corner of the Square, and situated in an area of sky devoid of bright stars, is magnitude 2.49 Markab, the light from which has taken around 130 years to reach us. The name of this star is derived from the Arabic *'mankib al-faras'* meaning 'the Horse's Shoulder' whilst that of the red giant Scheat, located at the north-western corner of the Square, comes from the Arabic *'al-saq'* meaning 'the Shin'. The reddish glow of Scheat can be detected in binoculars, the light from this magnitude 2.44 star having set off on its journey towards us nearly 200 years ago.

October 15th
Pegasus lies in a fairly barren area of sky, and it is an interesting exercise to try to count the number of stars you can detect with the naked eye within the Square. Those with really keen eyesight may be able to spot around two dozen, although dark, moonless skies are essential for the best results.

October 16th
The three stars Homam, Matar and Enif lie to the west of the Square of Pegasus. The origins of these names are all uncertain, that of magnitude 3.41 Homam possibly derived from the Arabic for 'the Lucky Stars of the Hero' and that of the magnitude 2.93 yellow giant Matar probably originating in the Arabic for 'rain'.

The brightest star in Pegasus, and marking the horse's head, is Enif, the roots of the name possibly lying in the Arabic *'anf'* meaning 'nose', although Arabic astronomers themselves sometimes referred to this star as the horse's mouth. Shining with a magnitude of 2.38, Enif is fairly remote, its light having taken something like seven centuries to reach us.

October 17th
A little to the north-west of Enif can be found the beautiful globular star cluster M15, discovered by the Italian astronomer Jean Dominique Maraldi in 1746. Located at a distance of over 33,000 light years, this object was described by the German astronomer Heinrich Ludwig D'Arrest as a: *'Most magnificent cluster, very bright...'*

With a magnitude of 6.2, the M15 cluster lies just below

the threshold of naked eye visibility and is an easy target for binoculars or a small telescope. The accompanying finder chart should prove useful in helping to locate the cluster by star hopping your way north westwards from the guide star Enif. However, M15 is bright enough to be detected by carefully sweeping the area with a pair of binoculars, providing the sky is dark and clear. Once found, the cluster should appear as a small diffuse patch of light, telescopes being needed to resolve any individual stars.

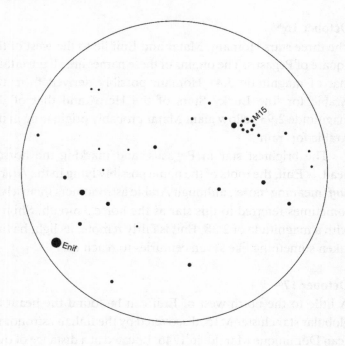

October 18th

Lying immediately to the west of Pegasus is the tiny constellation Equuleus (the Little Horse), introduced by

Ptolemy on his list of 48 constellations drawn up in the 2nd century AD. Taking the form of a tiny trapezium of faint stars, it is by no means conspicuous although it can be made out with the naked eye provided the sky is really dark and clear. Using the star Enif in Pegasus (see October 16th) as a guide, as shown on the chart, carefully sweeping the area with binoculars should help you resolve the triangle formed from the three stars Kitalpha, Gamma and Delta, from which the rest of this faint constellation can be picked out. Equuleus is visible in its entirety from anywhere north of latitude 77°S, putting it within the view of observers in almost any inhabited part of the world.

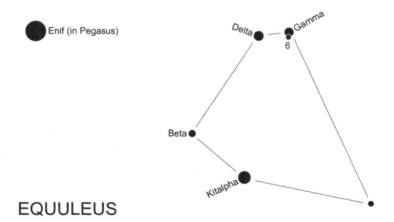

EQUULEUS

October 19th

The brightest star in Equuleus is Kitalpha, its name derived from the Arabic *'qit at al-faras'* meaning 'the Section of the Horse'. Shining with a magnitude of 3.92, Kitalpha lies at a distance of around 190 light years. Somewhat closer to us is magnitude 4.47 Delta Equulei, the light from which has taken just 60 years to reach us. Beta Equulei shines at magnitude 5.16 from a distance of 330 light years.

The white giant Gamma forms a wide double with the magnitude 6.07 star 6 Equulei. Gamma shines at magnitude 4.70, its light having set off towards us 118 years ago. However, the relationship between Gamma and 6 Equulei is nothing more than a line of sight effect, the latter being located at a distance of around 440 light years, nearly four times that of Gamma. Provided the sky is exceptionally dark, clear and moonless, you may be able to pick out the faint glow from 6 Equulei and so resolve this pair with the naked eye, although you will probably need a pair of binoculars to bring out both stars.

October 20th

Seven o'clock sounds from city-wards, and the deep, low vibrations come tremulous to the ear, as it were the passing bell for the dead hours. A gloomy pall shuts out the stars; from it the rain descends in torrents, bespattering the sheet whereon I write. The grayness of the sky is not uniform, but is broken up into light and shade, for the moon is upon the full, and her light illumines those regions where the cloud-pall is least opaque. The luminous places serve but to impart a weird grandeur of contrast to this earth-dropping sky, so absolutely starless and so merely suggestively moonlit. Autumn's storms are now set in, foully conspiring to eclipse the glories of the starry heavens. In this expansive county of Yorkshire, as in much of Western Europe, have there been severe rains; and disasters by sea multiply with this saddening relapse from September's brilliance. A boisterous, unastronomic October night is this! Adieu, then, to its gray sky, to its hollow-sounding blasts, and its wildly driving rain. Night waits for her companion stars, but waits in vain.

*

October 21st

Orion, returning to us for the winter, has now stepped proudly into the night sky by eleven o'clock, and balances himself on his right foot on my east-south-east horizon. Castor and Pollux, the Twins, are conspicuous by half-past nine, when Betelgeuse and Bellatrix, the giant's shoulders, are visible.

October 22nd

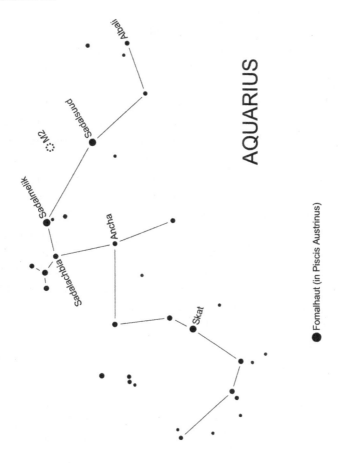

The constellation Aquarius (the Water Carrier) can be found to the south of Pegasus. An imaginary line drawn from Scheat through Markab, both in the Square of Pegasus, and projected southwards will eventually lead you to the bright star Fomalhaut in the constellation Piscis Austrinus (see October 26th). Roughly three-quarters of the way from Markab and Fomalhaut the line passes immediately to the east of the star Skat in Aquarius. Once Skat has been identified, you should have no problem tracing out the rest of Aquarius. The whole of this constellation can be seen from anywhere south of latitude 65°N, with only portions of the group being visible from the northernmost reaches of Russia, Europe, Canada and Alaska.

There are several legends attached to this constellation and the character it depicts, one of which identifies it as Ganymede, the son of King Tros of Troy. Jupiter had numerous attendants to serve him, one of which was Hebe, the goddess of youth, her duties including the pouring out of wine and nectar for the gods. Unfortunately, Hebe had to resign her office following a fall and Jupiter needed to replace her. Assuming the form of an eagle, Jupiter set off on his mission and, as he flew over the earth, noticed a beautiful youth tending sheep on a hillside. He promptly gathered him up in his talons and whisked him off to Olympus. The captured youth was Ganymede who, following his abduction and subsequent relocation in Olympus, was instructed in his duties by Jupiter, one of which was to pour wine and nectar for the gods.

October 23rd

The brightest star in Aquarius is the magnitude 2.90 yellow supergiant Sadalsuud which shines from a distance of around 540 light years. Although the precise meaning of the name is not known, it probably derives from the Arabic *'sa'd al-su'ud'* which may translate as 'the Luckiest of the Lucky (Stars)'. A short way to the north east of Sadalsuud is the magnitude 2.95 Sadalmelik, another yellow supergiant whose light has taken around 520 years to reach us. Sadalmelik probably derives its name from the Arabic *'sa'd al-malik'* which translates as 'the Lucky (Stars) of the King'. Shining with a magnitude of 3.86 from a distance of 160 light years, Sadalachbia appears to take its name from the Arabic for 'the Lucky (Stars) of the Tents'.

Lying at a similar distance to Sadalachbia is Skat, its name derived from the Arabic *'al-saq'* meaning 'the Shin'. The light from Albali, located at the westernmost point of the constellation, has taken just over 200 years to reach us, a little longer than the orange giant Ancha which lies at a distance of 190 light years. These two stars derive their names from the Arabic for 'swallower' and 'hip' respectively.

October 24th

Discovered by the Italian astronomer Jean Dominique Maraldi in 1746, and located a little to the north of the star Sadalsuud, is the globular cluster Messier 2. Lying at a distance of 37,500 light years, and with a diameter estimated to be around 175 light years, M2 is one of the largest known globular clusters.

M2 lies a short way to the north of Sadalsuud and forms a right-angled triangle with this star and the nearby Sadalmelik. With an overall magnitude of 6.3 this object is easily seen in binoculars, through which it will appear as a fuzzy ball of light with no individual stars resolved. However, even a small telescope may reveal some of the individual stars around the edge of the cluster. The finder chart shows how to star hop your way to M2 using the prominent guide star Sadalsuud as your starting point.

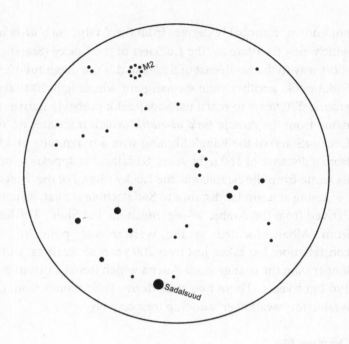

October 25th

The stars come out early as October closes in. By half-past five Vega is glittering not far to the west of the meridian, and even Deneb, at the head of the Cross, is clearly visible. Arcturus, that beauteous star of eve, shines in splendid solitariness in the west. How Arcturus does linger in the western sky! It is like a sparkling jewel on the hem of the rich robe of the departing day.

October 26th

As mentioned previously (see October 22nd) Fomalhaut, the brightest star in the constellation Piscis Austrinus (the Southern Fish) can be located by following a line drawn from Scheat through Markab, both in the Square of Pegasus. Projecting this line southwards will eventually lead you to Fomalhaut. For observers at mid-northern latitudes, October evenings reveal Piscis Austrinus lying low over the southern horizon, and managing to see it at all presents something of a challenge unless the sky is particularly dark and clear. However, the entire group is visible from anywhere south of latitude 53°N, and those observing from Argentina, South Africa, Australia and similar latitudes during October evenings will see brilliant Fomalhaut at or near the overhead point.

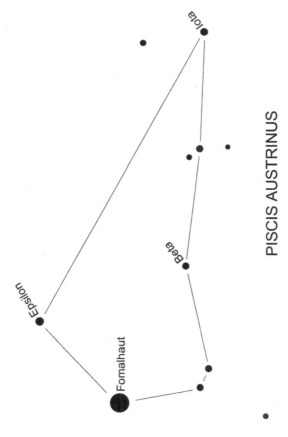

The line from the Square of Pegasus passes through Aquarius (the Water Carrier) and old star charts depict the Southern Fish lying on its back drinking the liquid being poured by Aquarius. Echoing this is the fact that the name of this star is derived from the Arabic *'fam al-hut al-janubi'* meaning 'the Mouth of the Southern Fish'. Fomalhaut itself shines at magnitude 1.17 from a distance of 25 light years.

The rest of the stars forming Piscis Austrinus are all relatively faint in comparison, the next brightest being magnitude 4.18 Epsilon Piscis Austrini, located just to the north west of Fomalhaut and whose light has taken nearly 500 years to reach us. Marking the westernmost point of the constellation is Iota, a white giant star shining at magnitude 4.35 from a distance of just over 200 light years.

Apart from picking out the constellation itself, Piscis Austrinus offers little to the backyard astronomer, although Beta Piscis Austrini is worth a closer look. Beta is a double star with pale yellow and white components of magnitudes 4.4 and 7.9 which can be resolved in small telescopes.

October 27th

Lying immediately to the south of Piscis Austrinus is the constellation Grus (the Crane), shown here with the bright star Fomalhaut as a guide. The whole of Grus is visible from latitudes south of 33°N and observers at mid-southern latitudes will see the constellation at or near the overhead point around this time of year.

This is another of the groups introduced by the Dutch navigators and explorers Pieter Dirkszoon Keyser and Frederick de Houtman following their expedition to the East Indies in the 1590s (see May 10th). It depicts the long-necked bird, a crane, and first appeared on the celestial globe produced

by Petrus Plancius in 1598 as well as in the star atlas
Uranometria produced by Johann Bayer in 1603.

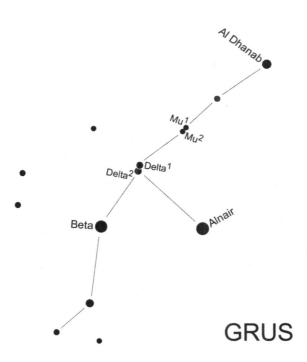

The brightest star in Grus is bluish-white Alnair, which
shines with a magnitude of 1.73 from a distance of 101 light

years. This star derives its name from an abbreviation of the Arabic for 'the Bright One from the Fish's Tail' alluding to the fact that Grus was formed from stars located immediately to the south of Piscis Austrinus and which originally formed the tail of the Southern Fish. The name of the magnitude 3.00 Al Dhanab, a star which takes its name from the Arabic for 'the Tail', is another reminder that this region once formed the tail of Piscis Austrinus. The light from Al Dhanab has taken just over 210 years to reach us making it somewhat more distant than the magnitude 2.07 red giant star Beta Gruis which shines from a distance of around 175 light years.

The two stars Delta[1] and Delta[2] form a wide naked eye optical double. The magnitude 4.12 red giant Delta[2] shines from a distance of 330 light years, around 20 light years further away than the magnitude 3.97 yellow giant Delta[1] the light from which has taken around 310 years to reach us. The two yellow giant stars Mu[1] and Mu[2], located a little way to the north west of the Delta pair, form another naked eye double. Although these two stars both lie at roughly 270 light years away, observation has shown that they are not gravitationally linked and simply happen to lie in more or less the same line of sight as seen from our planet.

October 28th

Another of the constellations introduced by the Dutch navigators and explorers Pieter Dirkszoon Keyser and Frederick de Houtman following their expedition to the East Indies in the 1590s (see May 10th), Indus (the Indian) represents an American native Indian. Indus lies immediately to the south west of the constellation Grus and is visible in its entirety from latitudes south of 15°N. The star Alnair in Grus (see October 27th) is shown here as a guide, along with the star

Peacock in the constellation Pavo (see August 6th) which can be found to the south west of Indus.

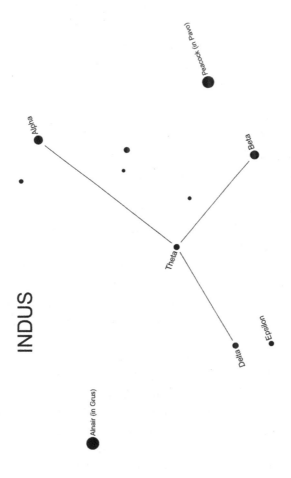

None of the stars in Indus are particularly bright and none are named. The brightest is Alpha Indi, an orange giant shining at magnitude 3.11 from a distance of 98 light years. Another orange giant is magnitude 3.67 Beta Indi, the light from which set off towards us over 600 years ago. The somewhat undistinguished form of Indus is completed by magnitude 4.39 Theta and magnitude 4.40 Delta, two stars of almost identical brightness. Of particular note is the magnitude 4.69 Epsilon Indi which, at a distance of just 11.8 light years, is one of the nearest of the naked eye stars.

October 29th

Our final port of call during this visit to the stars of the southern hemisphere, before we once again divert our attentions to the northern skies, is the constellation Microscopium (the Microscope) which was devised by the French astronomer Nicolas Louis de Lacaille to represent the microscope. It takes the form of a tiny elongated rectangle of faint stars located immediately to the west / north west of the trio of constellations Piscis Austrinus, Grus and Indus. The chart shows the group along with the four stars Iota Piscis Austrini, Alnair and Al Dhanab (both in Grus) and Alpha Indi as a guide to locating this faint constellation.

The whole of Microscopium can be seen from latitudes south of 45°N, although none of the stars in the constellation are in any way prominent, the brightest being the yellow giant Gamma Microscopii which shines at a dismal magnitude 4.67 from a distance of around 230 light years. This is flanked by magnitude 4.71 Epsilon to the east and magnitude 4.89 Alpha to the south west. Theta[1] and Iota complete the group.

By all means take time out to locate and identify Microscopium, if only to congratulate yourself in doing so. Patrick Moore once described this constellation as being '...totally unremarkable...' This writer agrees with him.

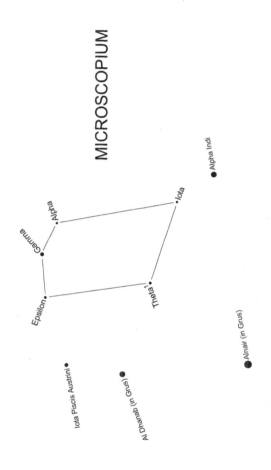

October 30th

During the evenings at this time of year observers at mid-northern latitudes will see the constellation Andromeda high in the sky, a little way to the south of the overhead point and stretching out from the north eastern corner of the Square of Pegasus (see October 13th). The whole of Andromeda is visible from latitudes north of 37°S, the consequence of which is that from South Africa, the southern reaches of South America and most of Australia, this group will be seen fairly low down towards the north. Hence it may well be lost to view unless the sky close to the northern horizon is clear and free of any light pollution.

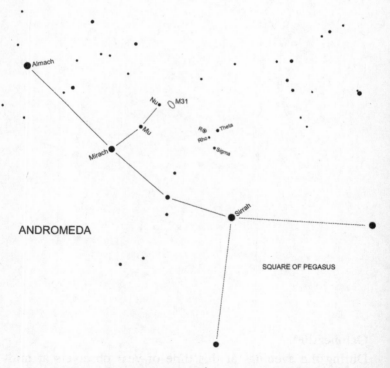

According to legend, Andromeda was the daughter of King Cepheus and Queen Cassiopeia of Ethiopia. Such was

Andromeda's beauty that her mother boasted of it far and wide, even claiming that she was fairer than the Nereids, the nymphs of the sea. This angered Poseidon, the god of the sea, who sent a ferocious monster (see December 2nd) to terrorise the country. Not at all pleased with the situation, the hapless King Cepheus appealed to the gods for a solution, following which he was commanded to offer his daughter Andromeda as a sacrifice to the creature. Andromeda was chained to a rock to await her fate, although help was at hand in the shape of Perseus, who was passing by at the time following his beheading of Medusa the Gorgon (see November 12th). Perseus slew the monster and released Andromeda, claiming her for his bride. The Greek goddess Athene eventually placed Andromeda in the sky, close to Perseus and her parents Cepheus and Cassiopeia, where she can be seen to this day.

October 31st

The three main stars in the group – Sirrah, Mirach and Almach – are all of roughly the same apparent brightness. Sirrah, whose name is derived from the Arabic *'surrat al-faras'* meaning 'the Horse's Navel', shines at magnitude 2.07 from a distance of 97 light years. The origins of its name hark back to a time when Sirrah was considered as being a member of the adjoining constellation Pegasus, the Winged Horse. Somewhat more distant is Mirach. Located to the east of Sirrah, and lying at a distance of around 197 light years the name of this magnitude 2.07 red giant star is taken from the Arabic *'al-mi'zar'* meaning 'the Girdle' or 'the Loin Cloth'.

Further still to the east is the orange giant Almach which forms one of the most beautiful double stars in the night sky. Shining from a distance of a little over 350 light years, the tints of the magnitude 2.30 and 5.10 yellowish and greenish-blue components of Almach are easily discernible in small telescopes.

NOVEMBER

November 1st

And now has entered the Month of Fogs; in England's cycle of the seasons a world-famous month. What profound despair it brings to the northern sky-student! But November is at least honest, and that is more than can be said for 'merrie' May (See May 1st).

November 2nd

By far the most famous object in Andromeda is Messier 31, more popularly known as the Great Andromeda Galaxy. This can be located by following a line from Mirach through the two fainter stars Mu and Nu and can be seen as a faint and extended misty patch of light just to the west of Nu. This huge island universe lies at a distance of around 2.5 million light years and, with the possible exception of M33 (see November 6th), is the most distant object visible to the unaided eye.

Both the Andromeda Galaxy and our own Milky Way Galaxy are spiral in shape, although the Andromeda Galaxy is roughly half as big again as our own. To the naked eye this object reveals itself as a faint misty patch and has often been described as being cloud-like in appearance. As long ago as the 10th century the Persian astronomer Al-Sufi noted it as being ' ...*a little Cloud... which belongs to the three (stars) which are above the girdle...*' and in 1614, the German astronomer Simon Mayr described it as resembling '...*the light of a burning candle, shining through translucent horn, when seen at night from afar.*'

Prior to the 20th century the Andromeda Galaxy, along

with other objects of its type, had been thought of as a gas cloud located within the confines of the Milky Way. In the 1920s, however, the American astronomer Edwin Hubble proved that M31 was a galaxy in its own right and was located outside our Milky Way. By proving the existence of galaxies beyond our own, Hubble's work dramatically altered our understanding and concept of the universe.

Unfortunately, because the galaxy lies at an angle to us, the full beauty of the spiral shape is lost. When seen through binoculars M31 appears as an elliptical blur of light and small telescopes fare little better. Larger telescopes may reveal a bright oval nucleus and traces of the spiral arms. However, perhaps the greatest satisfaction in viewing the Andromeda Galaxy is knowing what it is. It certainly impressed Joseph Elgie and, although his words were written before the work of Edwin Hubble, they still have relevance...

...the great Nebula of Andromeda will be readily found. This object is sunk to an appalling depth in space, and is gaseous in nature, much brighter in the centre than at the edges. It is very weird-looking; a vast Solar System, probably, in process of making. Its glow seems to palpitate as I gaze at it tonight. And what an uncanny feeling one has that there is something very mysterious behind it..

So, out yonder in abysmal space, where the Andromeda nebula dimly glows to-night, one can conceive a gathering of the forces of star-matter for ever pushing outwards the sun-spangled borders of our universe.

November 3rd

Andromeda plays host to the Mira-type (see December 4th) variable star R Andromedae which can be found a little way to the south west of M31, lying very close to the tiny triangle of stars formed from Theta, Rho and Sigma Andromedae.

R Andromedae varies between magnitudes 5.8 and 14.9 over a period of 409 days. When at its brightest it can just be made out with the naked eye and its reddish tint should be easily identifiable in binoculars. However, bear in mind that, as is the case with other stars of this type, if you search and have difficulty in finding it, this may well be because it is at or near minimum magnitude. With a little patience you will, over the course of time, see R Andromedae come into view as it brightens, from when you can watch it attain maximum magnitude before decreasing in brightness again. Although much of its cycle can be followed through binoculars, you will need a telescope to keep it in view when at or near its dimmest. Another definite target for the backyard astronomer!

November 4th
During November evenings, the diminutive constellation of Triangulum (the Triangle) can be seen immediately south of a line between Mirach and Almach in the neighbouring Andromeda. Almach is shown here as a guide, along with the bright star Hamal in the neighbouring constellation Aries (see November 9th). From southern locations such as South Africa, Australia and New Zealand this group can be seen over the northern horizon a little way above Andromeda, the whole of the constellation being visible from latitudes north of 53°S.

Triangulum is unusual in that it is one of the small number of constellations that actually resembles the object that it is supposed to depict, its three main stars forming a small, elongated triangle which, once spotted, is unmistakeable. Alternative names for this tiny constellation include Delta, or Deltoton, by which it was known to Greek and Roman astronomers due to the resemblance of the constellation to the Greek capital letter Delta (Δ). The shape of the group led to it being associated with Egypt and, in particular, with the delta of the Nile. The Latin author Hyginus recorded that the group was considered by some astronomers to have a shape not unlike that of the island of Sicily, home of Ceres, the goddess of agriculture, the island originally being known as Trinacria due to its three promontories.

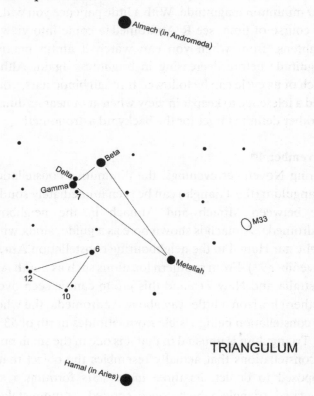

November 5th

The brightest star in Triangulum is the magnitude 3.00 white giant Beta Trianguli which lies at a distance of around 125 light years. Slightly fainter is Metallah, the name of this magnitude 3.42 star deriving from the Arabic *'al-muthal-lath'* meaning 'the Triangle'. The light from Metallah has taken a little over 60 years to reach us. Magnitude 4.03 Gamma Trianguli shines from a distance of 112 light years. Delta and 7 Trianguli both lie close to Gamma, this trio of stars forming a pretty little group when viewed through binoculars.

November 6th

Triangulum is home to the spiral galaxy M33, also know as the Triangulum Spiral Galaxy or Pinwheel Galaxy. Discovered by the French astronomer Charles Messier in 1764, and described by him as '*...a whitish light of almost even brightness...*', this object is the third-largest member of what is known as the Local Group, a collection of galaxies of which our own Milky Way Galaxy and the Great Andromeda Galaxy (see November 2nd) are also members.

Lying at a distance of around 3 million light years, M33 has a tiny nucleus, or central region, together with huge sweeping spiral arms. This gives the galaxy a very low surface brightness resulting in it being easily blotted out by moonlight or any form of light pollution. The overall magnitude of M33 is around 6 and, provided the sky is exceptionally dark and clear, you may just be able to make out the galaxy with the naked eye. Located a short way to the north west of the star Metallah, you should be able to pick up its faint glow through binoculars by following the line of stars from Metallah as shown on the accompanying finder chart. The rule is to look for a faint and extensive patch of light rather than a more concentrated light source. If you can mount your binoculars on a camera tripod that will keep them steady and should help in picking out faint diffuse objects such as the Triangulum Spiral Galaxy.

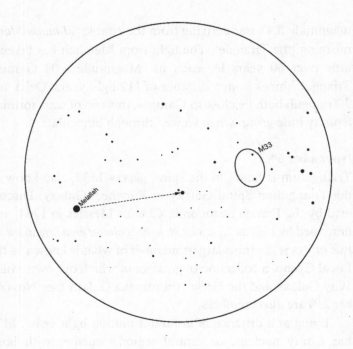

November 7ᵗʰ

While you're looking at Triangulum, check out the much-smaller triangle of fainter stars located just to the southeast of the group. This is Triangulum Minus and was introduced to star charts by the Polish astronomer Johannes Hevelius in 1687, at which time he renamed the main constellation Triangulum Majus.

Often erroneously named Triangulum Minor, Triangulum Minus was created from the southern parts of his Triangula (the plural form of Triangulum) from the fifth-magnitude stars 6, 10 and 12 Trianguli. This tiny triangle of faint stars is no longer recognised as an individual constellation on modern star charts.

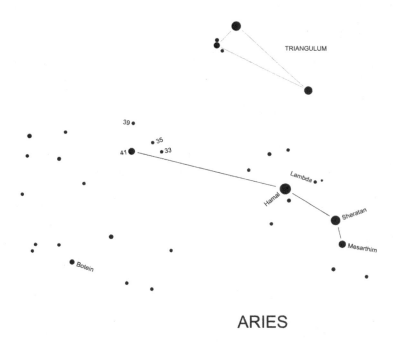

ARIES

Located immediately to the south of Triangulum is the small but well-defined constellation Aries (the Ram) and, although not particularly prominent, the bent line of three stars that form the head of the Ram lie in an otherwise isolated area of sky. The constellation is shown here along with the main stars in neighbouring Triangulum as a guide to identification. Aries is completely visible from latitudes north of 59°S putting it within visual reach of backyard astronomers across the world.

The legend behind this constellation is intriguing, Aries being associated with the legend of Jason and his quest to seek out the Golden Fleece. The marriage of King Athamas and his wife Nephele was not a happy one, and Athamas decided to turn his attentions towards Ino, daughter of King Cadmus of Thebes. However, Ino turned out to be a rather wicked stepmother, taking a disliking to her two step-children Phrixus and Helle. She hatched a plot to have them killed which, naturally, prompted the children to try and escape. This they duly did, with the help of their mother Nephele, on a magical winged ram with a golden fleece. Unfortunately, during the flight Helle was frightened by the experience and fell off the ram, plunging to her death in the channel between Europe and Asia, the Dardanelles (which was named the Hellespont by the Greeks in her memory). Her brother Phrixus, however, survived and eventually landed safely in Colchis. Phrixus sacrificed the ram to Zeus (perhaps displaying a certain amount of ingratitude towards the poor animal), who promptly placed it amongst the stars where we can see it to this day.

The fleece came into the possession of King Aeetes of Colchis who hung it on a sacred tree guarded by a fearsome serpent. When Jason and the Argonauts came in search of the fleece King Aeetes was reluctant to hand it over. However, with the help of Aeetes' daughter Medea, Jason managed to avoid the attentions of the serpent, retrieve the fleece and make his escape.

November 9th

Shining at magnitude 2.01 from a distance of 66 light years the orange giant Hamal is the brightest star in Aries and takes its name from the Arabic *'al-hamal'* meaning 'the Lamb'. Sheratan lies even closer, the light from this magnitude 2.64 star having set off on its journey towards us 59 years ago. Botein derives its name from the Arabic *'al-butain'* meaning 'the Little Belly', this magnitude 4.35 yellow giant star lying at a distance of 170 light years.

November 10th

Mesarthim is a lovely double star, its magnitude 4.2 and 4.4 white components easily resolvable in small telescopes. The fact that Mesarthim is a double star was first noted by the English philosopher and astronomer Robert Hooke in 1664. Lambda Arietis, located immediately to the west of Hamal, is another double star. The magnitude 4.8 and 7.4 components of Lambda are just resolvable through binoculars and a small telescope will bring them out well.

November 11th

In 1613 the Dutch celestial cartographer Petrus Plancius introduced the tiny constellation Musca Borealis (the Northern Fly) on a celestial globe produced by him in 1613 (see May 10th). Formed from the four stars now designated 33, 35, 39 and 41 Arietis, Musca Borealis was located a little way to the north east of Hamal. Plancius originally named this constellation Apes (the Bee) following which it was the subject of several name changes, including that by the German astronomer Jakob Bartsch, who named it Vespa (the Wasp) on his celestial map published in 1624, and Johannes Hevelius who renamed it Musca (the Fly) in 1687. It eventually became Musca Borealis to avoid confusion with the southern constellation Musca Australis (the Southern Fly) which existed at the time, and the name of which has subsequently been reduced to Musca.

November 12th

Located to the east of Andromeda, the constellation of Perseus depicts the legendary Greek hero of the same name. The constellation is shown here along with the star Almach in Andromeda as a guide to locating this famous group. From locations in northern Australia, South Africa and central South America most of the constellation will be seen over the northern horizon, albeit very low down in the sky, and at least portions of Perseus will be permanently hidden from view from latitudes south of these.

Perseus was the son of Zeus and Danae, she being the daughter of King Acrisius of Argos. Acrisius had been warned by an oracle that he would one day be killed by his grandson so, as a precaution, he imprisoned his daughter in a heavily-guarded tower in order to keep away any prospective suitors. However, her plight was noticed by Jupiter who decided to visit her. One thing led to another and eventually Danae bore Jupiter a son, who she named Perseus. Naturally this angered Acrisius who promptly placed Danae and her son into a wooden chest and threw them out to sea at the mercy of the elements. Danae prayed to the gods to help her.

The prayers seem to have been heeded as the chest was eventually washed up on the shores of the island of Seriphos. King Polydectes of Seriphos took both mother and child into his care and raised Perseus as his own.

Polydectes fell in love with Danae and wanted to marry her although she did not return his affections. This angered Polydectes and he insisted she obey. Perseus stood up for his mother and, to get rid of him, Polydectes sent Perseus on a mission to prove his bravery. The mission was to slay Medusa, one of the three Gorgons. This wasn't a straightforward task, however, as Medusa had serpents instead of hair and anyone looking at her would instantly be turned into stone. However, Perseus accepted the challenge and the gods, who had looked over Perseus throughout his childhood, decided to lend him a hand. Pluto lent Perseus a magic helmet which rendered the wearer invisible and Mercury gave him his own winged sandals which gave Perseus the power of rapid flight. To round off the assistance, Minerva gave Perseus her polished shield.

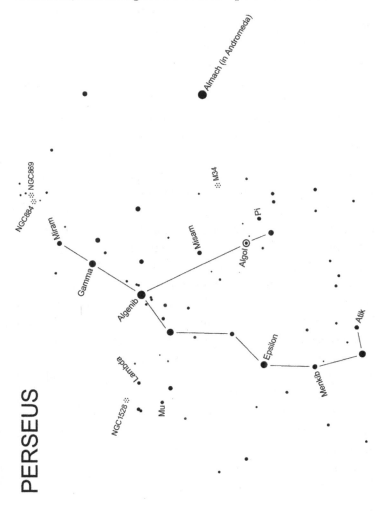

Perseus set off and eventually reached the home of the Graeae, three horrible sisters who shared one eye and one tooth between them, passing them from one to another to use in turn. The Graeae were the only living beings who knew where the Gorgons lived. In order to get this information from them, Perseus approached them wearing the helmet given to him by Pluto and took the eye from the sisters, offering it back if they told him where he could locate Medusa. This they did and Perseus continued his mission.

He eventually arrived at his destination and, wary of not being able to look at the Gorgons directly in fear of being turned to stone, used Minerva's shield as a mirror to locate Medusa. Without looking at her directly, and using only her reflection, he came across the sleeping Medusa and promptly cut her head off. Holding it behind his back to avoid looking at it he rapidly departed back towards Seriphos. On his way he came across the princess Andromeda, daughter of King Cepheus and Queen Cassiopeia, chained to a rock (see October 30th) awaiting sacrifice to a sea monster. In the best Greek tradition, Perseus swooped down and killed the monster, freeing Andromeda and taking her to safety. He married Andromeda and took her back to Seriphos. Hearing that Polydectes was still ill-treating Danae, he showed him the head of Medusa, turning him into a rock. Perseus then returned to his native Argos where King Acrisius had been imprisoned by a usurper to the throne. Perseus disposed of the unlawful usurper and freed Acrisius from his prison, the King benefiting at the hands of the very person he had come to fear. However, the decree of the oracle was always going to be fulfilled. During an athletics contest, a discus thrown by Perseus accidentally hit and killed his grandfather.

After a long and prosperous life Perseus died and was

placed among the stars alongside his wife Andromeda and his in-laws Cepheus and Cassiopeia. The sea monster sent to kill Andromeda is also nearby, represented by the constellation Cetus (see December 2nd). To complete the scenario, the head of Medusa is depicted by the star Algol (see November 14th).

November 13th

The brightest star in Perseus is the white supergiant Algenib, its name being derived from the Arabic *'al-janb'* meaning 'the Side or Flank'. Algenib shines at magnitude 1.79 from a distance of around 580 light years. Located at the southern end of Perseus is Atik, a magnitude 3.84 blue supergiant whose light has taken over 850 years to reach us. Just to the north of Atik we find Menkib, the light from this magnitude 3.98 star having set off towards us around 1,200 years ago.

A little to the north of Algenib is the magnitude 2.91 yellow giant star Gamma Persei, which shines from a distance of around 250 light years. Miram is the northernmost of the brighter stars in Perseus, this magnitude 3.77 orange giant being located at a distance of nearly 900 light years. Relatively close in comparison is magnitude 3.79 Misam, the light from this yellow giant star having set off on its journey towards us just 113 years ago.

November 14th

Algol is one of the most famous variable stars in the entire sky. Its name is derived from the Arabic *'ra's al-ghul'* meaning 'the Demon's Head' and, according to legend, depicts the severed head of Medusa the Gorgon held by Perseus. Algol's changes in brightness may have been known to Arabic astronomers around the 10th century, although the earliest recorded observations of its variability were made by the Italian astronomer Geminiano Montanari. In 1667, Montanari noticed that Algol was shining at less than its usual brightness, his subsequent series of observations confirming that Algol was indeed variable. However, it was the astronomer John Goodricke who made the first accurate measurements of its period of variability. It was also Goodricke who first suggested that Algol was a binary and that the variations in brightness were due to the occasional eclipse of a brighter star by a fainter companion.

Algol is the prototype eclipsing binary and, at a distance of 93 light years, is the closest object of its kind. As Goodricke stated, it is indeed a system of two stars in orbit around each other, with one star considerably fainter than its companion. The plane of their orbit is almost exactly lined up with our position in space and the fainter star regularly passes in front of, or eclipses, its brighter companion. When this occurs, the overall light output from Algol decreases from magnitude 2.1 to 3.4 before climbing again. The entire sequence takes around 10 hours with a well-determined period between successive times of minimum brightness of 2.867 days (2 days, 20 hours, 48 minutes, 56 seconds). By making a series of random checks on Algol over several nights, you should eventually be able to detect its fluctuations from which point you can follow its changes in magnitude by comparing it to nearby stars.

...and the elements still conspire to hide the stars, as though they were envious of their radiant beauty. Scarce had I taken my notes of Perseus and Algol last night than the clouds rolled up, and this morning there was a thick mantle of snow.

November 15th

Discovered by Charles Messier in 1764, the open star cluster Messier 34 shines with an overall magnitude of 5.5 from a distance of around 1,500 light years. Messier noted this object as being: *'A cluster of small stars...'* while the German astronomer Johann Elert Bode described it as: *'A star cluster, visible to the naked eye.'*

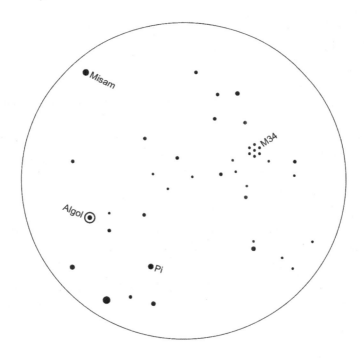

If the sky is really dark and clear you may be able to pick M34 up without any optical aid, although a pair of binoculars will make the search easier. Using the finder chart, you can star hop your way to the cluster working from the guide stars Algol, Misam and Pi Persei. Binoculars should show M34 as a distinct nebulous patch and even a small telescope will resolve some of the individual stars in this cluster.

November 16th

Located near the border between Perseus and the neighbouring constellation Cassiopeia, the two open star clusters NGC 869 and NGC 884 are visible to the naked eye under clear, dark skies. Collectively known as the Sword Handle Double Cluster, attention was drawn to them as long ago as the 2nd century AD by the Greek astronomer Ptolemy who referred to them as being: *'At the tip of the right hand (of Perseus) and is misty [nebulosa]'*

Both NGC 869 and NGC 884 are located around 7,500 light years away, their overall magnitudes being 4.4 (NGC 869) and 4.7 (NGC 884). Binoculars will show the clusters quite well and small telescopes will reveal the splendour of these two beautiful objects. Although they lie quite close to each other in the sky, a wide field of view is needed in order to see both clusters at once.

The Sword Handle Double Cluster lies in a rich section of the Milky Way and time spent carefully sweeping this area with binoculars or a telescope at low magnification is well rewarded. Why not try and follow the example of the English astronomer Thomas William Webb when he points out to us that: *'Night after night the telescope might be employed in sweeping over its magnificent crowd of stars.'*

November 17th

Located near the north eastern border of Perseus and shining with an overall magnitude of 6.4, the open star cluster NGC 1528 is a fairly easy target for the backyard astronomer. Binoculars will help you seek out this cluster which can be found a little to the north of Mu and Lambda Persei. These two stars are shown on the finder chart which should help you to star hop your way to NGC 1528. Through binoculars you will see the cluster as a dim and slightly oval patch of light although even a small telescope will resolve some of its individual member stars.

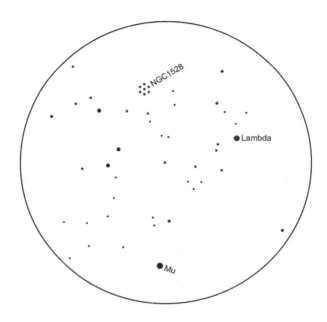

November 18th

We now move on to Camelopardalis (the Giraffe) which graces the far northern skies and is one of the faintest of the constellations. During November evenings, observers at mid-northern latitudes will see this somewhat obscure constellation a little way to the north east of the overhead point. In theory, the whole of Camelopardalis is visible from latitudes north of 5°S although, because this is such a dim constellation and contains no bright stars, observers around the equatorial regions will struggle to make it out at all unless the sky above the northern horizon is clear and free of light pollution.

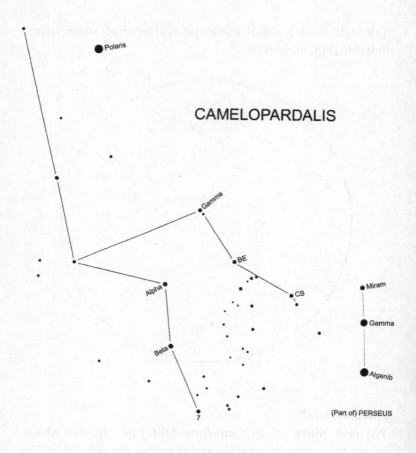

CAMELOPARDALIS

Polaris

Gamma

BE

Alpha

CS

Miram

Gamma

Beta

Algenib

7

(Part of) PERSEUS

*Very few amateur observers, I should imagine, have ever
definitely identified any star in the singularly barren-looking
constellation of Camelopardalis. The constellation, though it
sprawls over a large area of sky, actually requires a pretty clear
night before anything can be seen in it at all, so insignificant are
its stars.*

The stars forming Camelopardalis can be seen stretching away from the region of Polaris, and you should be able to pick out the constellation reasonably easily providing the sky is dark and free of moonlight. Polaris is shown here as a guide together with the trio of stars Algenib, Gamma and Miram in neighbouring Perseus (see November 12th).

Camelopardalis is long and straggling and indeed resembles the character it depicts, lying in an area of sky containing no bright stars and which consequently was left blank by Greek astronomers. Camelopardalis was originally devised by the Dutch astronomer Petrus Plancius in 1613 and was first depicted graphically in 1624 by the German astronomer Jacob Bartsch who included it in his star chart published that year.

The brightest star in Camelopardalis is Beta, a yellow supergiant which shines at magnitude 4.03 from a distance of around 850 light years. Slightly fainter is magnitude 4.26 Alpha while fainter still is Gamma, the light from this magnitude 4.59 star having set off towards us around 350 years ago.

Of particular interest in Camelopardalis is Kemble's Cascade. Named after the Franciscan Friar and amateur astronomer Lucian J. Kemble, this slightly-meandering chain of 20 or so unrelated stars, ranging between 5th and 9th magnitude, is a pretty sight when viewed through binoculars. Also known as the Waterfall, it stretches for a distance equal to around five times the diameter of a full Moon. To locate it, start from a point roughly a third of the way from the star BE towards CS. Kemble's Cascade can then be seen as a rambling line of stars extending roughly in the direction of the star 7, one of the southernmost stars in Camelopardalis. If the sky is fairly dark and moonless, and you sweep the area with binoculars, you should easily pick out this pretty collection of stars.

*

CASSIOPEIA

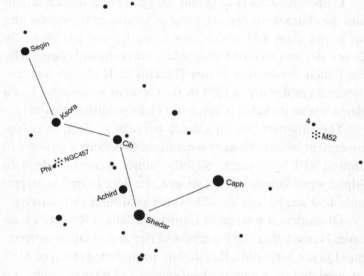

Along with the Plough (part of the larger constellation Ursa Major, the Great Bear) and Ursa Minor (the Little Bear), the prominent 'W' or 'M' formation of stars known as Cassiopeia completes the trio of conspicuous star groups that grace the far northern skies. The constellation represents the mythological

Queen Cassiopeia, wife of King Cepheus and mother to Andromeda, the beautiful maiden rescued by Perseus from the terrible sea monster (see November 12th).

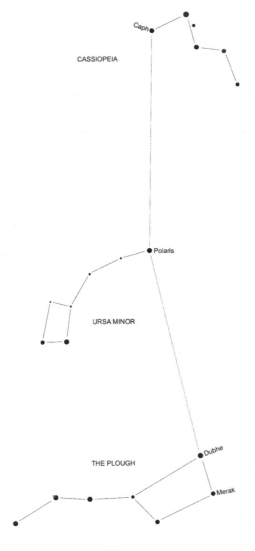

Cassiopeia stands out quite well and should be spotted fairly easily by observers at mid-northern latitudes, being located at or around the overhead point during autumn evenings. The entire constellation can be seen from locations to the north of latitude 12°S and portions of Cassiopeia can be seen from Australia, South Africa and all but the southern reaches of South America.

For observers in Great Britain and northern Europe, Cassiopeia is what we call a circumpolar constellation, which means that it never sets as seen from these latitudes. A general guide to locating Cassiopeia is to use the two end stars in the 'bowl' of the Plough, these being the two stars we use to locate Polaris, the Pole Star. If you follow the imaginary line from Merak, through Dubhe and past Polaris as shown on the opposite page, you will eventually arrive at the star Caph in Cassiopeia.

The constellation lies within the Milky Way and the whole area is seen to abound with stars. On a really clear night you should spot around fifty naked eye stars within the group, although binoculars will reveal many more scattered across this region of sky. Although most of these stars are below naked-eye visibility, their combined light produces the effect we call the Milky Way. While not usually very clear to city-dwellers, the Milky Way can be a superb sight when viewed under a really dark and moonless sky.

November 20ᵗʰ

Cassiopeia contains six prominent stars, the brightest of which is Cih whose light has taken around 550 years to reach us. Cih generally shines at magnitude 2.15, although this star is slightly variable and prone to sudden and unpredictable increases in brightness. Shedar, its name derived from the Arabic *'al-sadr'*, meaning 'the Breast', is a magnitude 2.24 orange giant star. Shining from a distance of around 220 light years, the orange tint of Shedar is easily seen in binoculars. Slightly fainter than Shedar is Caph, a white giant shining at magnitude 2.28 and lying at a distance of just 55 light years. Achird, located between Shedar and Cih, is a comparatively nearby star, its magnitude 3.46 glow reaching us from a distance of just 19.4 light years.

Marking the knee of Cassiopeia is magnitude 2.66 Ksora, the light from which set off on its journey towards us around a century ago. An alternative name for this star is Ruchbah, both names being derived from the Arabic *'rukbat dhat al-kursiy'* meaning 'the Knee of the Lady in the Chair'. The distinctive shape of Cassiopeia is completed by Segin which, at magnitude 3.35, shines from a distance of around 425 light years.

Facing due north, and looking high upward, the gaze meets with five stars of nearly equal brightness, in form resembling a sprawling capital "W". They make the principal outline of the constellation Cassiopeia, the Lady in the Chair. I cherish a kindly remembrance for Cassiopeia; it was the first star group I ever recognised, when, under almost heart-breaking difficulties, I was trying to learn the geography of the sky.

November 21st

Cassiopeia plays host to a number of open star clusters within reach of binoculars or a small telescope, one of which is Messier 52, discovered by Charles Messier in 1774. This collection of around 200 stars shines with an overall magnitude of 7.3 and is thought to lie at a distance in excess of 5,000 light years.

M52 can be found close to the star 4 Cassiopeiae and

located by star hopping through the field of stars from Caph as shown on the finder chart. A careful search should reveal this object as long as you remember to look for a small patch of light rather than an actual gathering of stars. Binoculars will show the cluster as a misty cloud although even a small telescope will resolve individual stars within this fine object.

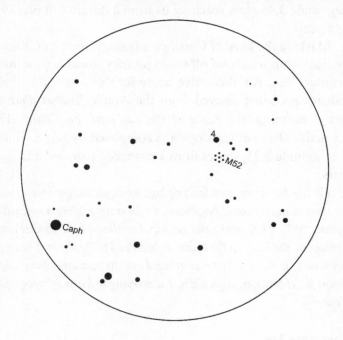

November 22nd

Discovered by William Herschel in 1787, and shining with an overall magnitude of 6.4, the open cluster NGC 457 lies adjacent to magnitude 4.95 Phi Cassiopeiae, forming a triangle with the two brighter stars Ksora and Cih. NGC 457 has been nicknamed the Owl Cluster due to the presence of two relatively bright stars which appear to lie on its edge. These two stars, the brighter of which is Phi, stand out quite well and give the distinct impression of being a pair of eyes staring back at you! Estimates as to the distance of NGC 457 vary, and this object may lie anywhere between 7,500 and 10,000 light years away. Whether the two stars alluded to are actually cluster members is open to debate, although the effect they give to the observer isn't!

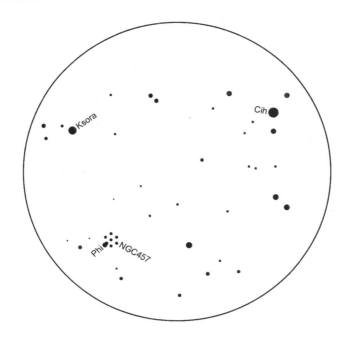

NGC 457 can be located with the finder chart which shows the field of faint stars in the region of Ksora and Cih together with Phi and the cluster itself. Binoculars will reveal NGC 457 as a distinct patch of light although even a small telescope should bring out a couple of dozen or so individual stars within the cluster.

November 23rd

Our next port of call is the large, but relatively inconspicuous constellation Cepheus. Following an imaginary line from Shedar through Caph, both in the neighbouring constellation Cassiopeia (see November 20th), as shown here will lead you to Cepheus.

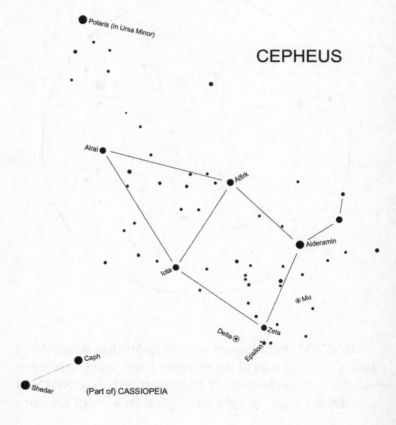

Like Cassiopeia, Cepheus is a circumpolar constellation for observers in Great Britain and northern Europe, meaning that it never sets as seen from these latitudes. As far as those observers further south are concerned, star gazers on or very close to the equator will see Cepheus low over the northern horizon around this time of year, although for those even further south most if not all of the constellation is permanently hidden from view.

Located slightly to the north west of the overhead point as seen from mid-northern latitudes, Cepheus is not the most conspicuous constellation. However, it does have a distinctive shape, even though it does not particularly resemble the character it depicts, this being King Cepheus, the husband of Queen Cassiopeia and father of the beautiful Princess Andromeda (see November 12th).

November 24th

The brightest star in Cepheus is Alderamin, marking the right shoulder of the legendary figure and shining at magnitude 2.45 from a distance of around 50 light years. To the north of Alderamin is the double star Alphirk which lies at a distance of nearly 700 light years and marks the waist of Cepheus. The magnitude 3.5 and 8.0 stars which make up the Alphirk system can be resolved through a small telescope which should reveal their blue and white tints.

A pair of binoculars will reveal a yellow-orange tint to the magnitude 3.21 orange giant Alrai, this star marking the left knee of Cepheus and whose light has taken around 45 years to reach us. Magnitude 3.50 Iota is another orange giant star although, being slightly fainter than Alrai, its colour is a little more difficult to make out. Completing the main form of Cepheus is the orange supergiant star Zeta Cephei which shines at magnitude 3.39, its light having set off on its journey towards us over 800 years ago.

November 25th

Although not an especially prominent constellation, Cepheus does contain a couple of objects of particular interest, these being the variable star Delta Cephei (see November 26th) and the red supergiant star Mu Cephei. Located near the southern border of Cepheus, estimates as to the distance of Mu Cephei vary, although it probably shines from somewhere between 2,500 and 3,000 light years away. This is one of the most luminous stars known and one of the largest stars visible to the naked eye. The astronomer William Herschel described this star as having '...*a very fine deep garnet colour*', leading to it being popularly known as Herschel's 'Garnet Star'. Mu Cephei is so huge that, if it was put in the place of our own Sun, its surface would extend out to well beyond the orbit of Jupiter.

The colour of Mu is very distinctive and therefore much easier to make out than other stars in Cepheus, and even modest optical aid, such as a pair of binoculars, will bring out the colour very well. Mu Cephei is a semi-regular variable, its magnitude ranging between around 3.40 and 5.10 over a period of between 2 and 2½ years. You can compare its brightness with the two nearby stars Zeta and Epsilon which shine at magnitudes 3.39 and 4.18 respectively.

From mid-northern latitudes Mu Cephei is circumpolar and can be seen all year round which means that, given clear skies, its cycle of variability can be continuously monitored. For backyard astronomers in the equatorial regions the star can be seen when favourably placed although for sky watchers south of central South America, central Africa and northern Australia this star never rises. However, if you can see it, the slightly-unpredictable Garnet Star is interesting and definitely well worth keeping an eye on!

November 26th

Also situated near the southern border of Cepheus is Delta Cephei, the prototype of perhaps the most famous class of variable star. Delta Cephei was the first star of this type to be recognised as a variable, this by the astronomer John Goodricke in 1784. Cepheids are short-period pulsating variables that are large and very luminous and can be seen over immense distances. Hundreds of Cepheids are known to astronomers, with periods ranging between as little as a day to around a couple of months or more. The period of Delta Cephei is 5.367 days, during which time it varies between magnitudes 3.5 and 4.3. As with Mu Cephei (see November 25th), you can compare the brightness of Delta with the two nearby stars Zeta and Epsilon.

An important relationship between the true luminosities and periods of Cepheid variables was announced by the American astronomer Henrietta Swan Leavitt in 1912. She was examining photographs of Cepheids in the Small Magellanic Cloud (see December 9th) when she noticed that Cepheids with shorter periods were always fainter than those whose periods of variability were longer. Because all the Cepheids under examination were at more or less the same distance from us, their apparent brightness seemed to reflect their true brightness.

Leavitt concluded that those with longer periods had greater actual luminosities and were indeed more powerful - the longer the period of a Cepheid, the brighter the star. Once the true brightness of the star had been determined, this was compared to how bright the star actually appeared in the sky.

From here, the distance to the Cepheid could be worked out. This is in much the same way as looking at two light bulbs of identical and known luminosity, but with one positioned further away than the other. If you compare the difference in apparent brightness (how bright they appear), and knowing the true luminosity (how bright they actually are) of each bulb, you can work out how far away they are from you.

Leavitt's pioneering work in determining this relationship allowed astronomers to calculate the distances to Cepheids which meant that distances to external galaxies in which Cepheids were observed could now be calculated. Indeed, it was following the observation of Cepheids in nearby galaxies by the American astronomer Edwin Hubble in the 1920s that he was able to show that these huge stellar gatherings were systems well outside our own.

November 27th

The constellation Lacerta (the Lizard) takes the form of a zigzag line of stars running from north to south and occupying the barren region between Cygnus to the west, Pegasus to the south and Cepheus immediately to the north, the small triangle formed from the three stars Delta, Zeta and Epsilon in Cepheus included here to help you locate this group. Lacerta can be seen in its entirety from locations north of latitude 33°S although because there are no particularly bright stars within this group, observers south of the equator may have difficulty seeing it at all unless the sky above their northern horizon is clear and free of light pollution.

Lacerta was introduced in the 17th century by the Polish astronomer Johannes Hevelius in order to fill a gap in this area of sky. The constellation is very faint and contains no stars brighter than fourth magnitude although, providing the sky is dark, clear and moonless you should have no problem locating the wandering form of this obscure constellation.

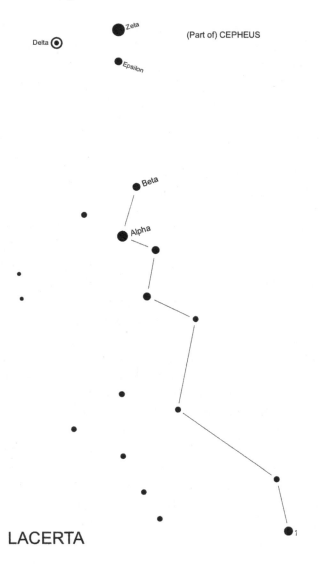

LACERTA

There are no legends attached to Lacerta and none of the stars have names. Its brightest star is Alpha Lacertae which, at a rather dismal magnitude 3.76 shines from a distance of around 100 light years. Located just to the north west of Alpha is Beta Lacertae, a magnitude 4.42 yellow giant whose light has taken 170 years to reach us. The southern tip of Lacerta is represented by 1 Lacertae, a magnitude 4.14 orange giant located at a distance of a little over 600 light years.

November 28th

Our next port of call is the constellation Pisces (the Fishes) which can be found straddling the sky around the south eastern borders of Pegasus. One fish, depicted by the two stars 82 and Tau Piscium, lies a little way to the south of the bright star Mirach in Andromeda, while the other fish can be found immediately to the south of the Square of Pegasus. When seen in the sky, the two fish are depicted as being tied together by a cord, although any significance that the Greeks, or earlier civilisations, placed in this cord is not known.

The chart shows Pisces, together with the Square of Pegasus and the star Mirach in Andromeda, and should enable you to locate the winding form of this faint group. Because Pisces lies just to the north of the celestial equator it is completely visible from almost all inhabited areas of the world.

Legend associates Pisces with Aphrodite and her son Eros, who were caught up in the battle between Zeus and the fearsome monster Typhon, this being the battle during which Pan assisted Zeus (see October 3rd). As we have seen, during the battle Pan concealed himself from Typhon by giving himself a fish's tail and diving into a river, Zeus eventually rewarding Pan by placing him in the sky where we see him today in the form of the constellation Capricornus. However, to get back to Aphrodite and Eros... according to legend, the pair took refuge from Typhon by hiding in the reeds that bordered the river. However, Aphrodite was worried that she would be seen and so dived into the river. It is at this point that the legend becomes a little unclear, and it isn't certain whether Aphrodite and Eros turned into fishes and swam to safety, or whether they were rescued by two fishes that happened to be swimming by. In either case, the two fishes (whatever their origin) are represented by the constellation Pisces.

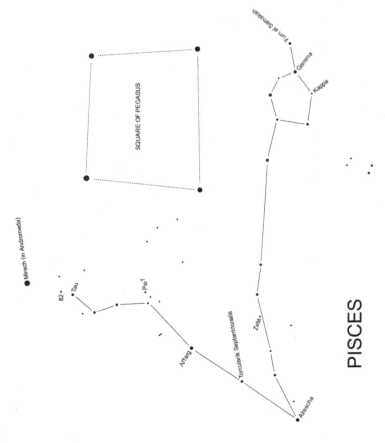

November 29th

The brightest star in Pisces is Al'farg, a magnitude 3.62 yellow giant shining from a distance of almost 350 light years. In terms of brightness, this is closely followed by the magnitude 3.70 Gamma Piscium whose light has taken around 140 years to reach us. Shining from a distance of 150 light years is the magnitude 3.82 Alrescha. The name of this star is derived from the Arabic *'al-risha'* meaning 'the Cord', its location within the constellation depicting the point at which two cords joining the fishes meet.

The most prominent part of Pisces is the 'Circlet' which represents the head of the western fish, and which contains the star Fum al Samakah. Located at a distance of over 400 light years, this magnitude 4.48 star derives its name from the Arabic for 'the Fish's Mouth' and is appropriately named bearing in mind its position relative to the westernmost of the two fishes. Perhaps the most imaginatively-named star in Pisces is the magnitude 4.26 Torcularis Septentrionalis, a yellow giant whose light set off towards us around 280 years ago. Its name is Latin for 'the Northern Press' although the reasons behind the star being given this strange name are lost in antiquity.

November 30th

There are a number of double stars in Pisces resolvable with only moderate optical aid including Psi[1] Piscium, the two 5th magnitude components of which are easily seen in a small telescope and may be glimpsed in binoculars. Another easy double for small telescopes is Zeta Piscium which has 5th and 6th magnitude components. Kappa, the Circlet's southernmost star, shines at magnitude 4.95 from a distance of around 160 light years. If you check this star out with binoculars or a small telescope, you will see what appears to be a nearby companion star. However, the proximity of this star to Kappa is merely a line of sight effect, the light from the magnitude 6.26 orange giant companion having taken over 350 years to reach us.

DECEMBER

December 1ˢᵗ

*The double-shaded nights of drear December have come at last, as if
to prepare the pall for the dying year. The days, too, are night-ridden,
for the cold, low-circling sun serves but to accentuate the gloom.*

*December, like November, has no amity for the star-student (I
speak, of course, of the star-student in these latitudes of Britain). The
nocturnal gloom is to him a fearful Hydra which even Alcides' hands
could ne'er have overcome. For him "the twinkling stares the sky
bespred" but seldom. Hermes' wand itself would often fail to touch
them into being.*

December 2ⁿᵈ

The constellation Cetus (the Whale or Sea Monster) represents
the sea monster (see October 30ᵗʰ) sent by Poseidon, the god
of the sea, to which the beautiful princess Andromeda,
daughter of King Cepheus and Queen Cassiopeia of Ethiopia,
was to be sacrificed. As we have seen, Perseus saved the day
(and Andromeda into the bargain) by killing the monster,
following which it was placed in the sky where it can be seen
to this day alongside the other characters depicted in the legend.

The constellation can be found to the south and south east
of Pisces (see November 28ᵗʰ), and the star Alrescha in Pisces
is included on the chart as an aid to identification. Cetus is best
placed for observation during October and November and can
be seen in its entirety from virtually anywhere south of central
Canada, northern Europe and northern Russia with at least

part of the group visible from any location on the planet.

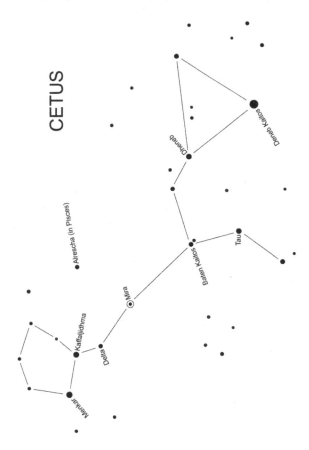

CETUS

Deneb Kaitos

Dheneb

Alrescha (in Pisces)

Baten Kaitos

Tau

Mira

Kaffaljidhma

Delta

Menkar

December 3rd

The brightest star in Cetus is Deneb Kaitos, a magnitude 2.04 yellow giant whose light has taken around 95 years to reach us and which depicts the sea monster's tail. Slightly fainter is the magnitude 2.54 red giant Menkar. Shining from a distance of around 250 light years, this star derives its name from the Arabic *'al-minkhar'* meaning 'the Nostrils'. Named from the Arabic *'batn qaitus'* meaning 'the Sea Monster's Belly', the orange giant star Baten Kaitos shines at magnitude 3.74 from a distance of 234 light years.

The light from magnitude 3.49 Tau Ceti has taken just 11.9 years to reach us, making it one of the closest stars to our solar system. Located a short way to the north west of Tau is Dheneb which, at magnitude 3.46, shines from a distance of around 120 light years. Southernmost of the circlet of stars forming the head of Cetus is magnitude 3.47 Kaffaljidhma, the light from which set off towards us around 80 years ago.

December 4th

The most famous object in Cetus is the long period variable Mira, the star which gave its name to all the other variable stars of its kind. Mira also holds the distinction of being the first variable to be discovered. On 13th August 1596 the Dutch astronomer David Fabricus observed the star, mistaking it for a nova (a star that suddenly flares up to several times its original brightness before returning to its original state). It was next spotted in 1603 when the German astronomer Johann Bayer catalogued it as a 4th magnitude star, including it as Omicron Ceti in his star atlas *Uranometria*. Not long after this Omicron Ceti disappeared from view, only to reappear almost a year later. Subsequent observation finally revealed its true nature. Because Omicron Ceti was the first star known to vary in brightness, it was naturally regarded as being highly unusual, and the Polish astronomer Johannes Hevelius named it Mira, meaning 'wonderful', in his book *Historiola Mirae Stellae* published in 1662 and in which he describes the star.

Mira-type variables are long period variable stars whose brightness oscillates over periods of several months. They are all pulsating red giants, their amplitudes (ranges in brightness from maximum to minimum) averaging out at around 5 or 6 magnitudes, although some are known to vary by as much as 9 or 10 magnitudes. The variations are by no means regular and substantial differences between successive cycles of variability occur. Their periods can be anything from less than 100 days to 700 days or more, although successive periods can differ markedly. Mira itself varies between around magnitude 3 to magnitude 9 or 10 although on one occasion, during observations made by William Herschel in 1779, it almost reached 1st magnitude. At other times however it has barely attained 4th magnitude. In addition, its period of variability, although averaging out at 331 days, has been known to vary dramatically, durations as short as 304 days and as long as 355 days having been recorded.

Located at a distance of around 400 light years, Mira is the brightest of the long-period variables and only moderate optical aid is required to follow its complete cycle. It is easily located roughly two-fifths of the way from Delta Ceti to Baten Kaitos as shown on the chart and at times it can be seen with the naked eye. However, for most of its cycle of variability it cannot be seen without the help of either binoculars or a small telescope.

Continued observation of Mira over a period of several weeks will reveal its changes in magnitude although, as is the case with any variable star which remains at or near minimum brightness for extended periods, Mira may well be out of view when you look for it. If this is the case, keep an eye open and Mira will eventually reappear, following which you can keep a check on its progress.

*

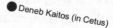

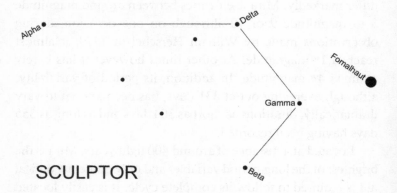

SCULPTOR

We are now approaching the end of our year-long journey around the skies, travelling southwards and continuing our journey back to the constellations of the southern heavens. Located to the south of the star Deneb Kaitos in Cetus, and to the east of the bright star Fomalhaut in Piscis Austrinus (see October 26th), is the tiny constellation Sculptor (the Sculptor). Both Deneb Kaitos and Fomalhaut are shown here as guides to locating this faint constellation, the whole of which is visible to observers south of latitude 50°N. However, because there are no bright stars in this group it may be difficult to make out for star gazers at mid-northern latitudes unless the sky above their southern horizon is dark, clear and free of light pollution.

Originally called Apparatus Sculptoris, the name of this group has since been shortened to Sculptor. It was one of the constellations devised by the French astronomer Nicolas Louis de Lacaille following his stay in South Africa during 1751 and 1752. The constellation was intended to represent a sculptor's workshop and takes the form of a curved line of faint stars, none of which are named and none of which are at all prominent.

The brightest star in this somewhat dismal group is Alpha Sculptoris, a magnitude 4.30 blue giant shining from a distance of over 750 light years. This is closely followed in prominence by the magnitude 4.38 Beta, the light from which has taken 175 years to reach us. Gamma Sculptoris is an orange giant, its magnitude 4.41 glow emanating from a distance of 180 light years. Completing the main outline of the constellation is Delta which, shining at magnitude 4.59, lies at a distance of around 140 light years.

December 6th

We now check out the area of sky immediately to the south of Sculptor where we find the slightly-more prominent constellation Phoenix (the Phoenix) that represents the legendary bird of the same name that rises from its own ashes. According to mythology, the phoenix lived a long life, following which it built for itself a nest of spices and then set fire to the nest. During this apparently rash process the bird was burned to ashes, from which it came forth again with new life.

This group is another of the constellations introduced by Pieter Dirkszoon Keyser and Frederick de Houtman following their expedition to the East Indies in the 1590s (see May 10th) and can be found slightly to the north of a line between Fomalhaut in Piscis Austrinus (see October 26th) and the bright star Achernar in Eridanus (see December 29th). When viewed from the southern hemisphere, both these stars are very prominent at this time of year and both are included on the chart as a guide to locating Phoenix. Both guide stars, as well as Phoenix itself, can be seen from anywhere south of latitude 32°N although the best views of this faint group are to be had from regions much further south than this.

Phoenix can be seen in its entirety from most of Mexico, northern Africa and India and from places south of these, although it is always low in the sky when viewed from places north of the equator. Its leading star is Ankaa, the name of which is derived from the Arabic *'al-anqa'* meaning 'the Fabulous Bird', an allusion to the constellation as a whole. This orange giant star shines at magnitude 2.40 from a distance of 85 light years. The second-brightest star in the group is the magnitude 3.32 yellow giant Beta Phoenicis, slightly to the north east of which is Gamma Phoenicis, a magnitude 3.41 red giant whose light has taken around 230 years to reach us.

December 7th

Although Phoenix doesn't hold a great deal of interest to the backyard astronomer, other than identification of the constellation and its main stars, it does play host to the Algol-type (see November 14th) variable Zeta Phoenicis, located slightly to the north west of the bright star Achernar and which completes the diamond-shape formed from Zeta itself together with Beta, Gamma and Delta. Shining from a distance of nearly 300 light years, this eclipsing binary ranges in magnitude from 3.92 to 4.42 over a period of 1.67 days (a little over 40 hours). The eclipse phase is easily visible to the naked eye and comparisons of its brightness can be made with Epsilon (magnitude 3.88) and the nearby Delta (magnitude 3.93) and Eta (magnitude 4.36).

December 8th

Moving deeper into the southern skies we now arrive at Tucana (the Toucan), located immediately to the south west of Phoenix and the bright star Achernar in Eridanus. The chart shows Achernar as a guide to locating both Tucana and the adjoining constellation Hydrus (see December 14th) which is also depicted here.

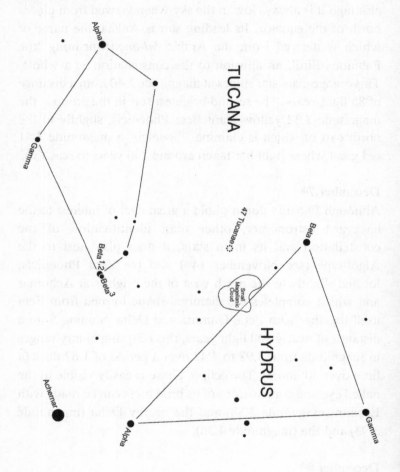

Taking the form of an irregular shaped circlet of stars, the constellation Tucana can be seen in its entirety from anywhere in the southern hemisphere and lower northern latitudes. Tucana is another of the southern constellations introduced by Pieter Dirkszoon Keyser and Frederick de Houtman (see May 10th), the group depicting the well-known South American bird with a huge bill and which first appeared on the celestial globe produced by Petrus Plancius in 1598. It's leading star is Alpha Tucanae, a magnitude 2.87 orange giant whose light has taken around 200 years to reach us. Next in order of brightness is Gamma, the light from this magnitude 3.99 star emanating from a distance of just 75 light years.

December 9th

Although only relatively small, the constellation Tucana contains a number of objects of interest to the backyard astronomer, not least of which is the Small Magellanic Cloud (SMC), a dwarf irregular galaxy and a member of the Local Group of Galaxies (see Glossary). Located at a distance of 190,000 light years, the SMC has a diameter of around 7,000 light years and lies close to the border between Tucana and the adjoining constellation Hydrus (the Little Water Snake) (see December 14th). Although this object was known to many ancient civilizations, it was only following accounts of the circumnavigation of the Earth by the Portuguese explorer Ferdinand Magellan in the early-16th century that its presence became more widely known. Magellan's contribution eventually resulted in the Small Magellanic Cloud (and the nearby Large Magellanic Cloud – see December 22nd) being named in his honour.

The SMC has a fairly low surface brightness and consequently is best viewed from dark locations away from street lights and other light pollution. It can be seen with the naked eye as a hazy, elongated patch of light and binoculars show it quite well. Careful sweeping of the Small Magellanic Cloud with a telescope or good binoculars will reveal the presence of a number of nebulae and star clusters.

December 10th

Another target for the backyard astronomer is the beautiful triple star Beta Tucanae. Beta[1] and Beta[2] form a double star with magnitude 4.36 and 4.53 blue-white components and which can be resolved in a small telescope. Magnitude 5.07 Beta[3] lies close by. The Beta[1,2] pair is resolvable from Beta[3] with the naked eye provided the sky is really dark and clear, and presents a lovely sight when seen through binoculars. All three stars appear to be gravitationally bound to each other and to share a common motion through space.

December 11th

Tucana also contains the globular cluster 47 Tucanae, rated as being one of the finest globular clusters in the sky and second only to Omega Centauri (see May 9th) in terms of visual impact. Shining with an overall magnitude of around 4.5 it is easily visible to the naked eye as a hazy, star like object. 47 Tucanae was discovered by the French astronomer Nicolas Louis de Lacaille who described it as being: *'Like the nucleus of a fairly bright comet.'*

Lying at a distance of over 16,000 light years, 47 Tucanae is a huge system with a diameter of 120 light years and a total actual luminosity of over a quarter of a million times that of the Sun. Binoculars with magnifications of 10x or more, or a small telescope, will resolve individual stars at the cluster's edge, the degree of resolution increasing rapidly as larger instruments are turned towards the cluster.

*

December 12ᵗʰ

Our final port of call in Tucana is the globular cluster NGC 362 which is less condensed and somewhat fainter than 47 Tucanae. Discovered in August 1826 by the Scottish astronomer James Dunlop, NGC 362 shines with an overall magnitude of 6.4 from a distance in the order of 28,000 light years. It lies just below naked eye visibility and binoculars will be needed in order to see it against the backdrop of star fields at the edge of the Small Magellanic Cloud. As with 47 Tucanae, small telescopes will start to resolve individual cluster stars.

December 13ᵗʰ

Alas! The winter shadows now fall on day's decline. Yonder sou'-western sun-fled sky was all afire a while ago, only to die out as though the year had died out with it.

December 14ᵗʰ

The constellation Hydrus (the Little Water Snake) is another of the groups introduced by Pieter Dirkszoon Keyser and Frederick de Houtman in the 1590s (see May 10ᵗʰ). It can be found bordering Tucana (see December 8ᵗʰ), both constellations being depicted on the same chart. One of the brightest stars in Hydrus, Alpha Hydri, lies a little way to the south of Achernar in Eridanus (see December 29ᵗʰ), this star being included on the chart for reference. Hydrus can only be seen in its entirety from regions around the equator and locations further to the south.

As is the case with many of the constellations that lie in the region of the south celestial pole, Hydrus contains no particularly bright stars, and none have individual names. This unimpressive group takes the form of a small triangle made up from its three principal stars. The brightest of these is magnitude 2.82 Beta Hydri which, at a distance of just 24.3 light years, is one of our nearer stellar neighbours. Shining at magnitude 2.86, Alpha Hydri is slightly fainter and more remote, its light having taken 72 years to reach us. Completing the triangle is the red giant Gamma Hydri whose magnitude 3.26 glow set off towards us a little over 200 years ago.

December 15th

Midnight in mid-December! A silence most profound. Earth is silent, as though it were stricken dumb with adoration before the display of starry grandeur which the sky unfolds; Heaven is silent, for though Nature has many voices, the stars have none; they pursue their diverse ways soundless as space itself. Let us listen as we might no strains of celestial music would ever reach our ears.

December 16th

The constellation Octans (the Octant) is another of the groups introduced by the French astronomer Nicolas Louis de Lacaille. It represents the octant, a navigational instrument invented by the English mathematician John Hadley which was designed to measure the altitude of stars and other celestial objects above the horizon while at sea. Because Octans is located at the south celestial pole (see below) it can only be seen in its entirety by star gazers located in the southern hemisphere.

To find the constellation, first of all locate the main trio of stars forming Hydrus (see December 14th) together with Theta Octantis, all of which lie in the region of the Small Magellanic Cloud. These stars, together with nearby Achernar in Eridanus, are depicted on the chart to help you track down the constellation Octans. Starting at Theta Octantis the rest of

Octans, including the triangle formed from Delta, Nu and Beta
Octantis, can then be picked out.

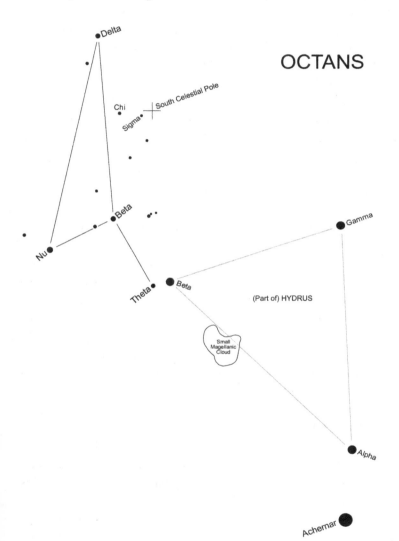

Theta is an orange giant shining at magnitude 4.78 from a distance of around 220 light years, not quite as far away as magnitude 4.31 Delta, another orange giant star whose light has taken almost 300 years to reach us. The magnitude 3.73 glow of Nu, the brightest star in Octans, set off on its journey towards us 69 years ago. Completing the main outline of Tucana is Beta, a magnitude 4.13 star located around 150 light years away.

As we have seen (see March 13th) the north (and south) celestial poles are the points on the celestial sphere through which extensions of the Earth's axis of rotation would pass. The north celestial pole is marked by Polaris (the northern Pole Star) in Ursa Minor, its southern equivalent being Sigma Octantis, which can be seen to lie a short distance from the south celestial pole. However, shining at a somewhat-feeble magnitude 5.46, Sigma is barely visible to the naked eye and cannot be seen without optical aid unless the sky is really dark and clear. To locate Sigma, first of all pick out the main shape of Octans, then follow the line from Beta towards Delta. The two faint stars Chi and Sigma Octantis will be seen near this line. Patience may be required, so do persist in your search. Once you do manage to locate Sigma, you will realise how fortunate those in the northern hemisphere are to have such a relatively bright pole star as Polaris!

December 17th
Moving back northwards we find, located just to the south west of the star Furud in Canis Major (see January 10th), the small and somewhat-shapeless Columba (the Dove). This constellation was devised by the Dutch celestial cartographer Petrus Plancius in 1592 in order to help fill out this otherwise-empty region of sky. Its leading star is the magnitude 2.65

Phakt which shines from a distance of around 260 light years. Beta Columbae, located just to the south east of Phakt, is an orange giant star which, at magnitude 3.12, lies at a distance of 87 light years. The 16th century Arabic astronomer Al Tizini knew these two stars collectively as *'Al Aghribah'* meaning 'the Ravens'. The rest of Columba is made up of the quartet of 4th magnitude stars Gamma, Delta, Epsilon and Eta.

Sirius

COLUMBA

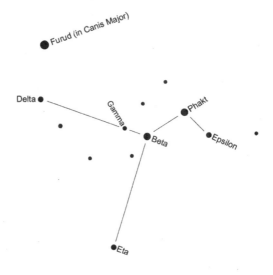

The whole of Columba is visible from latitudes south of 47°N and you should have little trouble locating this constellation, particularly as its two leading stars are reasonably bright and that there are useful guide stars in the shape of Furud and brilliant Sirius, both in Canis Major and both of which are shown here.

December 18th

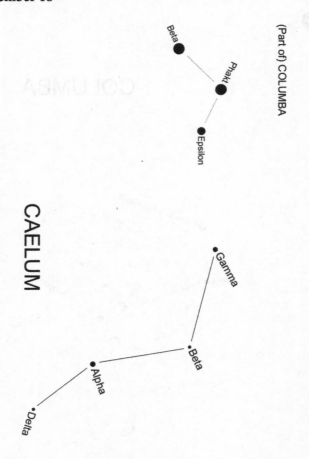

The constellation Caelum (the Graving Tool) was devised by the French astronomer Nicolas Louis de Lacaille to fill the gap between Columba and Eridanus (see December 28th) and takes the form of a short zig-zag line of faint stars located to the west of Columba. As a guide to locating Caelum the three stars Beta Columbae, Phakt and Epsilon Columbae are included on the chart. The whole of this constellation is visible to backyard astronomers in the central United States, southern Europe and from locations further south than these.

Caelum represents the burin, or graving tool, of the engraver and can be located with the naked eye providing the sky is dark and clear. There are no prominent stars in Caelum, the brightest member of the constellation being Alpha, a white magnitude 4.44 star shining from at a distance of around 65 light years. The 5th magnitude trio Beta, Gamma and Delta complete this obscure group.

December 19th

The tiny constellation Pictor (the Painter's Easel) can be found to the south of Columba and Caelum and immediately to the west of the bright star Canopus in Carina (see February 13th), this star being included on the chart for reference. Another of the constellations devised by Nicolas Louis de Lacaille and intended to represent a painter's easel and palette, this group is unimaginative to say the least. Taking the form of a bent line of three stars, it is visible in its entirety from locations along the equatorial regions and south from there. Observers in South America, South Africa, Australia and New Zealand will see the brilliant star Canopus riding high in the sky a little to the south of the overhead point during late evenings in December. Once this star is located the unimpressive collection of stars forming Pictor can be found.

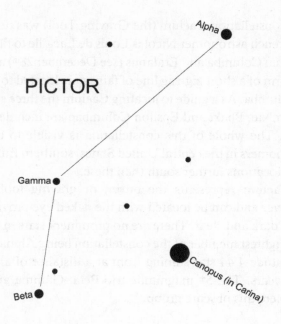

PICTOR

Alpha

Gamma

Beta

Canopus (in Carina)

The brightest star in the group is Alpha Pictoris which, at magnitude 3.24, shines from a distance of 96 light years. Somewhat closer to us is Beta, a magnitude 3.85 star whose light has taken just 63 years to reach our planet. Completing the main trio of stars in Pictor is Gamma. This light from this magnitude 4.50 orange giant set off on its journey towards us around 180 years ago.

December 20th

Orion at midnight strode the southern sky like a Colossus. What an attention-compelling constellation Orion is! With its heroic proportions, its conspicuous stars, Betelgeuse, Rigel and Bellatrix; its jewel-sparkling Belt; its pendant Sword; and its stupendous nebula, it excites the highest admiration of astronomer and casual observer alike.

December 21st

Dorado (the Goldfish) is another of the constellations introduced by Pieter Dirkszoon Keyser and Frederick de Houtman in the 1590s (see May 10th), appearing on the celestial globe produced by Petrus Plancius in 1598. Dorado is visible in its entirety from locations south of latitude 20°N and tracking this group down should not present too much of a problem. If you extend an imaginary line from Canopus through a point roughly midway between Beta and Gamma Pictoris (see December 19th) roughly twice as far again you will eventually reach Alpha Doradus. The star Canopus together with the main outline of Pictor are included on the chart as a guide to locating Dorado.

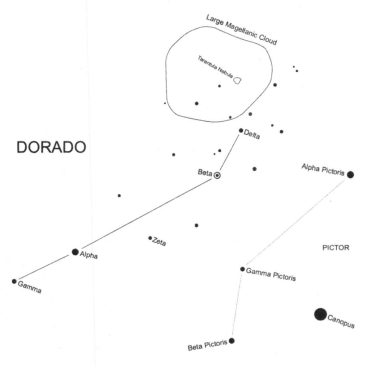

Shining at magnitude 3.30 from a distance of around 170 light years, Alpha is the brightest star in the constellation, closely followed in prominence by Beta Doradus. Located at a distance of around 1,000 light years, Beta is a Cepheid variable (see November 26th), its magnitude ranging between around 3.40 to 4.10 over a period of 9.84 days. Comparisons of its brightness can be made with the nearby Zeta (magnitude 4.71) and Delta (magnitude 4.34), the latter of which, together with Gamma Doradus, completes the line of stars that forms Dorado.

December 22nd
The constellation of Dorado is notable chiefly for the presence of the Large Magellanic Cloud (LMC) which lays on the border of Dorado and the adjoining constellation Mensa. Most of the LMC lies within Dorado itself and, like its counterpart the Small Magellanic Cloud (see December 9th), this galaxy is a member of the Local Group of Galaxies. Situated at a distance of over 160,000 light years, the LMC is a sizeable system measuring around 14,000 light years across. It is plainly visible to the unaided eye and repays time spent sweeping it with binoculars or a telescope. The LMC is visible even in moonlit skies and has been likened in appearance to a detached portion of the Milky Way.

The Tarantula Nebula (NGC 2070) is the brightest part of the entire Large Magellanic Cloud. Its name arises from the fact that its spidery outer filaments and streamers, stretching away to cover an area of space some 1,000 light years across, resemble the legs of a gigantic tarantula. NGC 2070 is by far the largest-known diffuse nebula within the Local Group of Galaxies, and the fact that it can be identified with the naked eye at a distance of 160,000 light years bears testimony to its colossal size and brilliance.

The Tarantula Nebula was originally thought to be a star, although its true nature was determined by Nicolas Louis de Lacaille who described it as: *'(Like the nucleus of a fairly bright comet)... but fainter.'* It is one of the most active regions of star formation known. At its heart is a massive recently-formed star cluster measuring some 35 light years in diameter and producing most of the energy which is causing the gas in the Tarantula Nebula to shine.

December 23rd

MENSA

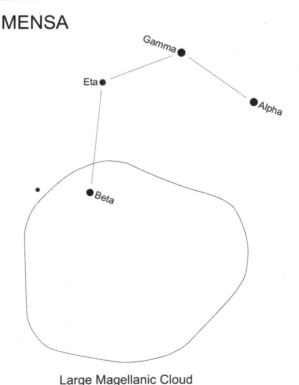

Large Magellanic Cloud

Other than through the fact that part of the Large Magellanic Cloud lies within its boundaries, the diminutive constellation Mensa (the Table Mountain) has little going for it. Visible from regions on or to the south of the equator, this is another of the constellations devised by Nicolas Louis de Lacaille and represents the Table Mountain near Cape Town, from where Lacaille charted the southern skies during his stay there in 1751 and 1752.

As well as being one of the smallest groups in the entire sky, it is also the dimmest, with its two leading stars Alpha and Gamma shining at magnitudes 5.08 and 5.18 respectively. However, the tiny circlet of stars comprising Beta, Eta, Gamma and Alpha Mensae, which forms the main part of Mensa, can be traced out either with the naked eye (under exceptionally dark and clear skies) or with the help of binoculars, by following its path away from the southern borders of the Large Magellanic Cloud.

Dcember 24th

The tiny constellation Reticulum (the Net) is yet another of the groups introduced into this region of sky by the French astronomer Nicolas Louis de Lacaille during his stay in South Africa. It represents the reticule used in the eyepiece of his telescope by Lacaille to measure the positions of stars.

The star Beta Reticuli forms a triangle with Alpha and Gamma in the neighbouring constellation Hydrus (see December 14th). The three main stars in Hydrus, together with the brilliant Achernar in Eridanus (see December 29th), are included on the chart to help you identify the group. These four stars, together with the whole of Reticulum, are visible in their entirety to star gazers on or south of the Earth's equatorial regions.

Reticulum takes the form of an approximately diamond-shaped pattern of stars, the brightest of which is Alpha Reticuli, a magnitude 3.33 yellow giant shining from a distance of around 160 light years. The magnitude 3.84 glow of orange giant Beta has taken 100 years to reach us whilst magnitude 4.44 Epsilon Reticuli, more or less completing the main outline of Reticulum, lies at a distance of just 59 light years.

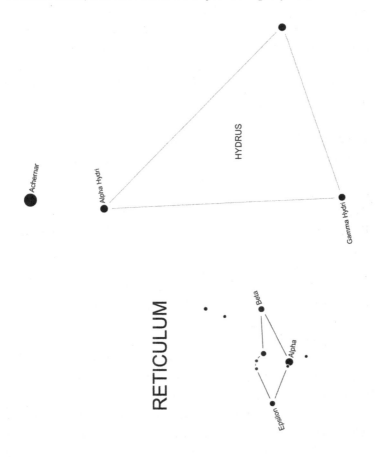

December 25th

The night of Christmas Day comes quickly and long ere the bells call us to church the stars come out. Indeed, at half-past four the brighter ones may be discovered without difficulty if the sky should be very clear. There is one at this hour which twinkles rapidly rather low in the east. It is Aldebaran, though the sky is too light – even the eastern sky – for any of this star's co-Hyads to be seen. There is another twinkling point away up in the north-east. That is Capella, alone of the Auriga stars revealed. And just a glimpse of the Pole Star can be caught, but so elusive is that famous object at half-past four that its discovery may be considered as hopeless to one who has but a general idea of its position. In the west – exactly opposite to Aldebaran – is Vega, as distinguished from its bluish-white brilliance as for its present location.

December 26th

Another of the constellations introduced by Nicolas Louis de Lacaille, Horologium (the Pendulum Clock) is visible in its entirety from latitudes south of 23°N and lies between Reticulum (see December 24th) and the bright star Achernar in Eridanus (see December 29th), these being included on the chart for guidance.

Looking nothing like the object it is supposed to depict, and bearing testimony to the vivid imagination of Lacaille more than anything else, Horologium comprises a bent line of faint stars at one end of which is Alpha Horologii, a magnitude 3.85 orange giant located at a distance of 115 light years and forming a wide pair with magnitude 4.93 Delta. These two stars are not physically connected, the light from Delta having taken around 180 years to reach us.

Beta, located at the opposite end of the constellation, is a white giant whose feeble magnitude 4.98 glow has reached us from a distance of around 300 light years. Located a little to the north of Beta is magnitude 5.12 Mu Horologii, the light from which star set off on its journey towards us around 140 years ago.

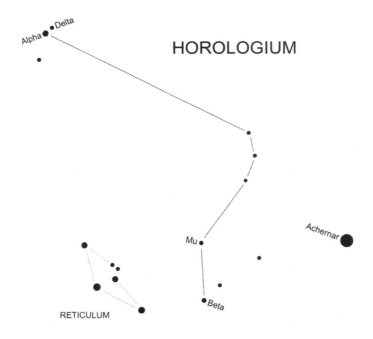

December 27th

The tiny and somewhat shapeless constellation Fornax (the Furnace) was devised by Lacaille to depict a chemical furnace and was introduced to highlight the importance of chemistry to his contemporaries. As with many of the groups devised by Lacaille the constellation bears little resemblance to the object it depicts, the main form of the group (if indeed it can be said to have one) is that of a short bent line of faint stars. It can be found bordering the southern regions of the long and winding constellation Eridanus (see December 28th), both constellations being depicted on the same chart.

The whole of Fornax is visible to star gazers located to the south of latitude 50°N but, as with many of Lacaille's imaginative creations, is not particularly prominent, so patience may be required to track it down. The brightest star in Fornax is Alpha which, at magnitude 3.80, shines from a distance of just 46 light years. The magnitude 4.45 yellow giant star Beta Fornacis lies at a distance of 173 light years, less being than half the distance of Nu, the light from this magnitude 4.68 star having taken 370 years to reach us.

December 28th

The long and winding constellation Eridanus (the River) extends from Achernar, deep in the southern hemisphere to a point a little way to the north west of the bright star Rigel in Orion (see January 4th). Achernar is one of the brightest stars in the sky and is, as we have seen, a useful guide to locating many of the faint constellations located around it. As its name suggests, the constellation Eridanus depicts a river, although the precise identification of this river is open to debate. The Greek astronomer Eratosthenes took it to represent the River Nile, although the Akkadians identified it as being the River Euphrates.

The River Eridanus features in the legend attached to Phaeton, the son of Apollo, the god of the Sun, and the nymph Clymene. Phaeton persuaded his father to let him drive the chariot of the Sun across the sky and Apollo eventually agreed, warning his son of the potential dangers. Phaeton set off on his journey but was unable to control the steeds pulling the chariot. A catastrophe seemed on the cards and to avert this Zeus hurled a thunderbolt at Phaeton, striking him down and hurling him into the River Eridanus far below.

Although portions of Eridanus are visible from anywhere in the world, this long and winding constellation can be seen in its entirety from most of Mexico and India, north Africa and latitudes to the south of these.

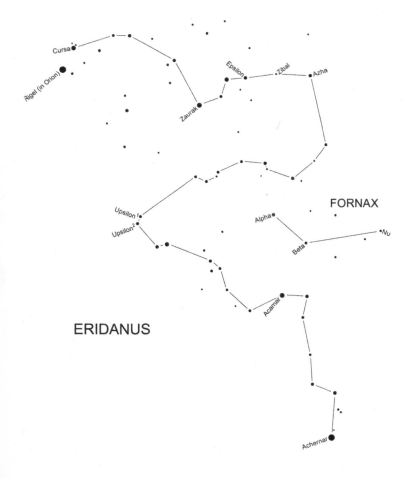

December 29th

The brightest star in Eridanus is Achernar which, at magnitude 0.45, shines from a distance of 140 light years. The name of this star is derived from the Arabic *'akhir al-nahr'* meaning 'the River's End', fitting in view of its location at the southern end of the constellation. Located near the northern end of Eridanus is the appropriately-named magnitude 2.97 red giant Zaurak, its name derived from the Arabic *'zauraq'* meaning 'Boat'. The light from Zaurak set off towards us around 200 years ago.

Of particular interest is the magnitude 3.72 Epsilon Eridani which, shining from a distance of just 10.5 light years, is one of our closest stellar neighbours. Immediately to the west of Epsilon is Zibal, a magnitude 4.80 white giant star whose light has taken 110 years to reach us. Slightly to the west again is Azha, a magnitude 3.89 orange giant star shining from a distance of 135 light years.

Moving further south, and navigating around the bend of the River Eridanus, we eventually arrive at the pair of stars Upsilon[1] and Upsilon[2] Eridani. Shining at magnitude 3.81 from a distance of 214 light years, the yellow giant Upsilon[2] is marginally brighter than its magnitude 4.49 orange giant neighbour Upsilon[1], the light from which taken around 125 years to reach us. Upsilon[1] and Upsilon[2] form just one of several wide pairs of stars scattered along the entire length of the constellation.

December 30th

There are a number of double stars in Eridanus, one of which is definitely worth mentioning. The Arabic *'akhir al-nahr'*, from which the name of Achernar is derived, also gives rise to the name of Acamar. Located at a distance of 160 light years,

Acamar is widely regarded as being one of the finest double stars in the southern sky, its magnitude 3.4 and 4.4 components easily resolvable in a small telescope.

Acamar marks the original end of the river Eridanus, the stars south of this point being inaccessible to Greek astronomers. It wasn't until explorers ventured into the southern hemisphere that additional stars were seen, this resulting in the original constellation Eridanus being extended to the south and to a new termination point marked by the bright star Achernar.

December 31st

Making our way northwards from Achernar along the full course of the river depicted by Eridanus we eventually arrive at Cursa, the magnitude 2.78 star marking the river's northern extremity. The light from this star set off towards us 89 years ago, although our journey around the sky has taken a single year. From Cursa we can identify the nearby brilliant star Rigel, located just to its south east and one of the leading stars in the constellation Orion, the group from where we commenced our odyssey around the sky exactly a year ago. Hopefully the journey has been a rewarding one for you, the backyard astronomer, and has introduced you to many of the wonders the night sky holds. Joseph Henry Elgie summed it up well, and with more than a degree of pathos, when he said:

> *Another year begins to-morrow, and the stars will*
> *enter upon another round, to pass again in stately*
> *procession before us, and to afford one more reminder*
> *that our sojourn upon earth shortens. It is for us to see,*
> *while we may, that we have sojourned not in vain.*

GLOSSARY

ALTITUDE

When referring to the altitude of a star or other object in the sky, this means the angular distance of that object above the horizon. For example, if a star is at the zenith, or overhead point, its altitude is 90° and if it is on the horizon, its altitude is 0° (see The Celestial Sphere pp 6-15).

ASTERISM

A grouping or collection of stars, located within a constellation, that form an apparent and distinctive pattern as seen from Earth. Examples include the False Cross (formed from stars in Carina and Vela) (see February 17th); the Square of Pegasus in Pegasus (see October 14th); the Summer Triangle (formed from stars in Lyra, Cygnus and Aquila) (see September 2nd and 4th); the Teapot in Sagittarius (see August 14th); and the Plough in Ursa Major (see March 7th).

AVERTED VISION

Averted vision is a useful technique for observing faint objects which involves looking slightly to one side of the object under observation. By doing so you allow the light emitted by the object to fall on a more sensitive part of the retina. Although you are not looking directly at the object, it is surprising how much more detail comes into view. This technique is also useful when observing double stars which have components of greatly contrasting brightness. Although direct vision may not reveal the glow of a faint companion star in the glare of a much brighter primary, averted vision may well bring the fainter star into view (see also February 4th for William Herschel's comments on averted vision).

BINARY STAR
See Double Star

CELESTIAL EQUATOR
A projection of the Earth's equator onto the celestial sphere, equidistant from the celestial poles and dividing the celestial sphere into two hemispheres (see The Celestial Sphere pp 6-15).

CELESTIAL POLES
The points on the celestial sphere directly above the north and south terrestrial poles around which the celestial sphere appears to rotate (see The Celestial Sphere pp 6-15).

CELESTIAL SPHERE
The imaginary sphere of stars surrounding the Earth (see The Celestial Sphere pp 6-15).

CIRCUMPOLAR STAR
A star which never sets from a given latitude (see The Celestial Sphere pp 6-15).

CONSTELLATION
A constellation is an arbitrary grouping of stars forming a pattern or imaginary picture on the celestial sphere. Many of these have traditional names and are associated with folklore and mythology. There are 88 official constellations which together cover the entire sky, each one of which refers to,

defines and identifies that particular region of the celestial sphere. As a result, every object that we see in the sky is described as being within one particular constellation or another.

DOUBLE STARS

Double stars are two stars which appear to be close together in space. Most of these are comprised of stars that are gravitationally linked and orbit each other, forming a genuine double-star system (also known as a *binary* star). Some double stars, however, (known as *optical* doubles) are nothing more than chance alignments, being made up of two stars that only happen to lie in the same line of sight as seen from Earth.

ECLIPTIC

The apparent path of the Sun through the sky. The ecliptic passes through a band of constellations called the Zodiac (see The Celestial Sphere pp 6-15).

EQUINOX (AUTUMNAL)

Occurring in late-September, the point at which the apparent path of the Sun, moving from north to south, crosses the celestial equator (see The Celestial Sphere pp 6-15).

EQUINOX (VERNAL)

Also known as the spring equinox, and occurring in late-March, the point at which the apparent path of the Sun, moving from south to north, crosses the celestial equator (see The Celestial Sphere pp 6-15).

GALAXY

A vast collection of stars, gas and dust bound together by

gravity and measuring many light years across. Galaxies occur in a wide variety of shapes and sizes including spiral, elliptical and irregular and many are so far away that their light has taken many millions of years to reach us. Our solar system is situated in the Milky Way Galaxy, a spiral galaxy containing several billion stars. Located within the Local Group of Galaxies (see below), the Milky Way Galaxy is often referred to simply as the Galaxy.

INDEX CATALOGUE (IC)

References such as that for IC 2391 (in Vela) and IC 2602 (in Carina) are derived from their numbers in the Index Catalogue (IC), published in 1895 as the first of two supplements (the second was published in 1908) to his New General Catalogue of Nebulae and Clusters of Stars (NGC) by the Danish astronomer John Louis Emil Dreyer. Between them, the two Index Catalogues contained details of an additional 5,386 objects (see also New General Catalogue).

LIGHT YEAR

To express distances to the stars and other galaxies in miles would involve numbers so huge that they would be unwieldy. Astronomers therefore use the term 'light year' as a unit of distance. A light year is the distance a beam of light, travelling at around 186,000 miles (300,000 km) per second, would travel in a year and is equivalent to just under 6 trillion miles (10 trillion km).

LOCAL GROUP OF GALAXIES

Our own Galaxy is one of a gravitationally-bound collection of galaxies known as the Local Group which contains over 50 individual members. These include the Andromeda Galaxy

(M31) (see November 2nd), the Large Magellanic Cloud (see December 22nd), the Small Magellanic Cloud (see December 9th), the Triangulum Spiral Galaxy (M33) (see November 6th) and many others. The two largest members are the Andromeda Galaxy and our own Milky Way Galaxy.

Galaxies are usually found in groups or clusters. Apart from our own Local Group, many other groups of galaxies are known, typically containing anywhere up to 50 individual members. Even larger than the groups are clusters of galaxies which can contain hundreds or even thousands of individual galaxies. Groups and clusters of galaxies are found throughout the universe.

MAGNITUDES

The magnitude of a star is purely and simply a measurement of its brightness. In around 150BC the Greek astronomer Hipparchus divided the stars up into six classes of brightness, the most prominent stars being ranked as first class and the faintest as sixth. This system is known as *apparent magnitude* and classifies the stars and other celestial objects according to how bright they actually appear to the observer. In 1856 the English astronomer Norman Robert Pogson refined the system devised by Hipparchus by classing a 1st magnitude star as being 100 times as bright as one of 6th magnitude, giving a difference between successive magnitudes of $\sqrt[5]{100}$ or 2.512. In other words, a star of magnitude 1.00 is 2.512 times as bright as one of magnitude 2.00, 6.31 (2.512 x 2.512) times as bright as a star of magnitude 3.00 and so on. The same basic system is used today, although modern telescopes enable us to determine values to within 0.01 of a magnitude or better. Negative values are used for the brightest objects including the Sun (-26.8), Venus (-4.4 at its brightest) and Sirius (-1.46). Generally speaking, the faintest objects that can be seen with the naked eye under good viewing conditions are around 6th magnitude, whilst binoculars will allow you to see stars and other objects down to around 9th magnitude.

MILKY WAY

The Milky Way is visible as a faint pearly band of light and is created by the combined glow of stars scattered along the plane of our Galaxy's disc as seen from Earth. Given clear, dark skies, it is easily visible to the unaided eye and any form of optical aid will show that it is made up of many thousands of individual stars. Our solar system lies within the main plane of the Milky Way Galaxy and is located inside one of its spiral arms. The Milky Way is actually our view of the Galaxy, looking along the main galactic plane. The pearly glow we see is the combined light from many different stars and is visible as a continuous band of light stretching around the celestial sphere. Although the vast majority of these are too faint to be seen without optical aid, their combined light produces the glow that can be seen crossing the sky on dark, clear nights.

NEBULA

Nebulae are huge interstellar clouds of gas and dust. The word is from the Latin *'nebula'* meaning 'mist' or 'vapour'. There are three main types of nebula.

Emission nebulae contain young, hot stars. These stars emit copious amounts of ultra-violet radiation which reacts with the gas in the nebula causing the nebula to shine at visible wavelengths and with a reddish colour characteristic of this type of nebula. In other words, emission nebulae *emit* their own light. A famous example is the Orion Nebula (M42) in the constellation Orion (see January 9th) which is visible as a shimmering patch of light a little to the south of the three stars forming the Belt of Orion.

Reflection nebulae, as their name suggests, shine because they *reflect* the light from stars. The stars that exist in and around reflection nebulae are not hot enough to actually cause the nebula to give off its own light. Instead, the dust particles within them simply reflect the light from these stars. The stars in the Pleiades star cluster (M45) in Taurus (see February 4th) are surrounded by reflection nebulosity. Photographs of the Pleiades cluster show the nebulosity as a blue haze, this being the characteristic colour of reflection nebulae.

Dark nebulae are clouds of interstellar matter which contain no stars and whose dust particles simply blot out the light from objects beyond. They neither emit nor reflect light and appear as dark patches against the brighter backdrop of stars or nebulosity, taking on the appearance of regions devoid of stars. A good example is the Coal Sack in the constellation Crux (see April 29th), a huge blot of matter obscuring the star clouds of the southern Milky Way.

NEW GENERAL CATALOGUE (NGC)

References such as that for NGC 3242 (in Hydra) and NGC 4755 (in Crux) are derived from their numbers in the New General Catalogue of Nebulae and Clusters of Stars (NGC) first published in 1888 by the Danish astronomer John Louis Emil Dreyer and which contains details of 7,840 star clusters, nebulae and galaxies (see also Index Catalogue).

PLANETARY NEBULA

Planetary nebulae consist of material ejected by a star during the latter stages of its evolution. The material thrown off forms a shell of gas surrounding the star whose newly-exposed surface is typically very hot. Planetary nebulae have nothing whatsoever to do with planets. They derive their name from the fact that, when seen through a telescope, some planetary nebulae look like luminous discs, resembling a gaseous planet such as Uranus or Neptune. An excellent example is the famous Ring Nebula (M57) in Lyra (see September 21st).

SOLAR SYSTEM
The collective description given to the system dominated by the Sun and which includes the planets, minor planets, comets, planetary satellites and interplanetary debris that travel in orbits around our parent star.

SOLSTICES
The positions in the sky at which the Sun is at its maximum angular distance from the celestial equator (see The Celestial Sphere pp 6-15).

STAR
A self-luminous object that shines through the release of energy produced by nuclear reactions at its core. Stars come in a whole range of different colours, sizes and temperatures, our Sun being a fairly average, medium-sized yellow star.

STAR COLOURS
Stars are seen to have many different colours, a prominent example being the bright red Betelgeuse in the constellation of Orion, which contrasts sharply with the nearby brilliant blue-white Rigel which marks Orion's foot. Our own Sun is yellow and Procyon, the brightest star in Canis Minor, also has a yellowish tint. Other stars with conspicuous colours include orange-red Aldebaran in Taurus, the red supergiant Antares in

Scorpius and Mu Cephei in Cepheus. Mu Cephei, or the Garnet Star, is probably the reddest star visible to the naked eye in the northern skies, and binoculars will bring out the colour very well.

The colour of a star is a good guide to its temperature, the hottest stars being blue and blue-white with surface temperatures of 20,000 degrees or more. Classed as a yellow dwarf, the Sun is a fairly average star with a temperature of around 6,000 degrees. Red stars are much cooler still, with surface temperatures of only a few thousand degrees. Betelgeuse in Orion and Antares in Scorpius are both red giant stars that fall into this category.

STAR NAMES

Over 200 stars have proper names, usually of Roman, Greek or Arabic origin. However, only a couple of dozen or so are used regularly, examples of which include Arcturus in Boötes, Spica in Virgo and Betelgeuse in Orion.

The system whereby Greek letters are assigned to stars was introduced by the German astronomer Johann Bayer in 1603. Bayer's system is applied to the brighter stars within any particular constellation, which are given a letter from the Greek alphabet, followed by the genitive case of the constellation in which the star is located. This genitive case is simply the Latin form meaning 'of' the constellation. Examples are the stars Alpha Boötis and Beta Centauri which translate literally as 'Alpha of Boötes' and 'Beta of the Centaur'.

As a rule, the brightest star in a constellation is labelled Alpha, the second brightest Beta, the third brightest Gamma and so on, although there are some constellations where the system falls down. An example is Gemini where the principal star (Pollux) is designated Beta Geminorum, the second brightest (Castor) being known as Alpha Geminorum.

There are only 24 letters in the Greek alphabet, which means that the fainter naked eye stars need an alternative system of classification. The system in popular use is that devised by the English Astronomer Royal John Flamsteed in which the stars in each constellation are listed numerically in order from west to east. Although many of the brighter stars have both Greek letters and Flamsteed numbers, the latter are generally used only when a star does not have a Greek letter, as is the case with 61 Cygni.

STAR CLUSTERS

Although most of the stars that we see in the night sky are scattered randomly throughout the spiral arms of the Galaxy, many are found to be concentrated in relatively compact groups, referred to by astronomers as star clusters. There are two main types of star cluster – open and globular. Open clusters, also known as galactic clusters, are found within the main disc of the Galaxy and have no particularly well-defined shape. Usually made up of young hot stars, over a thousand open clusters are known, their diameters generally being no more than a few tens of light years. They are believed to have formed from vast interstellar gas and dust clouds within our Galaxy and indeed occupy the same regions of the Galaxy as the nebulae. A number of open clusters are visible to the naked eye including Praesepe (M44) in Cancer (see March 25th) and perhaps the most famous open cluster of all the Pleiades (M45) in Taurus (see February 4th).

Globular clusters, as their name suggests, are huge spherical collections of stars located in the area of space surrounding the Galaxy. With diameters of anything up to several hundred light years globular clusters typically contain tens of thousands of old stars and little or none of the nebulosity seen in open clusters. When seen through a small telescope or binoculars, they take on the appearance of faint, misty balls of greyish light superimposed against the background sky. Although some form of optical aid is usually needed to see globular clusters, there are three famous examples which can be spotted with the naked eye. These are the Great Hercules Cluster (M13) in the constellation Hercules (see July 3rd), Omega Centauri in Centaurus (see May 9th) and 47 Tucanae in Tucana (see December 11th).

VARIABLE STARS
Variable stars are stars whose brightness varies over a period of time. There are many different types of variable star, although the variations in brightness are basically due either to changes taking place within the star itself, such as L^2 in Puppis (see February 25th) or Mira in Cetus (see December 4th), or the periodic obscuration, or eclipsing, of one member of a binary star by its companion, such as Algol in Perseus (see November 14th).

ZENITH
The point in the sky directly above the observer.

ZODIAC
The band of 12 constellations which straddles the ecliptic through which the Sun and planets appear to travel throughout the year. The constellations forming the Zodiac are Aries, Taurus, Gemini, Cancer, Leo, Virgo, Libra, Scorpius, Sagittarius, Capricornus, Aquarius and Pisces (see The Celestial Sphere pp 6-15).

FURTHER READING

If you have enjoyed your journey around the night sky, and want to find out even more about the wonders the universe has to offer, the books listed below should be of interest. They contain lots of useful information for the backyard astronomer and will help expand on what you have learned from The Stars Night By Night. Although some of the books listed may be currently out of print they are generally still accessible either from online sources or from more-traditional second hand book shops.

Binocular Highlights, Gary Seronik.
An excellent and readable book which takes the form of a tour of 99 celestial sights for the binocular user. As well as providing observing tips, it explains what to look out for when choosing binoculars for star gazing.

The Cambridge Guide to the Constellations, Michael E. Bakich.
A comprehensive, thorough and well illustrated guide to the constellations.

Deep-Sky Wonders, Walter Scott Houston.
For those who want to take things further, this inspirational book offers a deeper look at what the night sky has to offer and truly captures the spirit of observational astronomy.

A Dictionary of Modern Star Names, Paul Kunitzsch and Tim Smart.

An excellent source of information on the origins and meanings of over 250 star names.

Messier's Nebulae and Star Clusters Kenneth, Glyn Jones.

An up-to-date and in-depth guide to the objects in Charles Messier's Catalogue of nebulae and star clusters.

Night Scenes, Paul L. Money.

Published annually, this is an excellent monthly guide to astronomical events for the year. The information it contains includes lunar phases, positions of the planets, meteor showers, comets and eclipses.

The Practical Astronomer, Brian Jones.

An introduction to astronomy and a practical guide to observing and understanding the night sky.

Starlight Nights: The Adventures of a Star-Gazer, Leslie C. Peltier.

A beautifully written account which captures the passion of star gazing in a way that few books have.

Star Names – Their Lore and Meaning, Richard Hinckley Allen.

A somewhat unusual book exploring the vast heritage of folklore and history associated with the stars and constellations.

Star Tales, Ian Ridpath.

Explores the mythology behind the stars and constellations. Beautifully illustrated.

INDEX

Index to Constellations, Stars and Deep-Sky Objects
(v = variable star; o = obsolete constellation)

47 Tucanae   333
61 Cygni   240

Acamar   351
Achernar   351
Achird   310
Acrab   196
Acrux   121
Acubens   98
Adara   45
Agena   127
Ain   60
Al Dhanab   281
Al Tarf   98
Albali   276
Albireo 236
Alchita   157
Alcor   88-90
Alderamin   314
Aldebaran   56, 59
Al'farg   321
Alfecca Meridiana   209
Algenib (in Pegasus)   269

Algenib (in Perseus) 300
Algenubi 107
Algieba 107
Algol (v) 300
Algorab 157
Alhena 50
Alioth 88
Alkalurops 139
Alkes 158
Almach 286
Alnair 280
Alnilam 41
Alnitak 41
Alpha Centauri 127
Alphard 114
Alphecca 173
Alphirk 314
Alrai 314
Alrescha 321
Alsciaukat 96
Alshain 232
Alsufi 266
Altair 231
Aludra 45
Alya 182
Ancha 276
Andromeda 284-290
Ankaa 330
Anser 251
Antares 196
Antlia 80-81
Apus 160-162

Aquarius 274-277
Aquila 230-233
Ara 202-204
Arcturus 136, 139
Argo Navis (o) 67
Aries 294-296
Arkab Posterior 212
Arkab Prior 212
Arneb 64
Arrakis 266
Ascella 212
Asellus Australis 98, 99
Asellus Borealis 98, 99
Asterion 142
Atik 300
Atria 160
Auriga 52-56
Azha 351
Azmidiske 75

Baten Kaitos 325
Bellatrix 41
Beta Centauri 127
Beta Doradus (v) 343
Betelgeuse 40
Boötes 136-140
Botein 295
Butterfly Cluster (M6) 199

Caelum 339-340
Camelopardalis 304-306
Cancer 97-100

Canes Venatici 140-144
Canis Major 43-46
Canis Minor 46-48
Canopus 66, 68
Capella 54
Caph 310
Capricornus 259-263
Carina 66-71
Carina Nebula 70
Cassiopeia 307-313
Castor 48, 49
Cebalrai 188
Centaurus 125-131
Cepheus 313-317
Cetus 323-326
Chamaeleon 133-135
Chara 142
Chi Cygni (v) 239
Christmas Tree Cluster (NGC 2264) 85
Cih 309
Circinus 135-136
Circlet, The 321
Coal Sack, The 123
Coathanger, The 253
Columba 337-339
Coma Berenices 144-149
Coma Star Cluster 147
Cor Caroli 142
Corona Australis 208-210
Corona Borealis 172-175
Corvus 155-157
Coxa 106

Crater 155-158
Crux 118-123
Cursa 352
Cygnus 233-241

Dabih 261
Delphinus 257-259
Delta Cephei (v) 316
Deneb 235
Deneb Algiedi 261
Deneb Dulfim 258
Deneb Kaitos 324
Denebola 106
Dheneb 325
Diadem 147
Diamond of Virgo 144
Dorado 342-344
Draco 263-267
Dschubba 196
Dubhe 88
Dumbbell Nebula (M27) 252

Eagle Nebula (M16) 183
Ed Asich 266
El Nath 54, 60
Enif 270
Equuleus 271-273
Eridanus 349-352
Eta Carinae Nebula 70
Etamin 266

False Cross 71, 74

Fomalhaut   279
Fornax   348-349
Fum al Samakah   321
Furud   45

Gemini   48-52
Ghost of Jupiter (NGC 3242)   116
Giedi   261
Gienah (in Corvus)   156
Gienah (in Cygnus)   235
Gomeisa   47
Great Andromeda Galaxy (M31)   288
Great Hercules Cluster (M13)   178
Great Peacock Cluster (NGC 6752)   206
Grumium   266
Grus   279-281

Hadar   127
Haedi (the Kids)   54
Hamal   295
Hercules   175-179
Herschel's Garnet Star (v)   315
Heze   153
Hind's Crimson Star (v)   65
Homam   270
Horologium   347-348
Hyades   60
Hydra   101-102, **110-118**
Hydrus   334-335

IC 2391   74
IC 2602   69

IC 4756   183

Indus   281-283
Izar   140

Jewel Box (NGC 4755)   122

Kaffaljidhma   325
Kaus Australis   212
Kaus Borealis   212
Kaus Media   212
Kemble's Cascade   305
Keystone, The   175
Kitalpha   272
Kochab   94
Kornephoros   177
Kraz   156
Ksora   310
Kuma   266

L² Puppis (v)   78
Lacerta   317-319
Lagoon Nebula (M8)   216
Large Magellanic Cloud (LMC)   343
Leo   104-108
Leo Minor   108-110
Lepus   63-66
Libra   168-171
Lupus   164-167
Lynx   95-96
Lyra   242-249

M2   276
M3   143
M4   198
M5   182
M6   199
M7   199
M8   216
M10 188
M11 226
M12 189
M13 178
M14 190
M15 270
M16 183
M17 217
M18 219
M19 191
M20 214
M21 217
M22 220
M23 213
M25 220
M26 228
M27 252
M29 238
M30 262
M31 288
M33 292
M34 301
M35 51
M36 55
M37 55

M38 55
M39 237
M41 45
M42 42
M44 99
M45 61
M46 77
M47 77
M48 114
M50 83
M52 310
M53 148
M54 221
M56 246
M57 247
M62 193
M67 100
M69 223
M79 65
M80 200
M92 179
M93 77
M104 153

Marfik (in Hercules) 179
Marfik (in Ophiuchus) 188
Markab 269
Markeb (in Puppis) 75
Markeb (in Vela) 74
Matar 270
Mebsuta 50
Megrez 88

Mekbuda 50
Menkalinan 54
Menkar 325
Menkent 128
Menkib 300
Mensa 344-345
Merak 88
Mesarthim 296
Metallah 291
Miaplacidus 69
Microscopium 283-284
Minkar 157
Mintaka 41
Mira (v) 325
Mirach 286
Miram 300
Mirzam 45
Misam 300
Mizar 88-90
Monoceros 81-85
Mu Cephei (v) 315
Muliphein 45
Muphrid 139
Musca 131-133
Musca Borealis (o) 296

NGC 362 334
NGC 457 311
NGC 869 303
NGC 884 303
NGC 1528 303
NGC 2070 343

NGC 2129 51
NGC 2244 84
NGC 2264 85
NGC 2547 75
NGC 3242 116
NGC 3532 70
NGC 3766 129
NGC 4755 122
NGC 5139 130
NGC 5822 167
NGC 5897 171
NGC 6025 160
NGC 6087 164
NGC 6193 203
NGC 6397 204
NGC 6709 232
NGC 6752 206

Naos 75
Nash 212
Nashira 261
Nekkar 139
Nihal 64
Norma 162-164
Nusakan 174

Octans 335-337
Omega Centauri (NGC 5139) 130
Omega Nebula (M17) 217
Omicron Ceti (v) 325
Omicron Velorum Cluster (IC 2391) 74
Ophiuchus 185-194

Orion 38-43
Orion Nebula (M42) 42

Pavo 204-206
Peacock 206
Pearl Cluster (NGC 3766) 129
Pegasus 267-271
Perseus 296-304
Phakt 337
Phekda 88
Pherkad 94
Phoenix 328-330
Pictor 340-341
Pinwheel Galaxy (M33) 292
Pisces 319-322
Piscis Austrinus 277-279
Pleiades (M45) 61
Plough, The 85
Polaris 90-94
Pollux 48, 50
Porrima 152
Praecipua 110
Praesepe (M44) 99
Prima Giedi 261
Procyon 47
Proxima Centauri 127
Puppis 75-78
Pyxis 78-80

R Andromedae (v) 289
R Centauri (v) 129
R Hydrae (v) 118

R Leonis (v)   108
R Leporis (v)   65
R Lyrae (v)   249
RR Scorpii (v)   201
R Scuti (v)   229
Ras Algethi   177
Ras Alhague   187
Rastaban   266
Regulus   105
Reticulum   345-346
Rigel   40
Rigil Centaurus   127
Ring Nebula (M57)   247
Rosette Nebula   84
Rotanev   258
Ruchbah   310
Rukbat   212

Sabik   187
Sadalachbia   276
Sadalmelik   276
Sadalsuud   275
Sadr   235
Sagitta   254-256
Sagittarius   210-224
Saiph   41
Scheat   269
Scorpius   194-201
Sculptor   327-328
Scutum   224-229
Scutum Star Cloud   226
Segin   310

Serpens 180-185
Sextans 102-103
Sham 256
Shaula 196
Shedar 309
Sheliak 245
Sickle, The 104
Sidus Ludoviciana 88-90
Sigma Octantis 337
Sirius 43, 45, 47
Sirrah 269, 286
Skat 276
Small Magellanic Cloud (SMC) 332
Sombrero Hat Galaxy (M104) 153
Spica 150, 152
Sualocin 258
Suhail 74
Sulaphat 245
Summer Triangle, The 233
Sword Handle Double Cluster
(NGC 869 and NGC 884) 303

Talitha 87
Tania Australis 87
Tania Borealis 87
Tarantula Nebula (NGC 2070) 343
Tarazed 231
Taurus 56-63
Teapot, The 213
Telescopium 206-208
Theta Carinae Cluster (IC 2602) 69
Thuban 266

Torcularis Septentrionalis   321
Triangulum   290-293
Triangulum Australe   158-160
Triangulum Minus (o)   293
Triangulum Spiral Galaxy (M33)   292
Trifid Nebula (M20)   214
Tucana   330-334

U Hydrae (v)   117
Unukalhai   181
Ursa Major   85-90
Ursa Minor   90-95

Vega   244
Vela   72-75
Vindemiatrix   152
Virgo   149-155
Volans   71-72
Vulpecula   249-254
Vulpecula et Anser   250

Wezen   45
Wild Duck Cluster (M11)   226
Winter Triangle, The   81-82

Yed Posterior   188
Yed Prior   188

Zaurak   351
Zavijava   152
Zeta Phoenicis (v)   330
Zibal   351

Zosma 106
Zuben Elakrab 170
Zuben Elakribi (v) 170
Zubenelgenubi 170
Zubeneschamali 170